Frank T.

THE DINKY TOY
PRICE GUIDE

Third Edition

A & C Black · London

Also by Frank Thompson

The Matchbox Toy Price Guide
The Triang/Minic Toy Price Guide
The Corgi Toy Price Guide

First published 1982 by Ernest Benn Ltd.
Second edition published 1987
Third edition published 1989 by
A & C Black (Publishers) Ltd.
35 Bedford Row, London WC1R 4JH.

ISBN 0–7136–3144–9

Printed and bound in Great Britain by William Clowes Limited,
Beccles and London

CONTENTS

INTRODUCTION

Although the world is full of companies making diecast toys, none is probably better known than that of Dinky which is why I chose it as the subject for my first price guide.

But there were other motives too for writing the book. I must admit that nostalgia for the toys themselves, coupled with memories of my childhood, also had a great deal to do with it. In my early school days I used to collect toys and models in the springtime and most of these came from the local tips or from the dustbins of the toyshops – if I was lucky enough to get them first, as other children had the same ideas. Coming, as I did, from a poor mining family, I never had the money to buy toys, nor could my parents afford to give me any.

It took me a good twenty years of hard work and research to compile this price guide. It was also, I believe, the first attempt to give prices which collectors could expect to pay for the many models listed in the book. To the uninitiated, some of these prices may seem remarkable, but the world of collecting contains little logic.

Personally, I had been telling people since the early 50's that one day every top auction house in the world would be selling Dinky models. Everyone laughed at me and even my wife thought many of my predictions were crazy. At last I proved everybody wrong and the world is now diecast toy swapping and collecting mad. As many as 400 swapmeets and fleamarkets dealing with Dinky toys take place every month in various parts of the British Isles, whereas not long ago a mere half dozen events took place in the whole country during the course of a year.

In 1933 a genius called Frank Hornby decided to enlarge his Meccano empire by introducing some miniature diecast models which he called 'Pocket Toys'. This name was later changed to 'Dinky Miniatures' and within a few years they became famous all over the world. The tiny toys were priced so that even the poorest admirer of a particular model ship, car, plane or whatever, could afford to buy a model.

The history of the company falls into three periods. The first from 1934 to 1964, known as the 'golden years' when original Dinky models were produced by the Hornby Dinky Company themselves. The second lasted from 1964 to 1969 when Lines Bros. took over the company and added still more to the range of products. During this period some of the best models were produced, including the Guy Vans, the Trojan range and the now much sought after Supertoys. But in 1970 there was a fresh take-over bid and many of the diecast models were replaced by plastic items which bore no resemblance to their predecessors at all. Even the boxes were changed and although this was bad news for the company, it was certainly good news for the investor-collector as it meant that those models made between 1934 and 1969 could only become more valuable and some in a very spectacular way.

Details of how to use the guide are included later in the introduction, but I think that a few general words about collecting might be helpful especially for the beginner.

Some of the models listed are really very valuable. Always handle each item with care and always buy mint and boxed models if possible. Many empty boxes themselves are worth a great deal of money. One important point to remember is that pre-war diecast toys are subject to metal fatigue and are therefore very delicate. Never try to clean models with polish or oil; they are best left in their original condition which is how collectors like to buy them.

Always beware of defects and shop-soiled items, especially the former. Many of these are often a waste of money and do not reach true market value. Always look for odd wheels, lights, tyres etc. By this I do not mean only genuine factory faults, but models which are deliberately made up by tradesmen with an intent to deceive the unwary. Always buy at a reliable shop.

In spite of what some dealers say, colours do often influence the potential value of an item. A special, or rare colour can mean extra pounds in your pocket. Although most models were made in standard colours, many had colour variants when the Dinky factory decided to use up odd cans of paint. An example of what I mean is Dinky 108 (Sam's Car) which is commonly seen in red. A silver model is probably worth double and the very rare blue version about five times that of the red.

It does not necesarily mean that because a model was made in 1936 that it will be more valuable than one that was made in 1966. There are many reasons why the later model could be rare, which would make it more expensive to buy. Commemorative items can be purely accidental, as were many of the pre-war models, whereas the more recent issues are intentionally designed for promotional or commemorative purposes. Something else which can make a particular model expensive is the advertisment attached to it. For example, the Players advertisement is much rarer that the Capstan one even though they are both attached to the same type of van. A Heinz bean tin on the side of a van is much easier to find and cheaper to buy than one with a Heinz sauce bottle on it.

Every post-war Dinky model has a definite mark or number connected with it, whereas many of the pre-war models have none at all. Beware of all forgeries and copies. The only way to tell is to seek the advice of an expert. Copies are always larger than the originals but if you are in real doubt of the authenticity of your model, make sure you have a signed affidavit from your dealer. Consult a solicitor as it is better to be safe than sorry.

Although thousands of models have been made, not only by Dinky, the early issues of all diecast toys are becoming increasingly hard to find as more and more people realise their full value. Nor is this collecting fever restricted to the British Isles. The scene is world-wide and covers every strata of society, all of them joined together by their common interest in Dinky toys.

Although the main interest in Dinky products is actually collecting the models themselves, many collectors specialise in searching for any catalogues and magazines which the Company produced. The older the catalogue the higher its value and a complete set is, naturally, worth still more. Many of the early models were advertised in the Meccano magazine and the most valuable of these were printed between 1911 and 1920. The last Dinky catalogue was produced in 1978. Although some people will say that 1979 was the final year, in fact the same catalogue was used for both years, apart from the handwritten addition of a few extra models.

Collectors should be very wary of some recent models. The name Dinky was transferred to a factory in Hong Kong and many of the boxes carrying the Dinky name still claimed to be 'Made in England'.

Many of the models which flooded the shops in pre-war days are priceless and the ones which were stacked in the shops and newsagents of the 1950's and 1960's have often become genuine collector's items. These models are normally unobtainable in regular toyshops and are to be found in fleamarkets, collector/dealer shops and antique shops all over the world. Auction Houses advertise them when they are available. Local and national papers show the growing number of town halls, race courses and showgrounds that are holding swapmeets and model sales which are much the best places to meet other collectors.

A final piece of advice. Take collecting seriously by all means, but never let it cause trouble between your friends or family.

Many people helped with the compilation of this book, but I would like to thank in particular my darling wife Anne, for the many hours she spent burning the midnight oil typing the script. I would like to give sincere thanks to the people in Liverpool where I spent four years research on the book in that area alone. Also, my thanks are due to those who gave me helpful advice on both prices and the content of the book, especially on the difficult, but important, years from 1934 to 1940.

INTRODUCTION TO THE THIRD EDITION

It gives me great pleasure to introduce the third edition of my Dinky Toy Price Guide.

There are, coincidentally, three important changes to this edition. The first is that the prices reflect the phenomenal increases that have taken place in the last year or so. The second is the exciting news of the relaunch of Dinky Toys by the Matchbox Company and the third is the extension of the coverage of French Dinky Toys.

The main increases in prices have been for mint and boxed models. Indeed, many of the early models are now so highly priced that they are out of the reach of the ordinary collector. Models which cost £12 or less in 1982 are now sold for £55 or more. A set of traffic lights available at £2 less than five years ago is now fetching £175 and a 49 Petrol Pump Set which, less than three years ago, could be bought for £1 is being sold for £265.

Even though newly produced models can never be the same as the originals the relaunch of Dinky Toys by Matchbox offers fresh opportunities for the collector. Details of the new models appear on page 312 but I would like to take this opportunity of thanking Jerry Tekerian and his staff of Matchbox for their hard work on this important project.

A further thirty models from the French factory have been included this time, reflecting the increased interest in this area of collecting.

If you find this book helpful please remember that I have also written price guides to Matchbox Toys, Triang-Minic Toys and Corgi Toys – all published by A & C Black.

Frank Thompson.

A NOTE ON THE PRICES

Any price guide is certain to cause controversy and in particular one to an area of collecting where prices are often rising very rapidly. It has to be said that, in some cases, there are wide differences in the price placed upon a model. For example a 905 Foden Flat Truck was recently auctioned at £110. The same model, in the same colour and in the same condition is on sale elsewhere at £375. In these cases I have tried to give a fair average price but do not be surprised at the level of variation you may encounter.

The prices were as accurate as possible at the time of going to press but things move so fast that you may well find that variations have taken place in the months that it has taken for the book to be produced. Often an item is as valuable as a person can afford to pay and this is particularly true of rare models where cost can become unimportant to the buyer. Nonetheless I would welcome comments from any collector, not only on prices, but on any other aspect of the guide.

EXPLANATIONS

To make it as easy as possible for the collector to find his or her model, I have set the book out in sections, each one devoted to a particular class or type of product. Within each section the models have been listed in numerical order of models, with all the necessary details of colour, tyres etc. Each entry gives the date that model was issued, deleted or had its number changed for some reason. Lengths and heights of each model are also given. Prices are listed for Mint and Boxed, Mint Unboxed and Good Condition. Some models never had individual boxes as they were sold in sets of six, or twelve, or as boxed sets. Therefore only Mint and Good Condition prices apply.

As many numbers were duplicated several times and became rather confusing, I have set out these numbers to the best of my ability. For instance, if the number 198 had more than one colour scheme attached to it, I would call one of them 198/A or just give a higher or lower price to that particular item.

If the model happened to be issued both in pre-war and post-war years, it will be distinguished by being given a small letter suffix pre-war and a capital suffix post-war. For example, the Reconnaissance Car which was issued in 1938 (officially 152b) is called 152b; the same model re-issued in 1946 and still classed as 152b in the catalogue, is now indicated as 152B.

If the same number is given to two different models, I have used an oblique stroke, but the details about the models themselves should be sufficient for identification.

Lengths are given in millimetres. Remember, however, the models are affected by expansion during manufacture or through metal fatigue in the case of old models.

The date of introduction will indicate the time when the model was first mentioned in a Dinky catalogue or magazine. Release dates for promotional items are as accurate as possible, and checks have been made with the relevant company or event associated with that model. Normally, these models were produced in a very limited edition and were sold out on the day and date in question. Deletion dates are also given, though these are sometimes uncertain. However, the information is as accurate as I can make it.

The original prices given are correct at the time a particular model was released. However, prices were often altered at a later date and not all shops sold toys at the recommended price.

There are various ways to identify models and you will find that on practically all Dinky toys the maker's name was shown, but there are exceptions. Dinky Toys; Meccano Ltd; Made in England; Supertoys; Made Overseas under Special Licence and patent numbers were used. In these cases the letters M N mean Maker's Name. Words in inverted commas such as 'Taxi' or 'Firestone Tyres' indicate the wording of a transfer or special paint job and have nothing to do with the words that were cast in metal. Many models are identified by authentic transfers and liveries of their large counterparts.

The wheels of many models were either smooth or ridged and sometimes this can be misleading in trying to date models.

IMPORTANT NOTICE

The prices given in this guide are the prices that you should expect to pay in order to buy an item. They are not necessarily what you should expect to receive when selling to a dealer. Although every care has been taken in compiling this price guide, neither the publisher nor the author can accept any responsibility whatsoever for any financial loss or other inconvenience that may result from its use.

ABBREVIATIONS

BOR	Opening boot at rear.
D	Driver. Separate, static or moveable.
DC	Diecast alloy. Usually Zamak except for early 22 series.
FTS	Finger tip steering, or Prestomatic as the factory called it.
H	Hook for towing. Either cast into body, or as separate attachment.
IP	Imitation plastic.
LHD	Left hand drive position for steering wheel.
MN	Manufacturer's name.
OB	Bonnet opens to reveal engine.
OD	Doors open.
P	Plastic. Either transparent in windows or on other parts of body.
PW	Plastic wheels.
RT	Rubber tyres. Does not include wheels or axles.
RW	Solid rubber wheels.
S	Seats or interior fittings.
SS	Independent suspension, springing etc.
SW	Steering wheel separate and not cast in.
SWIP	Side wood imitation panels
W	Windows.
WS	Separate plastic windscreen.

M/B	**Mint boxed**
M/U	**Mint unboxed**
G/C	**Good condition**

THE FAMOUS ATLANTEAN BUS

Of all the models made by Dinky none is more popular than the Atlantean Bus. There were three casting variations of the much admired and sought after first Atlantean bus.

The first casting was the Corporation Transport where the front entrance doors were fully extended to the bottom of the casting and the livery was a pinkish red or Post Office red and off-white with interior white seats.

The second casting had a small extension added to the main chassis which protruded into a space where the space immediately underneath the doors was recessed. This alteration continued until this model was withdrawn in 1966.

The third type of casting was the Green Corporation Transport model with the ribbed roof. These models were brought out in the following livery order. No. 1: Red and off-white with white interior. This model was first described in the 10th edition of the Dinky small catalogue in May 1962. No. 2: Red and off-white with white interior, Regent advertisements and with the 'Ribble' name on the sides. No. 3: Red and off-white with no advertisements but still had the name 'Ribble' on the sides. No. 4: First green issue with pale yellow and 'B.P. is the Key to Better Motoring' on sides. Red interior seating. No. 5: Second model issued in green 'B.P. is the Key etc.' in bright orange. Red interior seating. No. 6: Ribbed roof, green livery and red interior seating.

In 1973 the first casting came in red and white with 'Regent' adverts but no corporation transport transfers. The first advertising for the model number 292 in the Dinky catalogue of 1962 showed the Corporation Transport lettering and displayed a driver behind the wheel, but in the 1963 Dinky catalogue of January and July (11th edition) a different bus illustration was used. This model had a single line route indicator and 'Regent' adverts but the Corporation lettering and the bus driver were missing.

The next Dinky catalogue No. 12 issued in January 1964 had the same illustration in red and the driver was shown once more. The No. 293 Green version was advertised at 7/11d. but not illustrated. Both the February and August Dinky catalogue of 1965 showed a green bus with a much larger route indicator panel and with B.P. adverts and Corporation lettering.

By the year 1966 the style of the Dinky catalogues changed altogether as the new ideas of Lines Bros. took over. They had one model to a small page (pocket size) and the red Atlantean bus had been done away with and in its place a new view of the offside of the green model appeared with full lettering. This model also appeared in the 2nd edition of the Dinky catalogue 1966 and in the No. 3 issue of 1967, and also in the No. 4 issued of 1968.

The model was not illustrated nor listed as a model in the No. 5 Dinky catalogue of 1969 (May issue). The green Atlantean with the ribbed roof was first illustrated in 1967 and the box had a fine picture of the model on it. Boxes are very important when getting a good price for your models. The first bus issue had a full colour illustration on the front of its box. On the back of the box there were important notes about the public service of the vehicle. The 'Ribble' version used the same box but the word 'Ribble' was stamped in ink in the bus style of printing on the opening flap of the same box. The later 293 box had a smart colour illustration and showed the red seating and took almost the whole of the front cover and rear of the box but this illustration was different as far as model appearance was concerned.

I hope this added information will help satisfy the great number of bus collectors, although I would be pleased to hear comment and variations from any of the readers of this catalogue.

AGRICULTURAL VEHICLES

MODEL	M/B	M/U	G/C

No. 22e. Farm Tractor — £850 £450 £150

Green, yellow and red, and in blue.
Metal wheels with SW. cast in H.
Price 9d. Issued December 1933.
Deleted 1940. 70mm. DC.

No. 22e. Farm Tractor — £850 £450 £150

Blue and white with red wheels.
Otherwise as before.

**No. 27A. 'Massey Harris'
Farm Tractor** — £75 £40 £20

Red and yellow. SW/DH. Front
swivel. Price 5/-. Issued June 1948.
Renumbered 300 in 1954. Deleted
1960. 89mm. DC/TP.

**No. 27AK. Farm Tractor and
Hay Rake** — £150 £75 £45

Red and yellow. Price 8/6d. Issued
March 1953. Renumbered 310 in
1954. Deleted 1960. 157mm.
DC/TP/Wire.

**No. 27B. 'Halesowen' Harvest
Trailer** — £45 £20 £10

Brown and red with tow-bar and
removable front and back supports. H.
Price 2/10d. Issued June 1949.
Renumbered 320 in 1954. Deleted
1960. 121mm DC.

**No. 27C. 'Massey Harris'
Manure Spreader** — £65 £25 £10

Red. Complete with tow-bar and
working parts in red. Letters 'Massey-
Harris manure spreader', on sides.
Price 3/9d. Issued October 1949.
Renumbered 1954. Deleted 1960.
113mm. DC. Late examples PW/RI.

No. 27G. Moto Cart — £45 £25 £5

Brown and green. S.W./D. with
tipping rear. Price 4/6d. Issued
December 1949. Renumbered 342 in
1954. Deleted 1960. 110mm. DC/RT.

No. 27H. Disc Harrow — £35 £20 £5

Red and yellow with discs which
rotate. Price 2/6d. Issued April 1951.
Deleted 1960. Renumbered 322 in
1954. 86mm. DC.

MODEL	M/B	M/U	G/C

No. 27J. Triple Gang Mower

£55 £25 £10

Red, yellow and green with working
blade. Price 6/6d. Issued October
1952. Renumbered 323 in 1954.
Deleted 1960. 114mm. DC

No. 27K. Hay Rake

£40 £20 £5

Red and yellow. The rake raises and
lowers. Price 2/11d. Issued 1953.
Renumbered 324 in 1954. Deleted
1960. 77mm. DC.

No. 27M. 'Land Rover' Trailer

£35 £15 £5

Orange or green with tow-bar, clip,
and 2 wheels. Price 2/6d. Issued April
1950. Renumbered 341 in 1954.
Deleted 1960. 79mm. DC/TP.

No. 27N. Field Marshall Farm Tractor

£95 £50 £30

Orange with front axle which swivels.
SW/D/H. Price 4/4d. Issued October
1953. Renumbered 301 in 1954.
Deleted 1960. 79mm. DC/TP.

No. 27N. Field Marshall Tractor (Special)

£2500

Black with tow-bar and special front
axle which swivels. Price 4/4d. Issued
October 1953. Deleted 1954. This
model was definitely produced in
1953 and not when model was
renumbered. 75mm. DC/TP.

No. 30N. Farm Produce Wagon

£75 £45 £20

Green and yellow, and blue and red.
Price 3/3d. Issued July 1950.
Renumbered 343 in 1954. Deleted
1960. 107mm. DC/TP/RT.

No. 300. 'Massey Ferguson' Tractor

	M/B	M/U	G/C
	£65	£30	£15

Red, with yellow wheels and blue driver. Front axle swivel. Price 4/11d. Issued 1960. Deleted 1965. 89mm. DC/P.

No. 300. 'Massey Harris' Tractor

£65   £30   £15

Red and yellow. Words 'Massey Harris' on sides. Price 4/-. Made in 1954. Deleted 1976. 89mm. DC.

No. 300. 'Massey Ferguson' Tractor

£65   £30   £15

Red and orange. Latter is rarer with the words 'Massey Ferguson' on sides. SW/D/H and plastic wheels at front. Front axle swivel. Price 4/11d. Issued 1960. Deleted 1965. This is the rubber tyred version. 89mm. DC/TP/P/RT.

No. 301. Field Marshall Tractor

£75   £35   £20

Orange with adjustable steering. SW/D/H. With front axle swivel. Price 4/2d. Issued 1954. Deleted 1964. 75mm. DC/TP

No. 301. Field Marshall Tractor (Special)

£2500

Black livery discovered in 1955. Adjustable steering. SW/D/H. Price 4/2d. Discovered 1956. Deleted 1956. 75mm. DC/TP. Rare model colour

No. 305. David Brown Tractor

£80   £35   £15

Red and yellow with brown or grey driver and movable front wheels. Price 9/11d. Issued 1965. Deleted 1970. 83mm.

MODEL	M/B	M/U	G/C
No. 305. David Brown Tractor	£80	£40	£15

Black, red and white. Colour
discovered in 1972. With lift-off hatch
and swivelling wheels. With or
without grey or brown driver. Price
9/11d. Issued 1965. Deleted 1970.
83mm.

	M/B	M/U	G/C
No. 305. David Brown Tractor	£450	£200	£150

Black with red wheels and blue driver.
This model appeared in 1967, but
only a few of this rare colour known.
Price 9/11d. Issued 1965. Deleted
1970. 83mm. DC/P.

	M/B	M/U	G/C
No. 308. 'Leyland' 384 Tractor	£65	£35	£20

Purple and cream with blue driver,
with the word 'Leyland' on sides.
Price 76p. Issued 1971. Deleted 1977.
86mm. DC/P.

	M/B	M/U	G/C
No. 308. 'Leyland' 384 Tractor	£135	£75	£40

Orange and black, with white plastic
wheels and driver. New colour for
1978. Price 87p. Issued 1977. Deleted
1980. 86mm. P.

	M/B	M/U	G/C
No. 310. Farm Tractor and Hay-Rake	£85	£45	£30

Red and yellow. Price 7/11d. Issued
1954. Deleted 1960. 157mm.
DC/TP/Wire.

	M/B	M/U	G/C
No. 319. 'Week's' Tipping Trailer	£40	£15	£3

Red and yellow. 2 wheels, tow-bar
and tipping body with hinged
tailboard. Price 4/6d. Issued June
1961. Deleted 1968. 105mm. DC/RT.

	M/B		
	£350		

Above model also found with red
top, with dark red wheels and yellow
chassis. Special collector's item in this
rare colour.

	M/B	M/U	G/C
No. 320. 'Halesowen' Harvest Trailer	£35	£20	£5

Red and brown. Tow-bar. Price 3/6d.
Issued 1954. Deleted 1960.
120/121mm. DC.

	M/B	M/U	G/C
No. 321. 'Massey Harris' Manure Spreader	£45	£30	£10

Red with silver blades which rotate.
Tow-bar and working parts at rear.
Price 4/5d. Issued 1954. Deleted
1960. 113mm, DC.

MODEL	M/B	M/U	G/C

Later model with yellow plastic wheels with very dark red body and white blades. — £25 £10 £5

No. 322. Disc Harrow — £30 £10 £5

Red and yellow. Tow-bar and rotating discs. Price 2/-. Issued 1954. Deleted 1966. 86mm. DC.

Model also exists in white and blue, rare colour, otherwise details as normal colour. — £30 £10 £5

No. 322. Disc Harrow — £25 £10 £5

Red and white with full working parts. Price 2/11d. Issued 1966. Deleted 1971. 79mm.

No. 323. Triple Gang Mower — £25 £10 £5

Red, yellow and green. With working blades. Price 5/3d. Issued 1954. Deleted 1963. 114mm. DC.

No. 324. Hayrake — £25 £10 £5

Red, yellow and silver. Rake which raises and lowers by lever. Price 3/9d. Issued 1954. Deleted 1964.

No. 325. 'David Brown' Tractor — £55 £25 £10

White, red and black with red pipe. Words 'David Brown' on sides. Price 9/11d. Disc Harrow optional as set. Price 12/11d. Issued 1966. Deleted 1974. 152mm. DC/P. (Price for single item).

Price for set with Harrow — £35 £25 £15

No. 325. 'David Brown' Tractor and Disc Harrow — £125 £60 £20

Red with white flash. Perfect matching pair. Only a few known in these colours. Price 12/11d. Discovered 1967. Deleted 1974. 152mm. DC/P with working parts.

No. 342. Moto-Cart — £30 £20 £5

Green and brown. S/W/D end tipper. Price 4/3d. Issued 1955. Deleted 1960. 110mm. DC/RT.

No. 343. Farm Produce Wagon — £60 £20 £10

Green and yellow. Dodge type. Price 3/6d. Issued 1954. Deleted 1964. 107mm. DC/TP/RT.

MODEL	M/B	M/U	G/C
Red and Blue.	£55	£20	£10
Red and Black. Very rare.	£350		

No. 381. Convoy Farm Truck

	£25	£10	£5

Cab and chassis with lemon and black bumpers. Dropping tailboard. Price £1.35. Issued 1977. Deleted 1980. 110mm. DC.

No. 381. Convoy Farm Truck

	£35	£15	£10

In yellow and brown with black bumper. With silver wheels and dark yellow chassis. Price £1.35p. Issued 1978. Deleted 1980. 110mm. DC.

No. 399. Farm Tractor and Trailer set

	£75	£35	£15

A 300 'Massey Ferguson' tractor and trailer. Price 13/11d. Issued 1969. Deleted 1975. 188mm. DC/P.

No. 563. Very Heavy Tractor

	£95	£40	£20

Red. Price 6/9d. Issued 1948. Renumbered 963 in 1954. Deleted 1959. 116mm. DC/TP. Rubber tracks.

Later model price (yellow).	£15	£10	£5

No. 973A. 'Eaton Vale' Artic. Tractor Shovel

	£15	£10	£7

Yellow and red, and later model in yellow. Silver lifting and lowering bucket, articulated main body action. Simulated hydraulic ram action. Price 15/11d. Issued 1971. Deleted 1975. 116mm.

AMBULANCES

No. 24a. Ambulance

£350

Red chassis with grey body. Model has a criss-cross chassis, a plain radiator, open windows with high frontage wings. Price 9d. Issued April 1934. Deleted 1938. 102mm. DC/RT.

No. 24a. Ambulance

£200

Red chassis with grey body with criss-cross chassis, open windows, high front wings and radiator with badge. Price 6d. Issued 1938. Deleted 1940. 102mm. DC/RT.

MODEL	M/B	M/U	G/C

No. 30f. Ambulance   £150   £100   £75

Red chassis with grey body. Red
crosses painted on sides and solid
moulded chassis with holes for
passengers. All windows open. Model
has a plain radiator. Price 9d. Issued
August 1935. Deleted 1938. 101mm.
DC/RT.

No. 30f. Ambulance   £150   £100   £75

Red chassis with grey body. Red
crosses painted on sides with solid
moulded chassis with holes for
passengers. All windows are open and
there is a radiator with badge. Price
6d. Issued 1938. Deleted 1940.
101mm. DC/RT.

No. 30F. Ambulance   £200   £150   £75

Black chassis with grey or cream
body. Red crosses painted on sides.
Moulded chassis, and all windows
open. Price 4/11d. Issued 1946.
Deleted 1947. 99mm. DC/RT.

No. 30F. Ambulance   £30   £20   £15

Cream with slotted chassis for
passengers. Price 4/11d. Issued 1946.
Deleted 1947. 99mm. DC/RT.

No. 30F. Ambulance   £70   £60   £50

Dark grey, otherwise as previous.
Rare colour.

No. 30F. Ambulance   £30   £25   £20

With black slotted chassis and white
tyres. Details as previous.

No. 30F. Ambulance   £65   £50   £40

Black chassis with cream body. Red
crosses painted on sides, moulded
chassis and no windows. Price 4/11d.
Issued 1947. Deleted 1948. 99mm.
DC/RT.

No. 30F. Ambulance   £200   £150   £100

With slotted chassis holes for
passengers. White tyres. Model has a
green chassis and no crosses on sides.
Otherwise details as previous model.
Rare.

MODEL	M/B	M/U	G/C

No. 30H. Daimler Ambulance

	£75	£35	£15

Cream with red crosses. Price 3/3d.
Issued January 1950. Renumbered 253
in 1954. Deleted 1960. 96mm.
DC/RT/TP.

No. 253. Daimler Ambulance

	£60	£25	£15

White with red crosses on sides.
Model also in cream with red crosses.
Price 2/9d. Issued 1954. Deleted 1964.
96mm. DC/TP/RT.

No. 253. Daily Service Daimler Ambulance

	£50	£20	£5

Some models have the red cross
missing and these are worth perhaps
five times more than the normal
model. Price 3/11d. Issued 1960.
Deleted 1969. 96mm. DC/TP/RT.

No. 263. Superior Criterion Ambulance

	£55	£30	£10

The word 'Ambulance' on windows.
LHD/SW/SS/FTS/S/W. with two
attendants, dummy roof light and
patient on stretcher. Opening doors.
Price 8/6d. Issued September 1962.
Deleted 1964. 127mm. DC/TP/P/RT.
Also available for the American
market.

No. 263A. Superior Criterion Ambulance

	£65	£30	£10

White and cream with red side
flashes, roof light, driver and
attendant and patient on stretcher.
Opening rear doors, silver hubs,
bumpers etc. Price 8/11d. Issued
1964. Deleted 1972. 127mm.
DC/RT/P.

No. 267. Superior Cadillac Ambulance

£55   £30   £15

Cream and red with patient on stretcher. Opening doors and roof light. Two-tone sides and red bonnet with silver bumpers, headlights etc. Word 'Ambulance' on the front and sides and also at the top of model. Price 13/11d. Issued 1964. Deleted 1970. 152mm. DC/P/RT.

No. 267A. Superior Cadillac Ambulance

£55   £30   £15

Completely all-red model, apart from cream flashes on sides. Details otherwise as previous.

No. 268. Range Rover Ambulance

£45   £25   £10

White. Price 15/6d. Issued 1973. Deleted 1978. 109mm. DC/P.

No. 274. Ford Transit Ambulance

£45   £25   £10

White with opening side and rear doors, complete with patient on stretcher. Ambulance roof sign and red cross with the word 'Ambulance' on side. Three windows at each side blacked out. Red cab interior. Price £1.25p. Issued 1977. Deleted 1980. 133mm. DC/P.

No. 276. Ford Transit Ambulance

£50   £30   £10

White and orange with black interior of cab. Red crosses on sides with word 'Ambulance' on sides and roof sign. Opening doors. Price 99p. Issued 1971. Deleted 1976. 129mm. DC/P.

MODEL	M/B	M/U	G/C

No. 276. Ford Transit Ambulance

	M/B	M/U	G/C
No. 276. Ford Transit Ambulance	£45	£20	£5

White. Price 99p. Issued 1971.
Deleted 1978. 129mm. DC/P.

No. 277. Superior Criterion Ambulance with flashing light

	£55	£30	£15

Two-tone colours of dark blue and
cream with two drivers. Flashing roof
light. White tyres. Silver trim on
bumpers, grille, etc. Opening rear
doors. Price 8/11d. Issued 1969.
Deleted 1972. 127mm. DC/P.

No. 227A. Superior Criterion Ambulance

	£60	£25	£10

Metallic blue with white roof. Word
'Ambulance' on windows. Two
drivers and opening rear door.
Flashing red light. Price 8/11d. Issued
December 1962. Deleted 1969.
127mm.
TP/P/RT/DC/LHD/SS/FTS/SW.

No. 277B. Superior Criterion Ambulance and flashing light

	£75	£40	£20

All blue body. Very rare colour.
Issued 1962. Deleted 1969. Other
details are 277/A.

No. 278. Vauxhall Ambulance

	£30	£15	£10

White with blue roof-light. Red
crosses on sides and the word
'Ambulance' on the front. With driver
and silver bumpers, grille, etc. Price
7/-. Issued 1964. Deleted 1972.
87mm. DC/P/RT.

No. 278A. Vauxhall Victor Ambulance

	£25	£15	£10

White, with red crosses on sides.
Dummy blue roof light. Opening rear
doors. Patient on stretcher. Price
6/11d. Issued July 1964. Deleted
1972. 91mm.
SW/SS/FTS/S/DC/TP/P/RT.

No. 288. Superior Cadillac Ambulance

	£50	£30	£15

White with orange panels along
bottom sides. Roof light and
ambulance sign with orange panel on
bonnet. Patient on stretcher. Price

4/11d. Issued 1964. Deleted 1970.
152mm. DC/P.

No. 288. Superior Cadillac Ambulance

	£45	£25	£10

White with red base line and silver
bumpers, hubs, etc. Patient on
stretcher and opening doors at side
and rear. The model with the opening
side door is a factory flaw and is a
rate item to find. Price 4/11d. Issued
1964. Deleted 1977. 142mm. DC/P.

Model with flaw. £150

No. 288. Superior Cadillac Ambulance

	£45	£20	£10

Cream, white and red. With opening
rear doors, roof lights and siren and
patient on stretcher. White interior.
Price 7/11d. Issued 1971. Deleted
1978. 152mm. DC/RT.

No. 288A. Danmak Special Superior Cadillac Ambulance

	£150

Black and white, made for the Danish
market. With roof light and sign,
patient on stretcher, opening doors at
rear. Equivalent English price 8/11d.
Issued 1964. Deleted 1971. 152mm.
DC/P.
This model would only be brought
back to England by tourists, or sent
by collectors on an exchange-basis.
Rare model.

MILITARY VEHICLES AND ACCESSORIES

No. 22f. Army tank

	£150	£100	£80

Green or grey with a rotating turret.
Rubber treads. Price 1/-. Issued
December 1933. Deleted 1940. 87mm.
DC. This early example was marked
'Hornby Series'.

	M/B	M/U	G/C
Price of model in grey	£100	£90	£80
Marked 'Dinky Toys' in green	£100	£90	£80
Marked 'Dinky Toys' in grey	£90	£80	£70

Mint examples are rare owing to
metal fatigue.

MODEL	M/B	M/U	G/C

No. 27D. Land Rover

£300 £250 £175

Dark green and black. Rare model
which definitely exists. Spare wheel
behind driver and screen. Price 3/9d.
Issued April 1950. Deleted 1960.
90mm. DC/RT/TP.
Remember, items such as the one
listed above can never be replaced if
stolen or damaged. Very rare model.

No. 30HM. Daimler Military Ambulance

£150 £100 £75

Green with red crosses on roof, sides,
and back. This model was also
numbered 253, made for the American
market only. English price 3/-. Issued
1951. Deleted 1960. 96mm.
DC/TP/RT.

Light or medium grey

£250 £200 £125

No. 301m. Daimler Military Ambulance

£750 £450 £350

Green. Special issue. Same model
copied later when brought out for the
American market post-war. Pre-war
model is rare and owing to metal
fatigue will only be found in
reasonable condition. Red crosses on
roof, sides and back. Price 3/-. Issued
1938. Deleted 1939. 96mm.
DC/RT/TP.

No. 37c. Royal Corps of Signals Dispatch Rider

£150 £100 £75

Khaki rider on green machine. Also
available in battlefront colours. Rider
has a blue and white arm-band. This
band was missing on certain models.
Model had white wheels or black
wheels, making a vast difference in
market value. Price 6d. Issued June
1938. Deleted 1940. 46mm. DC/RW.
Model with missing arm-band and
white wheels.

With missing arm-band and black wheels	£100	£60	£50
With arm-band and white wheels	£100	£70	£60
With arm-band and black wheels	£45	£30	£20

MODEL	M/B	M/U	G/C

No. 150a. Royal Tank Corps Officer

| | £10 | £7 | £5 |

Very rare model with khaki uniform. Price 2d. Issued February 1938. Deleted 1940.

No. 150b. Royal Tank Corps Private (sitting)

| | £4 | £3 | £2 |

Khaki. Price 1½d. Issued February 1938. Deleted 1940. DC.

No. 150c. Royal Tank Corps Private (standing)

| | £4 | £3 | £2 |

Khaki. Price 1½d. Issued February 1938. Deleted 1940. DC.

No. 150d. Army Driver

| | £5 | £4 | £3 |

Khaki. Price 1½d. Issued February 1938. Deleted 1940. DC.

No. 150e. Royal Corps NCO

| | £4 | £2 | £1 |

Khaki. Price 1½d. Issued February 1938. Deleted 1940. DC.

No. 151a. Medium Tank

| | £45 | £40 | £25 |

Matt green with white squadron markings. Rotating turret and aerial. Price 1/6d. Issued December 1937. Deleted 1940. 92mm. DC/TP/with chain.

No. 152a. Light Army Tank

| | £35 | £25 | £15 |

Matt green with rotating turret and aerial and white squadron markings and chain. Price 1/-. Issued December 1937. Deleted 1940. 68mm. DC.

No. 152/A2. Light Army Tank

Military green with rotating turret, aerial, white squadron markings and chain. Price 2/11d. Issued 1946. Deleted 1948. 68mm DC.

| With green pre-war baseplate | £35 | £25 | £15 |
| With post-war black baseplate | £30 | £20 | £10 |

No. 152A. Light Army Tank

| | £65 | £35 | £20 |

Black tracks and no squadron markings. Otherwise as before.

No. 152b. Reconnaissance Car

Military green with six wheels. Price 1/-. Issued February 1938. Deleted 1940. 89mm. DC/TP/RT.

MODEL	M/B	M/U	G/C
Green baseplate	£30	£25	£15
Black baseplate	£20	£15	£10

No. 152/B2. Reconnaissance Car

Green or brown with six wheels. Price
2/11d. Issued 1946. Deleted 1948.
89mm. DC/TP/RT.

Black baseplate and brown body	£25	£20	£15
Black baseplate and green body	£20	£15	£10

No. 153A. Jeep

Green. This is a US model with a
white star on the bonnet.
LHD/SW/TP with screen, four wheels
and one spare wheel at rear. Price
2/6d. Issued April 1946. Deleted
1948. 69mm. DC/TP/RT.

Model with flat bonnet	£25	£15	£10
Model with curved bonnet	£12	£10	£8

No. 160a. Royal Artillery NCO

	£3	£2	£1

Khaki uniform. Price 2d. Issued
August 1939. Deleted 1940. DC.

No. 160b. Royal Artillery Gunner (seated)

	£3	£2	£1

Khaki. Price 1½d. Issued August
1939. Deleted 1940. DC.

No. 160c. Royal Artillery Gunlayer

	£3	£2	£1

Khaki. Price 1½d. Issued August
1939. Deleted 1940. DC.

No. 160d. Royal Artillery Gunner (standing)

	£3	£2	£1

Khaki. Price 1½d. Issued August
1939. Deleted 1940. DC.

No. 161. Searchlight on Lorry

	£65	£50	£35

Green. Price 1/6d. Issued March
1939. Deleted 1940. 99mm. DC/RT.

No. 161a. A.A. Gun on Trailer

	£40	£30	£20

Green. Gun elevates and moves, etc.
Folding sides and holes in seats for
gunners. Tow-bar and hook. Price
1/6d. Issued March 1939. Deleted
1940. 115mm. DC/TP/RT.

MODEL	M/B	M/U	G/C

No. 161/B2. A.A. Gun and Trailer

| | £30 | £15 | £10 |

Green. The gun elevates etc. The sides fold down and there are holes in the seats for gunners. Tow-bar and hook. Price 3/3d. Issued 1946. Deleted 1948. 89mm. DC/TP/RT.

No. 162a. Light Dragon Motor Tractor

| | £50 | £25 | £10 |

Green. Green baseplate. Price 1/3d. Issued March 1939. Deleted 1940. 89mm. DC/with chain.

No. 162/A2. Light Dragon Motor Tractor

Dark green with chain. There are holes in the seats for driver etc. Some models have rubber wheels instead of chains. Price 3/11d. Issued 1946. Deleted 1948.

| Prices for model with rubber wheels and black baseplate | £55 | £30 | £20 |
| Price for model with chains and black baseplate | £50 | £30 | £15 |

No. 162b. Trailer

| | £45 | £20 | £10 |

Green. Green baseplate. Price 5d. Issued March 1939. Deleted 1940. 43mm. DC/RT.

No. 162/B2. Trailer

| | £25 | £15 | £5 |

Green. Tow-bar and hook. Black baseplate. Price 11d. Issued 1946. Deleted 1948. 54mm. DC/RT.

No. 162c. 18 Pounder Gun

| | £35 | £20 | £10 |

Green. Green baseplate. Price 5d. Issued March 1939. Deleted 1940. 78mm. DC/RT.

No. 162/C2. 18 Pounder Gun

| | £35 | £20 | £10 |

Green. With rubber tyres and black baseplate. Tow-bar and hook. Price 2/-. Issued 1946. Deleted 1948. 78mm. DC.

No. 170. Ford Fordor US Army Staff Car

| | £95 | £40 | £20 |

Special model made for the American market. Military green with white US star on nose. Equivalent price 4/6d. Issued 1957. Deleted 1958. 102mm. DC/TP/RT.

MODEL	M/B	M/U	G/C

No. 281. Army Military Hovercraft

	£45	£20	£10

Green. Black base with the word 'Army' and the model has gun and showing Union Jack on deck. Price 75p. Issued 1973. Deleted 1976. 139mm. DC/P.

No. 601. Paramoke

Military green or camouflage or battlefront colours. Latter is worth double. Complete with parachute in camouflage or plain military green. Green canopy on model with black tyres. An all-action model with plastic Speediwheels from approx. 1974. Price 8/3d. Issued 1966. Deleted 1978. 76mm. DC/P/RT.

Metal wheels and rubber tyres	£45	£20	£10
Plastic Speediwheels	£40	£25	£10

No. 602. Armoured Command Car

	£35	£20	£10

White and khaki with driver. Price 55p. Issued 1977. Deleted 1980. 57mm. DC/P.

No. 602/A. Armoured Command Car

	£30	£20	£10

Green with US Star and radar scanner. Price 75p. Issued 1975. Deleted 1978. 160mm. DC/P.

No. 603. Army Private (seated)

	£1	50p	25p

Khaki with peg attached to underbody to fix model to seat of vehicle. Price 3d. Issued 1950. Deleted 1968. Height 20mm.

No. 603/A. Set of Army Personnel

	£20	£10	£5

Green. Set of six in a box. Price 1/11d. Issued 1950. Deleted 1969-70.

No. 604. Army Personnel (drivers)

	£20	£5	£3

Khaki with new green and yellow boxes. Packed in numbers of six personnel per box. Issued 1960. Deleted 1973.

MODEL	M/B	M/U	G/C

No. 604/A. Land Rover Bomb Disposal Unit

	M/B	M/U	G/C
	£95	£35	£25

New 142nd scale in two-tone green with orange panels on sides. This is a bomb-disposal unit truck in this rare two-tone colour. This Land Rover had a blue-green roof light and the words 'Explosive Disposal' in red on the front headboard. Price 76p. Issued 1976. Deleted 1978. 160mm. DC/P.

No. 604/A2. Land Rover Bomb Disposal Unit

£35	£20	£10

Green with orange-red side panels. In 1/42nd scale with signs on headboard, 'Explosive Disposal'. Price 76p. Issued 1976. Deleted 1979. 160mm. DC/P.

No. 609. The 105mm Howitzer with Gun Crew

£55	£25	£10

Green. Price 99p. Issued 1976. Deleted 1979. 199mm. DC/P.

No. 612. Commando Jeep

£45	£20	£10

Two-tone green and black with two guns and driver. In new 1/42nd scale. Price 65p. Issued 1976. Deleted 1979. 105mm. DC/P.

No. 612/A. Commando Jeep

£35	£20	£10

Army battlefront camouflage colours. Also plain military green. Price 65p. Issued 1974. Deleted 1979. 108mm. DC/P.

No. 615. US Jeep and 105mm Howitzer

£45	£25	£15

Green with authentic US markings and driver. Price 18/11d. Issued 1968. Deleted 1978. 199mm. DC/P.

No. 616. AEC Artic with Chieftain Tank

£95	£35	£20

Green. Price 21/-. Issued 1968. Deleted 1978. 318mm. DC/P/RT.

No. 617. Volkswagen KDF and 50mm Gun

£50	£25	£15

Dark greyish green or German army colour. German cross on each side. Price 16/11d. Issued 1968/69. Deleted 1978. 159mm. DC/P. The gun was a Pak-anti-tank model.

MODEL	M/B	M/U	G/C
No. 618. AEC Artic with Helicopter	£65	£30	£15

Green. Price £1.25p. Issued 1976.
Deleted 1978. 318mm. DC/P.

No. 619. Bren Gun	£30	£20	£10

Green. Price 1/11d. Issued 1968.
Deleted 1972. 35mm. DC.

No. 620. Berliet Missile Launcher	£65	£30	£15

Green with full working parts. Price
14/11d. Issued 1968. Deleted 1971.
150mm. DC/P. The French Dinky
number was 816.

No. 621. Three Ton Army Wagon	£50	£25	£10

Green with full squadron markings.
Four wheels and one spare wheel.
Price 4/8d. Issued June 1954. Deleted
1963. 113mm. DC/TP/RT.

No. 622. Bren Gun Carrier	£45	£20	£10

Green. Price 75p. Issued 1975.
Deleted 1978. 125mm. DC/P. A
mistake in the mm of the model was
wrongly advertised on some of the
boxes (159).

No. 622/A. Ten Ton Army Truck	£75	£20	£10

Green. Six wheels and one spare and
holes for passengers inside model.
Price 6/10d. Issued May 1954.
Deleted 1963. 137mm. DC/TP/RT.
Very rare.

No. 623. Army Covered Wagon	£65	£25	£15

Green with squadron marking etc.
Four wheels and one spare. Price
3/7d. Issued March 1954. Deleted
1963. 105mm. DC/TP/RT.

No. 624. Daimler Ambulance	£200		

Fine model in green. Made especially
for the American market with red
crosses on roof, sides and back.
Equivalent price 4/6d. Issued 1954.
Deleted 1960. 96mm. DC/TP/RT.

No. 625. Six Pounder Tank Gun	£35	£15	£5

Green. Price 35p. Issued 1975.
Deleted 1978. 159mm. DC.

No. 626. Military Ambulance   £60   £25   £10

Green with red crosses on the roof, sides and back. Four wheels, one spare and opening doors at rear. Price 6/11d. Issued September 1956. Deleted 1962. 110mm. DC/TP/RT.

No. 630. Ferret Armoured Car   £35   £15   £10

Khaki. Price 54p. Issued 1973. Deleted 1978. 80mm. DC/P.

No. 641. Army 1 Ton Cargo Truck   £50   £25   £10

Green with army squadron markings, four wheels and holes for passengers inside truck. Price 3/9d. Issued August 1954. Deleted 1962. 79mm. DC/TP/RT.

No. 643. Army Water Tanker   £45   £20   £10

Green with squadron markings, four wheels and one spare. Price 4/3d. Issued January 1958. Deleted 1964. 89mm. DC/TP/RT.

No. 651. Centurion Tank   £75   £30   £15

Green with rotating turret and squadron markings. Price 7/11d. Issued 1954. Deleted 1961. 149mm. DC/RT.

No. 651/A. Centurion Tank   £75   £30   £15

Light green or medium green with Army markings etc. Price 10/11d. Issued 1961. Deleted 1971. 146mm. DC/P/Tracks.

No. 654. 155mm Mobile Gun   £35   £15   £5

Battlefront colours. Price 30p. Issued 1974. Deleted 1976. 151mm. DC/P.

No. 654. 155mm Mobile Gun   £35   £15   £5

Light or medium green. Price 36p. Issued 1976. Deleted 1979. 151mm. DC/P.

MODEL	M/B	M/U	G/C

No. 656. 88mm Gun   £35   £15   £5

1/35th scale in battlefront livery and markings. Model can be found in normal military green. Price 55p. Issued 1975. Deleted 1979. 218mm. DC/P.

No. 660. Tank Transporter   £100   £30   £15

Green with folding ramps at the rear. 6 × 6 wheels and one spare wheel. Price 17/6d. Issued June 1956. Deleted 1964. 335mm. DC/RT.

No. 660/A. Mobile A.A. Gun with crew   £55   £25   £10

Light or dark green. With three crew members. Black base. Price 78p. Issued 1978. Deleted 1980. 218mm. DC/P/RT.

No. 661. Recovery Tractor   £70   £30   £15

Green with six wheels and working crane. Price 9/6d. Issued June 1957. Deleted 1964. 134mm. DC/TP/RT.

No. 662. Static 88mm. Gun with crew   £35   £15   £5

A big gun which fires plastic shells. In 1/35th scale with three gun-crew figures. Camouflage or green livery. Price 55p. Issued 1975. Deleted 1978. 185mm. DC/P.

No. 665. Honest John Missile Launcher   £100   £50   £20

Green with ten wheels and one spare with elevating ramp. Firing rocket. Price 17/11d. Issued March 1964. Deleted 1969. 188mm. DC/TP/RT/P.

No. 666. Missile Erector Vehicle and Corporal Missile   £200   £50   £20

Green with working rockets, four wheels, one spare and two wheels. Price 30/11d. Issued November 1959. Deleted 1964. 240mm and 90mm. DC/TP/P/RT.

No. 667. Missile Servicing Platform Vehicle   £75   £45   £25

Green with side supports which fold down. Elevating platform, six wheels and one spare. Price 14/3d. Issued April 1960. Deleted 1961. 130mm vehicle only. O.A. 197mm. DC/TP/P/RT. Only a limited number made and a good investment.

MODEL	M/B	M/U	G/C

No. 667/A. Armoured Patrol Car
£50 **£20** **£10**

Battlefield grey livery. 1/48th scale.
Price 99p. Issued 1976. Deleted 1980.
80mm. DC/P.

Price for the normal green livery   **£9**   **£7**   **£5**

No. 668. Foden Army Truck
£350

Two-tone green with orange panels on
cab doors and white cab interior. In
1/42nd scale. Rare colour, although
there is a model in the normal
military green livery. Price £1.50p.
Issued 1976. Deleted 1978. 197mm.
DC/P.

Price for the normal colour of green   **£95**   **£30**   **£15**

No. 669. USA Universal Jeep
£45 **£20** **£10**

Green. This model was especially
made for the American market.
Equivalent price 2/9d. Issued 1956.
Deleted 1958. 83mm. DC/TP/RT.

No. 670. Armoured Car
£30 **£15** **£5**

Green with rotating turret and
squadron markings. Price 2/10d.
Issued September 1954. Deleted 1964.
73mm. DC/TP/RT.

No. 670/A. Armoured Car
£25 **£10** **£5**

Green and light green, with revolving
turret. Squadron markings and
numbers. Price 4/-. Issued 1965.
Deleted 1971. 73mm. DC.

No. 671. Mk 1 Corvette
£35 **£15** **£10**

Grey with black stripes and dark fawn
markings. with firing missiles. Price
76p. Issued 1976. Deleted 1979.
260mm. DC/P.

No. 672. OSA Missile Boat
£30 **£15** **£10**

Grey and black with firing missiles.
Price 76p. Issued 1976. Deleted 1979.
206mm. DC/P.

No. 673. Scout Car
£40 **£15** **£10**

Green. Holes in seat for driver and
passenger. Price 3/2d. Issued
November 1953. Deleted 1962.
68mm. DC/RT.

MODEL	M/B	M/U	G/C

No. 674. Austin Champ (promotional special)

£500 — —

White. With driver and spare wheel, Presented to several important staff members of UN Forces. Price £1. Issued 1965. Deleted 1971. 70mm. DC/P. Rare model. Mint and boxed only.

No. 674. Austin Champ

£45 £15 £10

Green. SW/TP. Four wheels, one spare and holes for driver and passenger. Tin plate windscreen. Price 3/2d. Issued 1954. Deleted 1964. 69mm. DC/RT.

No. 674/A. Austin Champ

£45 £15 £10

Green or camouflaged with driver and spare wheel on rear. Price 4/-. Issued 1965. Deleted 1971. 70mm. DC/P.

No. 675. Ford Fordor US Army Staff Car

£280

Green. Made for the American market. Equivalent price 4/6d. Issued 1966. Deleted 1967. 102mm. DC/TP/RT. Rare model.

No. 675/A. 153 Missile Firing Boat

£45 £15 £5

Grey, silver grey and black. Model runs along on concealed wheels. This was a model of the motor patrol boat used in many battles with great success by the Navy. Price 99p. Issued 1976. Deleted 1979. 170mm. DC/P.

No. 676. Armoured Personnel Carrier

£50 £30 £15

Green. With six wheels and rotating turret and squadron markings etc. Price 3/2d. Issued February 1955. Deleted 1962. 82mm. DC/RT.

No. 676/A. Daimler Armoured Car

£55 £25 £10

Green with squadron markings and numbers. Price 3/11d. Issued 1960. Deleted 1966. 72mm. DC/RT.

No. 677. Armoured Command
Vehicle

£70   £35   £15

Green with six wheels and squadron
markings. Price 5/4d. Issued April
1957. Deleted 1962. 134mm.
DC/TP/RT.

No. 678. Air-Sea Rescue
Launch

£55   £25   £10

Fawn and black complete with pilot
and dinghy. With RAF markings and
the word 'Rescue' on each side. Price
79p. Issued 1976. Deleted 1979.
170mm. DC/P.

No. 680. Ferret Armoured
Car

£45   £20   £10

Medium green with full squadron
markings. Price 54p. Issued 1972.
Deleted 1979. 80mm. DC/P.

No. 681. D.U.K.W.

£55   £25   £10

Light green with full squadron
markings. Price 54p. Issued 1972.
Deleted 1979. 127mm. DC/P.

No. 682. Stalwart Load
Carrier

£55   £25   £10

Green with six large black wheels and
black cab interior. Full squadron
markings. Price 90p. Issued 1972.
Deleted 1979. 132mm. DC/P.

No. 683. Chieftain Tank

£75   £30   £15

Green with full squadron markings
and rotating turret. With tracks. This
model fires plastic shells. Price
£1.60p. Issued 1972. Deleted 1979.
117mm. DC/P.

No. 683/A. Chieftain Tank

£75   £30   £15

Camouflaged, in the new 1/50th scale.
Price £1.76p. Issued 1972. Deleted
1979. 217mm. DC/P/Tracks.

MODEL	M/B	M/U	G/C
No. 686. 25 Pounder Field Gun	£35	£25	£10

Green with tow-bar. Price 2/9d.
Issued 1957. Deleted 1969. 90mm.
DC/RT.

No. 686/A. Trailer for 25 Pounder Field Gun	£35	£25	£10

Green. Price 1/9d. Issued 1957.
Deleted 1969. 58mm. DC/R/RT/TP.

No. 686. Convoy Army Truck	£55	£25	£10

Military green with black bumper and
silver wheels. Model had misprint of
number and should be 687 and this
wrong number on the box of model
makes it more valuable. Price £1.25p.
Issued 1978. Deleted 1979. 110mm.
DC/P.

No. 687. Convoy Army Truck	£50	£25	£10

Green with black bumper and
removable green canopy and silver
wheels. Price £1.25p. Issued 1977/78.
Deleted 1980. 110mm. D/P.

No. 688. Field Artillery Tractor	£45	£25	£10

Green with full squadron markings
and four wheels with one spare. Price
3/5d. Issued 1957. Deleted 1969.
81mm. DC/RT/TP.

No. 688/A. Field Artillery Tractor	£55	£25	£10

Green with full squadron markings.
Spare wheel at rear. Price 4/-. Issued
1960. Deleted 1969. 79mm.
DC/TP/RT.

No. 689. Medium Artillery Tractor	£75	£30	£20

Green. Excellent model of a six-wheel
drive vehicle used for towing medium
artillery and equipment over rough
and dangerous country. With full
squadron markings, driver and hook.
Price 8/9d. Issued 1957. Deleted
1962. 140mm. DC/TP/RT.

No. 690. Scorpion Tank	£65	£30	£15

Green with rotating turret and
camouflage net. Full military
markings. 1/40th scale. With four
round rapid firing gun. Price £1.25p.
Issued 1975. Deleted 1979. 120mm.
DC/P.

MODEL	M/B	M/U	G/C

No. 691. Striker Anti-Tank Vehicle

	M/B	M/U	G/C
	£45	£20	£10

Camouflaged. With five firing rockets singly or all together. In the new 1/40th scale. Price £1.55p. Issued 1976. Deleted 1979. 122mm. DC/P.

No. 692. 5.5 Medium Gun

| | £35 | £10 | £5 |

Green with tow-bar which splits, and elevating gun. Price 3/2d. Issued September 1955. Deleted 1962. 131mm. DC/RT.

No. 692/A. Leopard Tank

| | £55 | £30 | £15 |

Grey or green. Price £1.25p. Issued 1976. Deleted 1979. 198mm. DC/P.

No. 693.7.2. Howitzer Gun

| | £40 | £15 | £5 |

Green or grey. Gun elevates. Price 3/5d. Issued October 1958. Deleted 1963. 130mm. DC/RT.

No. 694. Hanomag 7.5cm Tank Destroyer

| | £40 | £20 | £10 |

Dark grey with German markings and number '145' on the sides. With large tracks and moveable front wheels. Price £1.55p. Issued 1976. Deleted 1979. 171mm. DC/P.

No. 694. Hanomag 7.5cm Tank Destroyer

| | £45 | £20 | £10 |

Green or grey. Price £1.55p. Issued 1976. Deleted 1979. 171mm. DC/P.

No. 696. Leopard Anti-Aircraft Tank

| | £55 | £20 | £10 |

Grey with full military markings and numbers. Price £1.25p. Issued 1976. Deleted 1979. 152mm. DC.

No. 697. 25 Pounder Field Gun Set

| | £60 | £20 | £10 |

Green. Price 10/6d. Issued 1964. Deleted 1971. 174mm. DC/T/P/RT.

No. 699. Leopard Recovery Tank

| | £65 | £30 | £20 |

Grey with full markings and numbers. Price £1.50p. Issued 1976. Deleted 1979. 147mm. DC/P.

MODEL	M/B	M/U	G/C

No. 739. AGM5 Zero-Sen

| | £35 | £15 | £5 |

Green and black with yellow lines and red circles. This is a model with a motor driver propeller. These planes did battle over the Pacific with great effect. Price £1.25p. Issued 1976. Deleted 1979. 184mm. DC/P.

No. 815. Panhard Armoured Car

| | £65 | £30 | £10 |

Green showing the French flag. With four wheels with tyres and four without and turret which rotates. Price 8/7d. Issued July 1962. Deleted 1964. 104mm. DC/RT/TP. Very rare model.

No. 817. AMX 13 Ton Tank

| | £75 | £30 | £10 |

Green with rotating turret. Rubber tracks. Price 12/6d. Issued July 1962. Deleted 1964. 107mm. DC/TP.

No. 822. M.3 Half-Track

| | £65 | £25 | £15 |

Green with rotating machine gun and rubber tracks. Price 9/11d. Issued July 1962. Deleted 1964. 121mm. DC/TP/RT.

No. 884. Brockway Truck with Bridge

| | £95 | £30 | £25 |

Green with ten wheels and inflatable pontoons. Price 38/-. Issued September 1962. Deleted 1964. 181mm. DC/TP.

No. 3284. Army Mogul Wagon

| | £30 | £15 | £5 |

Dark brown and fawn in battlefront livery with driver and passenger. Price 77p. Issued 1976. Deleted 1978. 236mm. DC/P.

No. 3287. Mogul Army Truck

| | £30 | £15 | £5 |

Dark green with light green cover. American star on bonnet. Price 77p. Issued 1976. Deleted 1979. 260mm. DC/P.

BUSES AND COACHES

No. 29c. Double Decker Bus   £500

Blue with white or cream roof. Words
'Dunlop Tyres' on sides. Stairs on
rear platform and the model has the
first type radiator (AEC). One of the
more sought after buses. Price 1/-.
Issued early 1938. Deleted 1939.
100mm. DC/RT.

No. 29c. Double Decker Bus   £450

Red and cream, or red and grey, or
green and white. The red and grey is
very rare indeed. With stairs on rear
platform and first type radiator.
Various adverts on the sides,
'Beecham Pills', 'Wild Woodbine The
Great Little Cigarette'. Price 1/-.
Issued March 1938. Deleted 1940.
100mm. DC/RT.

Red and grey (with Woodbine advt.)   **£3000**

No. 29C. Double Decker Bus   £110   £40   £25

Green or red bodywork and cream or
grey top. Model has the Type 1
radiator (AEC) and cutaway front
mudguard with no stairs. Various
adverts connected with model, and
many with no adverts at all. The
models with adverts are worth
considerably more than the plain type.
Price 2/10d. Issued October 1947.
Deleted 1955. 101mm. DC/RT.

No. 29C. Double Decker Bus   £80   £40   £25

Green with cream top. 'Dunlop, the
World's Master Tyre' on the sides.
With Type 2 radiator (GUY) with
straight front mudguards. Price 3/9d.
Issued 1950. Deleted 1954.
Renumbered same year to 290.
Deleted 1964. 101mm. DC/RT.

No. 29dz. Autobus   £750

Dark brown or silver. Model was
advertised in the *Meccano Magazine* in
the 1930s, but the model never sold in
England officially (unofficially it was).
Advertised price 10d. Issued 1937/39.
Deleted 1940. Very rare model.

MODEL	M/B	M/U	G/C

No. 27. Tramcar — £300 £200 £100

Red and white, advertising 'Lipton's Tea' on the sides.. Price 6d. Issued July 1934. Deleted 1938. 77mm. DC. Very rare.

No. 27. Tram Car — £300 £200 £100

Red and cream with Ovaltine adverts. Otherwise as before.

No. 27. Tram Car — £400 £300 £200

Green and cream with Ovaltine adverts. Otherwise as before.

No. 29. Double Decker Bus — £500 £400 £300

Green or yellow with white roof. Word 'Marmite' on the sides. This model also had various other adverts connected with it. The models with real high values are those advertising special events such as 'Exhibitions', 'The Great Circus Coming to Town', etc. Model has metal wheels and even though suffering greatly from metal fatigue they bring a fantastic price in the swapmeets and top-class sale rooms throughout the world. Price 6d. Issued July 1934. Deleted 1938. 69mm. DC.

No. 29. Double Decker Bus

Various two-tone colours exist in this model range. The most common are green and blue, although prices vary according to colours. With open rear window. Price 6d. Issued April 1935. Deleted 1940. 88mm. DC/RT.

Blue and green	£350	£250	£150
Yellow and brown	£500	£400	£250
Red and cream	£650	£500	£350

No. 29. Double Decker Bus — £400 £350 £250

Yellow, with the word 'Marmite' on sides. Otherwise as before.

No. 29b. Streamline Bus — £90 £50 £10

No advertising on this issue. Open rear windows. Price 6d. Issued April 1936. Deleted 1937. 88mm. DC/RT.

No. 29B. Streamline Bus — £250 £150 £50

Cream and red or green with no rear windows. Price 2/6d. Issued January 1948. Deleted 1950, 88mm. DC/RT.

MODEL	M/B	M/U	G/C

No. 29E. Single Decker Bus   £130   £60   £25

Cream with blue flashes, or green
with dark green flashes, or blue with
dark blue flashes. Price 3/3d. Issued
March 1948. Deleted 1952. 113mm.
DC/RT/TP.

No. 29F. Single Decker Bus   £75   £35   £25

Red with dark red and silver flashes.
This observation coach has 'Airport
Special' on sides. Price 3/3d. Issued
July 1950. Deleted 1951. 112mm.
DC/TP/RT. Rare model.

No. 29F. Observation Coach   £160   £80   £30

Grey with red flashes. With the words
'Observation Coach' on sides. Price
3/3d. Issued July 1950. Renumbered
280 in 1954. Deleted 1964. 112mm.
DC/TP/RT.

No. 29G. Luxury Coach   £250   £90   £35

Fawn with orange flashes. Price 3/1d.
Issued April 1951. Renumbered 281
in 1954. Deleted 1964. 113mm.
DC/TP/RT.

No. 29H. Duple Roadmaster Coach   £65   £30   £20

Blue with silver flashes. Price 4/4d.
Issued November 1952. Renumbered
282 in 1954. Deleted 1964. 119mm.
DC/TP/RT.

No. 111. Cinderella's Coach   £50   £15   £10

Gold with four white horses and
driver. Driver in pink with girl figure
inside. Made because of film 'The
Slipper and the Rose'. Price £3.75p.
Issued 1977. Deleted 1978. 242mm.
DC/P.

No. 111. Cinderella's Coacn   £100   £75   £50

Gold with four black or four white
horses. With driver and girl figure
inside. Special one-off model. Price
£7.50p. Issued 1977. Deleted 1978.
242mm. DC. Very rare.

No. 248. Continental Touring Coach

$75 $30 $10

One of the best investments Dinky produced in the 1970 period. Coach is the type which carries the various football teams around the country. Model is available in the various soccer-team liveries. Collect them all if you are lucky enough to find them. Basic colour of the model is white. The value of this item will depend on what soccer club colours are connected with it. Price £1.95p. Issued 1978. Deleted 1980. 164mm. DC/P.

No. 280. Observation Coach

$90 $25 $15

Cream with red flashes. This is a renumbering of 29F. Price 3/1d. Issued 1954. Deleted 1960. 112mm. DC/TP/RT.

No. 281. Modern Coach

$90 $30 $20

Fawn with orange flashes, or maroon with cream flashes. Price 2/11d. Issued 1954. Deleted 1960. 113mm. DC/TP/RT.

No. 281. Luxury Coach

$90 $30 $20

Blue with orange or fawn flashes. Deep yellow wheels, black tyres, silver radiator grille and lights. Price 3/6d. Issued 1954. Deleted 1960. 113mm. DC/TP/RT.

No. 282. Duple Roadmaster Coach

Blue with silver flashes, or red with silver flashes. This model was known as the 'Leyland Royal Tiger Bus'. Price 3/5d. Issued April 1954. Deleted 1961. 119mm. DC/TP/RT.

	M/B	M/U	G/C
Blue with silver flashes	£110	£70	£15
Red with silver flashes	£120	£75	£25

No. 283. BOAC Coach

$85 $35 $20

Blue with white roof. With word 'British Overseas Airways Corporation' and 'B.O.A.C.' on sides. Price 4/2d. Issued October 1956. Deleted 1963. 120mm. DC/TP/RT.

MODEL	M/B	M/U	G/C

No. 283. Single Decker Bus

£65 **£30** **£20**

Red with long wide white flashes on sides. With the words, 'Red Arrow'. Silver wheels, headlights, etc. Price 99p. Issued 1971. Deleted 1977. 167mm. DC/P.

No. 283. Single Decker Bus

£95 **£30** **£20**

Metallic red, with automatic opening doors and bell. Price 99p. Issued 1971. Deleted 1977. 167mm. DC/RT/P.

No. 289. London Transport Routemaster Bus

£55 **£20** **£10**

Red. There are many adverts connected with this model. Although there are other colours or liveries for this model the general colour is red. Any collector should consult an expert, or write to me c/o the Publishers with regard to the various values on adverts, etc. The more common adverts are 'London Transport', 'Esso Petrol', 'Tern Shirts' and 'Dunlop'. With driver and conductress. Price 4/2d. Increased to 8/11d after first year. Issued June 1964. Deleted 1966. 121mm. SW/DC/P/RT.

No. 289. London Routemaster Bus

£300

Red. With driver and conductress. Full destination signs on front and rear. Promotional models were a great attraction and this edition is very rare. Words, 'Festival of London Stores', on the sides. Price 9/11d. Issued 1965. Deleted 1966. 121mm. DC/RT/P.

No. 289. Routemaster Bus

£45 **£20** **£10**

Red with the words 'Esso Safety Grip Tyre' on the sides. Price £1.25p. Issued 1971. Deleted 1978. 121mm. DC/P.

No. 289. Routemaster Bus

£60 **£20** **£10**

Red, with words 'Kenning Car . . . Van & Truck Rental' or 'Hire' placed on a wide purple background with silver and plastic trim. Price £1.25p. Issued 1971. Deleted 1978. 121mm. DC/P.

MODEL	M/B	M/U	G/C

No. 289. London Routemaster Bus

| | £20 | £15 | £10 |

Red with the words 'Esso Grip', or 'Esso Safety Grip Tyres'. Also a new introduction of the three-colour variations of 'Schweppes' advert. Cream, white, or grey, otherwise details as previous. Price £1.50p. Issued 1976. Deleted 1978. 121mm. DC/P

No. 289 London Routemaster Bus (promotional)

| | £150 | £100 | £75 |

Gold, with the words 'Madame Tussaud'. Only a very limited number of these models were made, otherwise details as previous 289.

Red with the words 'Madame Tussaud'

| | £100 | £75 | £60 |

Red with the words 'Jackson's the Tailor'

| | £350 | £200 | £100 |

Red with the words 'Woolworth's Stores the Wonder Store for all the Family'

| | £300 | £200 | £100 |

No. 289. London Routemaster Bus

| | £75 | £30 | £15 |

Red, with driver and conductress. Words 'Schweppes' and 'London Transport' on sides. Price £1.50p. Issued 1976. Deleted 1978. 121mm. DC/P.

No. 289. London Routemaster Bus

| | £90 | £50 | £20 |

Red with the words 'Schweppes' and designs on the side. Model has thick black or gold lines around wording on sides. Only a few finished in this style for a special order. Price £1.50p. Issued 1976. Deleted 1978. 121mm. DC/P.

No. 290. Double Decker Bus

| | £60 | £30 | £20 |

Red, with cream roof and the words 'Dunlop, the World's Master Tyre' on sides. This was a Type 2 radiator (Guy). These models come with or without small headboards on the roof at the front, however the values are almost the same. Collectors look for these models in all parts of the world. Price 4/2d. Issued 1957. Deleted 1963. 103mm. DC/TP/RT.

MODEL	M/B	M/U	G/C
No. 290. Dunlop Double Decker Bus	£150	£70	£30

Green with cream roof. Type 3 radiator (Leyland). Price 4/2d. Issued 1957. Deleted 1963. 103mm. DC/RT/TP.

	M/B	M/U	G/C
No. 291. London Bus (Exide)	£175	£80	£25

Red with the words 'Exide Batteries' on sides. With number 73 on destination plates. Type 3 radiator (Leyland). Price 4/2d. Issued 1960. Deleted 1963. 103mm. DC/RT.

Note: For more details on the Atlantean bus see page 11.

	M/B	M/U	G/C
No. 291A. Atlantean City Bus (Kennings)	£65	£30	£15

Red and white. With opening doors.Price 8/11d. Issued 1960. Deleted 1966. 123mm. DC/RT/TP.

	M/B	M/U	G/C
No. 291. Atlantean City Bus	£60	£30	£20

Orange and white. With opening doors. Price 8/11d. Issued 1960. Deleted 1966. 123mm. DC/RT/TP.

	M/B	M/U	G/C
No. 292. Atlantean Bus	£110	£50	£25

Red and white. With the words 'Regent' or 'Corporation Transport' etc. Price 7/10d. Issued August 1962. Deleted 1966. 120mm. DC/P/RT/SW/D/S/W.

	M/B	M/U	G/C
No. 292A. Atlantean Bus	£65	£30	£15

Red and white with the words 'Ribble Transport' or 'Midland Red'. Price 7/10d. Issued July 1962. Deleted 1966. 120mm. DC/P/RT/SW/D/S/W.

	M/B	M/U	G/C
No. 293. Atlantean Bus	£65	£30	£15

Green and white. With the words 'BP is the Key to Better Motoring' and 'Corporation Transport'. Price 7/10d. Issued August 1963. Deleted 1966. 120mm. SW/D/S/W/DC/RT/P.

	M/B	M/U	G/C
No. 293. Atlantean Bus	£65	£30	£15

Green and cream with words in yellow and cream 'BP is the Key to Better Motoring'. With driver. Price 7/11d. Issued 1963. Deleted 1966. 121mm. DC/P/RT.

MODEL	M/B	M/U	G/C
No. 293A. Swiss Postal Bus	£220	£75	£30

Green with orange or cream roof and white interior. Also in yellow with cream roof. Price £1.35p. Issued 1975/6. Deleted 1978. 119mm. DC/P.

	M/B	M/U	G/C
No. 295. Atlantean Bus	£75	£30	£10

Yellow and black with the first version of 'Yellow Pages, Let Your Fingers do the Talking'. Has 'Yellow Pages' in reverse on the headboard. Price £1.35p. Issued 1973. Deleted 1976. 121mm. DC/P.

	M/B	M/U	G/C
No. 295. Atlantean Bus	£55	£20	£10

Yellow and black. As previous model only with 'Yellow Pages' correct on headboard. Price £1.35p. Issued 1973. Deleted 1976. 121mm. DC.

	M/B	M/U	G/C
No. 295. Atlas 'Standard Kenebrake' Bus	£50	£20	£10

Light blue and grey. With windows, steering wheel, seating and four wheel suspension. Price 3/9d. Issued May 1960. Deleted 1969. 86mm. DC/P/RT.

	M/B	M/U	G/C
No. 295. Atlantean Bus	£250	£100	£50

Yellow and black. Black band around the bus immediately above the doors with the words 'Yellow Pages' in white. Very rare colour. Price £1.35p. Issued 1976. Deleted 1977. 121mm. DC/P.

	M/B	M/U	G/C
No. 295A. Atlas 'Kenebrake Bus'	£350	£100	£50

Silver with 'Butlins Holiday Camp Special' on sides. Price 7/11d. Issued 1968/69. Deleted 1971. 90mm. DC/P.

	M/B	M/U	G/C
No. 296. Luxury Coach	£65	£20	£10

Royal blue with white or cream interior. Silver wheels and trim. Price 75p. Issued 1972. Deleted 1975. 119mm. DC/P.

No. 297. Silver Jubilee Bus

	M/B	M/U	G/C
	£75	£30	£15

Silver and black. With words 'The Queen's Silver Jubilee 1977' on the sides. Price £1.50p. Issued and deleted 1977. 123mm. DC/P.

No. 297. Silver Jubilee Bus

£75	£40	£20

Silver, with word 'National' in red and blue letters on each side, otherwise details as previous model. Price £1.50p. Issued and deleted 1977. 123mm. DC/P.

No. 297. Silver Jubilee Bus

£95	£30	£15

Silver with the words 'Woolworth's Stores Everybody Needs One!' Promotional model. Price £1.50p. Issued and deleted 1977. 123mm. DC/P.

No. 306. Luxury Coach Viceroy

£75	£30	£20

Metallic red. Price 96p. Issued 1973. Deleted 1975. 119mm. DC/P.

No. 949. Wayne School Bus Special

£100	£55	£30

Orange, with red trim. With words 'School Bus' on front. Price 12/9d. Issued 1961. Deleted 1964. 195mm. DC/P/TP/RT.

Green with white trim. Very rare livery

£100	£55	£30

No. 952. Vega Major Luxury Coach

£100   £30   £15

Grey and maroon. Word 'Lowland'
on sides. SW/SS/S/W. Six wheels,
flashing indicators and opening boot.
Price 21/-. Issued January 1964.
Deleted 1969. 242mm. DC/P/RT.

Metallic livery   £40   £30   £20

No. 952. Vega Major Luxury Coach

£125   £50   £30

Cream and chocolate or very dark
brown with blue and white seats.
Silver bumpers, grille, etc. Opening
boot and flashing indicators. Price
22/-. Issued 1968. Deleted 1971.
245mm. DC/P/RT.

Metallic livery. Rare model   £125   £35   £30

No. 952. Vega Major Luxury Coach

£95   £40   £20

White or off-white and dark red. With
flashing indicators. Opening boot.
Price 22/-. Issued 1971. Deleted 1973.
245mm. DC/P.

No. 953. Continental Touring Coach

£75   £60   £50

Pale blue with white roof. Also
medium red with cream roof and pale
green with white roof. Both with
words 'Dinky Continental Tours' on
sides. SW/W/Seats. Six wheels and the
same casting as 949. Price 13/6d.
Issued January 1963. Deleted 1964.
242mm. DC/P/RT/TP.

Rare colour of medium red with
cream roof   £250   £200   £100

Rare colour of pale green with white
roof   £300   £250   £150

CARAVANS

MODEL	M/B	M/U	G/C
No. 30g. Caravan	£100	£50	£30

Two-tone green. With two wheels and towing hook. Price 6d. Issued April 1936. Deleted 1940. 81mm. DC/RT/H.

No. 30G. Caravan	£130	£60	£40

Orange and cream. With two wheels and tow-bar. Words 'Caravan Club' shown on a small plaque in front. Price 2/6d. Issued January 1948. Deleted 1950. 81mm. DC/RT.

No. 117. Caravan	£35	£15	£10

Blue and cream. Four berth type with glass roof and full interior fitments. Price 6/-. Issued August 1963. Deleted 1965. 118mm. DC/RT/P/TP/SS/H.

No. 117. Four Berth Caravan with Transparent Roof	£30	£15	£10

Yellow with red interior, white door and tow-bar. Fine interior fittings. Price 7/-. Issued 1965. Deleted 1968. 132mm. DC/P/TP/RT.

No. 188. Four Berth Caravan	£50	£20	£10

Green and yellow with windows and interior fittings. Rare colour. Price 5/6d. Issued April 1961. Deleted 1963. 132mm. DC/TP/P/RT/SS/W/OD/S/HG.

No. 188A. Four Berth Caravan	£55	£30	£20

Cream and blue, or white and blue. Price 5/6d. Issued 1961. Deleted 1963. 132mm. DC/TP/P/RT.

No. 190. Caravan	£35	£15	£10

Cream and orange, with tow-bar. This model is suitable for attachment to almost every model car or Land Rover that Dinky ever made. Price 3/8d. Issued May 1956. Deleted 1960. 118mm. DC/TP/P/RT.

Red and brilliant white. Rare colour	£150	£75	£50
No. 190A. Caravan	£40	£20	£10

Cream and yellow with tow-bar. Price 3/8d. Issued July 1956. Deleted 1961. 118mm. DC/TP/P/RT.

SPORTS CARS AND SALOONS

No. 22a like all the 22 series was sold without a box as an individual model, although models were packed in half-dozens in plain boxes. They were made from diecast-lead, therefore no metal fatigue was possible, even though metal was often chewed by rats in warehouses and old stone built shops. Colours do vary and rare colours mean extra money to any collector.

MODEL	M/B	M/U	G/C
No. 22a. Sports Car	–	£200	£125

Cream with red wings, red interior, and unpainted solid metal wheels. One piece body casting with separate dashboard and windscreen casting. Price 6d. Issued December 1933. Deleted 1935. 82mm.

	M/B	M/U	G/C
No. 22b. Sports Coupé	–	£200	£125

Yellow with green wings and roof with unpainted metal wheels. One piece body. This is a standard colour model. The model is also known in red or cream with green wings. These are more valuable than the normal colours and if any collector wishes to write to me c/o my publisher, I will give a personal valuation. Price 6d. Issued December 1933. Deleted 1935. 82mm.

	M/B	M/U	G/C
No. 22g. Streamlined Tourer	–	£150	£100

Red or cream, also pale green or in a rare black livery. With separate wheel and windscreen casting slid into main body casting. Price 6d. Issued May 1935. Deleted 1940. 85mm. DC/RT.

	M/B	M/U	G/C
No. 22h. Streamlined Saloon	–	£150	£85

This is a 1934 Chrysler Airflow. One piece casting with no bumpers. Price 6d. Issued May 1935. Deleted 1940. 85mm. DC/RT.

	M/B	M/U	G/C
No. 23a. Racing Sports Car	—	£150	£100

The first issue of the 23A Racing cars represented an MG Magic Midget and was made in lead. There are two distinct colour schemes.
The first has a cream body with flash on upper surface of body and tail,

with circle on nose in orange or green.
Cream wheels with white tyres. Some
models have matching orange or green
tyres.
The second type has cream body with
orange stripes along the body sides,
representing the famous George
Eyston's 'Humbug', with cream or
coloured tyres. Price for both types
6d. Issued April 1934 and deleted in
1935, in favour of the second issue in
similar casting details. Second type
deleted in 1938. 94mm. DC/RT.

No. 23a. Racing Car or Sports Model

	–	£160	£35

Blue and white or blue and silver.
Also yellow livery with the flash and
numbers. Six exhausts, pipe and
silencer with a raised ridge, round
racing number and plated wheels.
Price 6d. Issued 1935. Deleted 1938.
94mm. DC/RT.

No. 23a. Racing Car

	–	£75	£35

Red with cream flash, and red or blue
with silver or cream flash with driver.
Six stem system, pipe and silencer
with no ridge. Price 9d. Issued 1938.
Deleted 1940. 94mm. DC/RT.

23A. Racing Car

Blue with flash (early post-war), red
with silver with red flash. No. 4 in a
circle on sides of car. The number is
body colour and surrounding circle is
flash colour. Black wheels and
pinched axles. Later models with
silver wheels and turned over axle
ends. One of the very early 1950
issues was made of lead and could be
the only lead post-war Dinky. Price
2/3d. Issued 1946. Renumbered 220
in 1954. Deleted 1955. 94mm.

Blue	–	£60	£15
Silver or red	–	£50	£15

No. 23b. Hotchkiss Racing Car

	–	£30	£15

Blue with white or red flash; yellow
with blue or black flash; and yellow
with red flash. Yellow with red flash
is very rare. This model is worth
much more than the other colours.

Racing numbers normally ('5') of
body colour in circles of flash livery.
Price 6d. Issued June 1935. Deleted
1940. 96mm. DC/RT.

No. 23B. Hotchkiss Racing Car   –   £100   £25

Red with silver flash, or silver with
red flash. Number in body livery, and
circle in flash livery. No. 5 on sides.
Price 2/11d. Issued 1946. Deleted
1948. 96mm. DC/RT.

No. 23c. Mercedes Benz
Racing Car   –   £130   £25

There are two pre-war castings for
this model. The first had no rivets
holding the moulded (tin-plate)
baseplate on: it was held in place by
crimping the body over the edge at
two places each side. Later the casting
was changed to accommodate rivet
pillars inside the body. This happened
in 1938. The colours for the two
variations are the same. Red, blue,
yellow or green, with racing numbers
of body livery in circles of contrasting
livery. Grille, exhaust pipe and driver
picked out in contrasting or natural
livery. Green is rare and worth
double. The name 'Mercedes Benz'
shows on model with No. 2 on sides.
Price 8d. Issued May 1936. Deleted
1940. 92mm. DC/RT/TP.

No. 23C. Mercedes Benz
Racing Car   –   £65   £15

Blue or silver. Blue model has black
circles around racing numbers, and
the silver has red circles. It has a
moulded tin-plate base with driver
cast in. Price 1/8d. Re-issued as large
open racing car with the name
'Mercedes Benz' in October 1947.
Deleted 1950. 92mm. DC/RT/TP.
Blue model worth double.

No. 23d. Auto-Union Racing
Car   –   £80   £25

Red or blue with driver slotted into
body. Circles are white or yellow
showing various numbers and, like
23C, early examples have no rivets
holding baseplate on. Price 7d. Issued
May 1936. Deleted 1940. 100mm.
DC/RT/TP.

No. 23D. Auto-Union Racing Car

	M/B	M/U	G/C
	–	£75	£20

Silver with moulded tin-plate baseplate and no driver. Auto-union red circle with '2' on sides. Price 1/11d. Issued 1950. Deleted 1955. 100mm. DC/RT/TP.

No. 23e. 'Speed of the Wind' Racer

	–	£95	£30

Blue or yellow with moulded tin-plate baseplate, although early examples had no baseplate rivets. Other colours in this model were red or green with driver cast into body. White circles with '1' on sides. Price 8d. Issued May 1936. Deleted 1940. 104mm. DC/RT/TP.

No. 23e. 'Speed of the Wind' Racer Special

£750

Red with silver flash. This is a very rare model and although 'Speed of the Wind' was a car used mainly for record-breaking attempts in 1935-36, driven by George Eyston, it did appear on certain race tracks in promotional ideas through the firm of 'Dinky'. The car also made a special appearance through the streets of Liverpool in 1936, from and to the Meccano factory in Binns Rd. A special team of almost 100 men were connected with the show. Special presentation boxes were made and they were autographed both by mechanics and driver. Price 5/-. 104mm. Driver cast in.

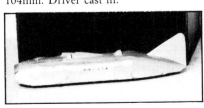

No. 23E. 'Speed of the Wind' Racing Car

£55 £20 £10

Silver or red with moulded tin-plate baseplate and driver cast in. Price 2/11d. Issued 1946. Deleted 1949. 104mm. Red model is worth double.

MODEL	M/B	M/U	G/C

No. 23E. 'Speed of the Wind' Racer

£55 £30 £20

Silver with plain tin-plate baseplate and driver cast in. The model was renumbered when colours were slightly altered to drivers, overalls, exhaust pipes and wheels. 'Speed of the Wind' written on baseplate. Price 2/11d. Issued 1949. Renumbered 221 in 1954. Deleted 1954. 104mm. DC/RT/TP.

No. 23F. Alfa-Romeo Racing Car

£45 £20 £10

Red with 'Alfa-Romeo' and white '8' on tail. Price 3/-. Issued 1952. Renumbered 232 in 1954. Deleted 1962. 100mm. DC/RT/TP.

No. 23G. Cooper-Bristol Racing Car

£45 £20 £10

Green. Model was renumbered 233 in 1954 with the driver cast in. The lettering 'Cooper British' or 'Bristol', with white '6' on tail. Price 2/9d. Issued February 1953. Deleted 1962. 89mm. DC/TP/RT.

No. 23G. Cooper-Bristol Racing Special

£350

White. A very rare model, otherwise details as green.

No. 23H. Ferrari Racing Car

£60 £20 £10

Blue with yellow nose and lettered 'Ferrari' with yellow '5' on the tail. Driver cast in. Price 3/-. Issued 1953. Renumbered 234 in 1954. Deleted 1962. 101mm. DC/RT/TP.

No. 23J. H.W.M. Racing Car

£40 £20 £10

Green with driver cast in. 'H.W.M.' with yellow '7' on the tail. Price 2/11d. Issued May 1953. Deleted 1960. 99mm. DC/RT/TP.

No. 23K. Talbot-Lago Racing Car

£50 £20 £10

Blue with driver cast in. 'Talbot-Lago' with yellow '4' on the tail. Price 2/6d. Issued September 1953. Renumbered 230 in 1954. Deleted 1960. 103mm. DC/RT/TP.

No. 23m. Thunderbolt Speed Car

	M/B	M/U	G/C
	£250	£50	£20

This was one of the very first Dinky models to be placed officially in an individual box worth more than many Dinky models. This explains the price difference in original price between this one and 23s, which is an identical casting. Light green and also dark green, the latter being the rarer of the two. Driver cast in. Union Jack flags on tail fin. Price 1/-. Issued 1938. Deleted 1940. 126mm. DC/RT/TP.

No. 23N. Maserati Racing Car   £50   £20   £10

Red with white flash and driver cast in. 'Maserati' with white '9' on tail. Price 2/8d. Issued June 1953. Renumbered 231 in 1954. Deleted 1962. 94mm DC/RT/TP.

No. 23p. Gardner's M.G. Record Car   £100   £40   £25

Green with driver cast in. 'M.G. Magnette' and Union Jack flag on sides, with M.G. badge on nose. White flashes along the sides. The change to 'M.G.' record car on the baseplate was possibly just pre-war, just as the dropping of the white flashes along the sides was post-war. Like the Thunderbolt, this model was issued pre-war with an individual box, with the scale drawings of the real car on the box lid. Price 1/-. Issued December 1939. Deleted 1940. 104mm. DC/RT/TP.

No. 23P. Gardner's M.G. Record Car   £45   £20   £10

Green with driver cast in. With Union Jack flag on sides, and M.G. badge on nose. Price 2/6d. Issued 1946. Deleted 1947. 104mm. DC/RT/TP.

No. 23s. Streamlined Racing Car   £125   £50   £20

Silver with driver cast in. Model has flags and also exists without flags. Black grille. There was a brief run of these models in lead which are worth double, provided that they are in good condition. Other colours exist, and colours mean extra money so check with myself or any other expert before you sell. Price 1/11d. Issued 1938. Deleted 1940. 126mm. DC/RT/TP.

No. 23S. Streamlined Racing Car

The colours of this model were blue, dark green, or silver with red or green details, grille and exhaust. Price 2/6d. Model was re-issued in January 1948, then renumbered 222 in 1954. 126mm. DC/RT/TP. Prices for colours vary.

	M/B	M/U	G/C
Blue	–	£75	£30
Green	–	£55	£30
Silver	–	£45	£20

No. 24b. Limousine

	M/B	M/U	G/C
	–	£350	

Colours recorded: maroon with black chassis, maroon with maroon chassis, maroon with grey chassis, cream with royal blue chassis, yellow with brown chassis, light blue with yellow chassis, yellow with black chassis. Plated or chromed wheels; black or coloured, white or coloured tyres on very early models; black tyres on later. The prices for any of the '24' series are for good unfatigued examples, other prices vary all according to condition and the eagerness of the collector. I advise all collectors to consult the very best of experts with regard to these models. It is possible to have either radiator type with or without spare wheel. There are at least 45 variations on the eight models in this series. 24b never had any kind of spare wheel. There are however, two body castings. The first has three horizontal bonnet louvres of equal length. The second has three louvres of different lengths, the top one being the longest. There are in fact a great number of minor changes to the chassis and radiator throughout the six year production run of the 24-series. I do not think that it matters to the value, as all models are very scarce. This is due to metal fatigue. The 24-series never had individual boxes, as they were packed

in boxes of eight. Original price 6d,
with or without badge. Issued April
1934. Deleted 1938. Price 9d. Reissued 1938. Deleted 1940. 98mm.

No. 24c. Town Sedan   –   £350   £150

Colours recorded: royal blue with
royal blue chassis, cream with royal
blue chassis, cream with black chassis,
light green with cherry red chassis,
cherry red with grey chassis, cream
with light green chassis. Wheels and
tyres as 24b. Criss-cross chassis and
radiator with or without badge. Side
mounted spare wheel on early models,
but this feature was later abandoned.
Separate dashboard and windscreen
casting. Price 1/-. Issued 1934.
Deleted 1940. 97mm. Painted or
nickel plated. DC/RT.

No. 24c. Super Streamlined
Saloon   –   £300   £150

Colours recorded: maroon with black
chassis, red with dark red chassis,
green with red chassis, red with black
chassis, black with red chassis. Wheels
and tyres as 24b. With criss-cross
chassis, plain radiator, no spare wheel
and 'single' side window. Price 9d.
Issued April 1934. Deleted 1938.
97mm. DC/RT.

No. 24d. Vogue Saloon   –   £300   £150

This model had the usual 24-series
variations. Colours recorded:
cream/royal blue chassis, pink/cherry
red chassis, pink/turquoise chassis,
green/black chassis, medium
blue/maroon chassis, blue/black
chassis. Wheels and tyres as 24b. The
spare wheel was never dropped on the
Vogue Saloon but later models
however had a very different body
shape with a domed roof. This model
was in fact a French Dinky Toy
casting, borrowed by the Liverpool
Binns Road Company when their own
casting had been re-modelled to make
the 36c Humber Vogue. Price 9d.
Issued April 1934. Deleted 1938.
97mm. DC/RT.

MODEL	M/B	M/U	G/C

No. 24f. Sportsman's Coupé

| | – | £300 | £150 |

Recorded colours: chocolate with buff chassis, beige with chocolate chassis, cream with royal blue chassis, yellow with brown chassis, and brown with chocolate chassis. Wheels and tyres as 24 b. This model is entirely different as regards casting compared with 36 Bentley. It has a higher domed roof line and lower bonnet line. With plain or badge radiator. Early models had side-mounted spare wheel. This feature was later dropped and the hole in the body was filled in. Price 9d. Issued 1934. Deleted 1940. 100mm. DC/RT.

No. 24g. Four Seater Sports Tourer

| | – | £300 | £150 |

Colours recorded: pale blue with brown chassis, cream with chocolate chassis, yellow with brown chassis, pale green with dark green chassis, green with black chassis, and light blue with black chassis. Wheels and tyres as 24 b. All 24 g , four seater sports tourers have the rear-mounted spare wheel and tyres. With open or solid screen radiator, with or without badge. Price 1/-. Issued April 1934. Deleted 1938. 98mm. DC/RT.

No. 24h. Two Seater Sports Tourer

| | – | £300 | £150 |

Colours recorded: red with red chassis, green with dark green chassis, cream with black chassis, red with green chassis, green with black chassis, yellow with black chassis. Wheels and tyres as 24b. As with 24 g , this model was only issued with a rear mounted spare wheel and tyres. With open or solid screen, and grille with or without badge. Price 1/-. Issued April 1934. Deleted 1940. 98mm. DC/RT.

No. 24kz. Peugeot Special Issue

| | – | £450 | £200 |

Colours recorded: dark blue, grey blue, maroon, white, green, red. Wheels are black with black or white tyres with sometimes 'Dunlop' stamped on side-walls. One-piece body casting with tin-plate bumper and no chassis. A version of this car with a tin-plate chassis was made in France between 1948/49, but the model was not imported. Models were purchased by people on holiday, or through friends living in France and brought to this country, The pre-war model was imported to England with 'Peugeot 402, Fab-en-France' cast inside body. Z means of French origin. Price 9d. Issued July 1939. Deleted 1940. 95mm. DC/TP/RT.

No. 25J. Jeep — £65 £20

Red or green, or pale blue with yellow wheels. Tin-plate windscreen. LHD/SW. With spare wheel at the rear. Price 2/6d. Issued 1947. Deleted 1948. 68mm. DC/TP/RT.

No. 25Y. Jeep — £65 £20

Red or dark green with maroon wheels. With tin-plate windscreen and spare wheel on right of body. LHD/SW. Price 4/4d. Issued September 1952. Renumbered 405 in 1954. Deleted 1962. 90mm. DC/RT/TP.

No. 27D. Land Rover £45 £20 £10

Green with cream seats, or orange with dark green seats. Not individually boxed until renumbered 340 in 1954. With screen and spare wheel behind orange driver. Price 3/9d. Issued April 1950. Deleted 1962. 90mm. TP/RT/DC.

No. 27D. Land Rover £55 £20 £10

Orange and blue. Red wheels, black windscreen and beige driver. Otherwise as before.

No. 27F. Estate Car £45 £20 £10

Brown and fawn or brown and grey. Latter colour is worth double as it is quite rare. Price 2/10d. Issued February 1950. Renumbered 344 1954. 105mm. DC/TP/RT.

MODEL	M/B	M/U	G/C

No. 30a. Chrysler 'Airflow' Saloon

| | – | £100 | £50 |

Green or cream. Also rare colour of dark blue which is worth double. Green or cream models were deleted in 1940. This model has no chassis and is identical to the earlier '32'. Price 9d. Issued June 1935. Deleted 1936. 103mm. DC/RT.

No. 30A. Chrysler 'Airflow' Saloon

| | – | £100 | £50 |

Green, cream, or pale blue. This model has no chassis. Price 1/11d. Issued 1946. Deleted 1948. 103mm. DC/RT.

No. 30b. Rolls Royce

| | – | £200 | £35 |

Colours recorded: royal blue with black chassis, pale grey with dark grey chassis, pale green with black chassis, dark grey with black chassis. The last colour is rare and worth double. With open chassis. Price 9d. Issued August 1935. Deleted 1950. 101mm. DC/RT.

No. 30B. Rolls Royce

| | – | £100 | £50 |

Dark blue or fawn, with black chassis. It has a plain or open chassis. Price 1/11d. Issued 1946. Deleted 1950. 101mm. DC/RT.

No. 30c. Daimler

| | – | £250 | £60 |

Green or cream with black chassis. Open chassis. Price 9d. Issued August 1935. Deleted 1940. 98mm. DC/RT.

No. 30C. Daimler

| | – | £150 | £50 |

Fawn, green or cream with black chassis, the latter two being worth at least double. With open or plain chassis. Price 1/11d. Issued 1946. Deleted 1950. 98mm. DC/RT.

No. 30d. Vauxhall

| | – | £300 | £150 |

Yellow body and brown chassis, yellow body with black chassis, or maroon body with black chassis. There are two varieties of this model: with or without spare wheel. There are also two varieties without spare wheels, and the model with spare wheel is worth at least double. Model

MODEL	M/B	M/U	G/C

has squared or shield radiator. Price
9d. Issued August 1935. Deleted
1940. 102mm. DC/RT.

No. 30d. Vauxhall

	–	£250	£100

Yellow body with brown chassis.
With squared or shield radiator, with
open chassis. With or without spare
wheel, although the one with spare
wheel is worth double. Price 9d.
Issued April 1939. Deleted 1940.
100mm. DC/RT.

No. 30D. Vauxhall

	–	£150	£50

Brown or green body with black
chassis. This model has a shield
radiator and no spare wheel. With
open or plain chassis. Price 1/11d.
Issued 1946. Deleted 1948. 98mm.
DC/RT.

No. 32. Chrysler 'Airflow' Saloon

	–	£250	£100

Maroon or blue, the latter colour
being rare and worth double. With
plated wheels otherwise identical with
30A. Price 9d. Issued January 1935.
Renumbered 30A in June 1935.
103mm. DC/RT.

No. 35a. Austin 7 Saloon

	–	£150	£60

Colours recorded: grey, red,
turquoise, dark blue, mid blue, pale
pink, and dark brown. The latter two
colours are quite rare and worth
do''ble. On some models the spare
wheel cover was picked out in a
contrasting livery. For example a pale
blue on a dark blue car. The change
from white to black tyres occurred in
1939. Price 3d. Issued 1936. Deleted
1940. 51mm. DC/rubber wheels.

No. 35A. Austin 7 Saloon

	–	£90	£30

Red, blue or grey with solid black
rubber wheels. Issued 1946. Deleted
1948. 51mm. DC. Went to retailers in
boxes of six.

No. 35az. Fiat Two-Seater Saloon

	–	£175	£75

Red, green blue, or pale grey. The
metal wheeled version was for the
French market only. For the export

market the model had white rubber
tyres similar to the English 35 series.
Marking on model 'Fab-en-France'.
Price 4d. Issued July 1939.
Deleted 1940. 59mm. Diecast with
metal wheels.

No. 35b. Racer

−	£150	£30

Silver or dark blue with white rubber
wheels only. No driver. Price 3d.
Issued 1935. Deleted 1939. 57mm.
DC.

No. 35b. Racer

−	£150	£30

Blue, yellow or red with driver and
white rubber wheels, although late
pre-war models had black wheels.
Price 3d. Issued 1939. Deleted 1940.
57mm. DC/RW.

No. 35B. Racer

−	£95	£40

Silver or red, with the latter being
worth almost double. Price 1/9d.
Issued 1946. Renumbered 200 in
1954. Deleted 1957. 57mm. DC.

No. 35c. M.G. Sports Car

−	£160	£40

Red, green, dark blue or maroon.
Solid white rubber tyres, except for
the later models which all had black
solid rubber wheels. All pre-war
models had the windscreen, steering
wheel, and spare wheel picked out in
silver. Price 3d. Issued 1936. Deleted
1940. 52mm. DC/RW.

No. 35C. M.G. Sports Car

−	£150	£60

Red or green, the latter colour being
worth almost double. Solid black
rubber wheels. Price 1/11d. Issued
1946. Deleted 1948. 52mm. DC/RW.

No. 35d. Austin 7 Tourer

−	£175	£60

Blue, yellow, or green, with solid
white rubber wheels and wire
windscreen. Late pre-war model had
casting with hole in seat for driver,
even though it was never issued with
a driver. As with 35A, some models
had the spare wheel cover picked out,
e.g. orange cover on yellow car with
the steering wheel painted silver. Price
4d. Issued 1938. Deleted 1940. 50mm.
DC/RW.

No. 35D. Austin 7 Tourer

	M/B	M/U	G/C
	–	£150	£45

Fawn, pale blue, red or grey. The latter being very scarce and worth double. Solid black rubber wheels and no windscreen. Price 2/6d. Issued 1946. Deleted 1948. 50mm. DC/RW.

No. 36a. Armstrong Siddeley Limousine

Grey, or dark blue with black moulded chassis and no driver. The 36-series were issued late pre-war with no figures but still had the slot in the baseplate. Many early post-war models have the slots. Early pre-war model had figures. Price 11d. Issued July 1938. Deleted 1940. 97mm. DC/RT.

	M/B	M/U	G/C
With figures	£250	£200	£100
Without figures	£150	£65	£50

No. 36A. Armstrong Siddeley

	M/B	M/U	G/C
	£90	£30	£20

Colours recorded and seen: grey, maroon, pale blue, dark blue, shire green, and off-white, all with black chassis. No drivers and Armstrong Siddeley radiator. Vertical bonnet louvres. Price 2/11d. Issued 1946. Deleted 1948. 97mm. DC/RT.

No. 36b. Bentley Two Seater Sports Coupé

Colours seen: yellow with black chassis, cream with black chassis, two-tone grey, yellow with maroon chassis. Moulded chassis with seats for passengers. Bentley radiator and no spare wheel. Price 11d. Issued July 1938. Deleted 1940. 100mm. DC/RT and tin-plate figures, also without figures. The model with the figures is worth nearly four times as much as the model without them.

	M/B	M/U	G/C
With figures	–	£250	£150
Without figures	–	£150	£50

No. 36B. Bentley Two Seater Sports Coupé

	M/B	M/U	G/C
	–	£35	£20

Colours seen: green, cream, brown and grey. No driver and Bentley radiator. Price 2/-. Issued 1946. Deleted 1958. 100mm. DC/RT.

No. 36c. Humber Vogue Saloon

Light blue with black chassis, two-tone green, silver grey with black chassis. Moulded chassis, with or without figures. Price 11d. Issued July 1938. Deleted 1940. 100mm. DC/RT.

With figures	–	£275	£150
Without figures	–	£150	£40

No. 36C. Humber Vogue — £150 £30

Brown with black moulded chassis, no driver and Humber radiator. Also in light blue. Price 2/-. Issued 1946. Deleted 1948, 97mm. DC RT.

No. 36d. Streamlined Rover Saloon

Colours recorded: light blue with black chassis, two-tone green, two-tone red, brown with black chassis which is a very rare colour and worth double. Moulded chassis with slot for driver, and double sided window. No spare wheel. Tin-plate figures. Price 11d. Issued July 1938. Deleted 1940. 100mm. DC/RT.

With figures	–	£275	£125
Without figures	–	£150	£50

No. 36D. Rover Saloon — £150 £70

Colours recorded: pale green, dark green, pale blue, dark blue, and medium green, all with black moulded chassis. No driver and Rover radiator. Price 1/11d. Issued 1946. Deleted 1948. 94mm. DC/RT.

No. 36e. Two Seater Sports British Salmson

Colours recorded: grey body and red chassis, royal blue and black chassis, black body and red chassis, two-tone grey, and two-tone red. Hole in seat for driver. With or without spare rubber wheel and Salmson radiator. Price 11d. Issued July 1938. Deleted 1940. 99mm. DC/RT.

With figures	–	£275	£150
Without figures	–	£150	£50

No. 36E. Two Seater British Salmson

	M/B	M/U	G/C
	–	£150	£40

Red, light brown, mid-blue, with black moulded chassis and no driver. With Salmson radiator and steering wheel cast in. Price 1/11d. Issued 1946. Deleted 1948. 93mm. DC/RT/solid screen.

No. 36f. Four Seater Sports British Salmson

Dark red, or salmon pink moulded chassis and red body. Also with the dark green chassis and green body, which is a very rare colour and worth double. Hole in seat for driver. Spare wheel optional and Salmson radiator. Price 11d. Issued July 1938. Deleted 1940. 98mm. DC/RT.

	M/B	M/U	G/C
With figures	–	£275	£125
Without figures	–	£50	£30

No. 36F. Four Seater British Salmson

	M/B	M/U	G/C
	–	£150	£50

Colours recorded: light green, dark green, light grey, dark grey, beige and the very rare maroon livery, all with black chassis. The last model is worth double. No driver and Salmson radiator. Steering wheel cast in solid green. Price 1/11d. Issued 1946. Deleted 1948. 96mm. DC/RT.

No. 38a. Frazer-Nash (B.M.W.) Sports Car

	M/B	M/U	G/C
	–	£175	£50

The seats for this model were in black or khaki. Body colours: light blue, light grey, or dark grey, the latter being rare. All models with bare metal baseplate. Price 10d. Issued June 1939. Deleted 1940. 82mm. DC/TP. All models for the 38 series are for models with perfect screens.

No. 38A. Frazer-Nash (B.M.W.) Sports Car

	M/B	M/U	G/C
	–	£100	£40

Blue or light grey with black painted baseplate, seats in khaki, but all the late export models had red seats and red wheels. Price 1/11d. Issued 1946. Deleted 1949. 82mm. DC/TP.

MODEL	M/B	M/U	G/C

No. 38b. Sunbeam Talbot Sports Car

	M/B	M/U	G/C
	–	£225	£75

Pale blue, or dark blue with dark blue seats, also in red with maroon seats. Bare metal baseplate. Price 10d. Issued 1939. Deleted 1940. 92mm. S/SW/WS/DC/TP.

No. 38B. Sunbeam Talbot Sports Car

	–	£150	£50

Colours recorded: red with maroon seats, blue with fawn seats, pale green with dark green seats, yellow with fawn seats, pale brown with khaki seats, and chocolate with fawn seats. The latter model is rare and worth double. Black painted baseplate and black chassis. Price 2/6d. Issued 1946. Deleted 1949. 92mm. DC/TP.

No. 38C. Lagonda Sports Coupé

	–	£175	£40

Red with dark red seats, dark green with black seats, grey with fawn seats, and brown with fawn seats, black painted baseplate. Price 2/6d. Issued February 1946. Deleted 1951. 102mm. DC/TP.

No. 38d. Alvis Sports Tourer

	–	£195	£60

Green body and brown seats with bare metal baseplate. SW/S/WS. Price 10d. Issued 1939. Deleted 1940. 95mm. DC/TP.

No. 38D. Alvis Sports Tourer

	–	£155	£40

Green with brown or black seats, maroon with red or black seats, and grey with black seats. Price 2/6d. Issued 1946. Deleted 1949. 95mm. DC/TP.

No. 38E. Armstrong Siddeley Coupé

	–	£100	£50

Pale grey with blue seats, light grey with pale blue seats, pale green with grey seats or the rare cream with black seats, worth double. With black chassis and black painted baseplate. Price 2/6d. Issued December 1946. Deleted 1950. 96mm. DC/TP.

MODEL	M/B	M/U	G/C

No. 38F. Jaguar Sports Car   –   £100   £50

Red with maroon seats, pale grey with
black seats, pale or dark blue with
fawn seats, or red with black seats.
Black chassis and black painted
baseplate. Price 2/9d. Issued
November 1946. Deleted 1949.
80mm. DC/TP.

No. 39B. Oldsmobile Six   –   £100   £50

Colours recorded: light grey, cream,
dark grey, dark brown, dark blue,
green, which is the rare colour and
worth double. With black chassis and
black painted baseplate. Price 2/9d.
Issued 1946. Deleted 1950. 100mm.
DC/RT/TP.

No. 39c. Lincoln Zephyr   –   £175   £40

Colours recorded: grey, light grey,
yellow, cream. Bare metal baseplate.
Price 10d. Issued 1939. Deleted 1940.
106mm. DC/RT/TP.

No. 39C. Lincoln Zephyr   –   £100   £50

Grey or brown with black chassis and
black painted baseplate. Price 2/9d.
Issued 1946. Deleted 1950. 106mm.
DC/RT/TP.

No. 39d. Buick Viceroy   –   £175   £50

Colours recorded: maroon, bright
green, deep blue, chocolate, which is
quite rare and worth double. Bare
metal baseplate. Price 10d. Issued
1939. Deleted 1940. 103mm.
DC/TP/RT.

No. 39D. Buick Viceroy   –   £100   £50

Colours recorded: maroon, dark or pale
grey, dull yellow or putty, dark brown,
dark red. Black chassis and black painted
baseplate. Price 2/9d. Issued 1946.
Deleted 1950. 103mm. DC/TP/RT.

No. 39e. Chrysler Royal   –   £175   £60

Blue, grey, green, or cream, the latter
being very rare, with bare metal
baseplate. Price 10d. Issued 1939.
Deleted 1940. 106mm. DC/RT/TP.

No. 39E. Chrysler Royal   –   £100   £50

Many shades of green. Also blue,
cream, or grey with black chassis and
painted black baseplate. Price 2/9d.
Issued 1946. Deleted 1950. 106mm.
DC/TP/RT.

MODEL	M/B	M/U	G/C

No. 39f. Studebaker 'State Commander'

| | – | £175 | £60 |

Green or yellow, with bare metal baseplate. Price 10d. Issued 1939. Deleted 1940. 103mm. DC/TP/RT.

No. 39F. Studebaker 'State Commander'

| | – | £100 | £50 |

Colours recorded: light blue, dark blue, olive green, light green, light grey, dark grey, dark brown, and chocolate. The latter two-tone model is very rare and worth five times the normal colour. Price 2/9d. Issued 1946. Deleted 1950. 103mm. DC/TP/RT.

No. 40A. Riley Saloon

| | £175 | £60 | £25 |

Medium or dull green, also in light green. Light or dark grey, dark blue and cream with black baseplate. Price 2/6d. Issued July 1947. Renumbered 158 in 1954. Deleted 1960. DC/TTP/RT.

No. 40B. Triumph 1800 Saloon

| | – | £150 | £45 |

Mid blue, fawn, black and light grey, which was the first type with rear axle pillars. Price 2/6d. Issued July 1948. Deleted 1949. 91mm. DC/TP/RT.

No. 40B. Triumph 1800 Saloon

| | £60 | £30 | £15 |

Mid blue, dark blue, dark grey or bright beige. This model was a second type with the rear axle held by a tin baseplate. Price 2/2d. Issued February 1949. Renumbered 151 in 1955. 91mm. DC/TP/RT.

No. 40D. Austin Devon

| | £60 | £30 | £15 |

Maroon, dark blue, grey, suede green and black. Rarer colour being the last named and worth considerably more. Price 1/9d. Issued January 1949. Renumbered 152 in 1954. Deleted 1956. 86mm. DC/TP/RT.

No. 40E. Standard Vanguard

| | – | £155 | £45 |

Fawn, maroon or the rare grey colour, with open rear wheels, plain boot with small print baseplate lettering and black chassis. Price 1/9d. Issued November 1948. Deleted 1950. 91mm. DC/TP/RT.

MODEL	M/B	M/U	G/C

No. 40E. Standard Vanguard — £150 £60 £25

Fawn or blue, covered rear wheels, plain boot, small baseplate lettering. Price 2/6d. Issued April 1950. Renumbered 153 in 1954. Deleted 1960. 91mm. DC/TP/RT.

No. 40F. Hillman Minx — £150 £60 £25

Light or dark green. Light or dark brown. Price 2/6d. Issued February 1951. Renumbered 154 in 1954. Deleted 1956. 88mm. DC/TP/RT.

No. 40G. Morris Oxford — £175 £50 £25

Dark green, very dark green, grey and fawn. Price 1/11d. Issued June 1950. Renumbered 159 in 1954. Deleted 1956. 93mm. DC/TP/RT.

No. 40J. Austin Somerset — £175 £50 £25

Red, pale blue. Dark blue and maroon. Price 2/4d. Issued March 1953. Renumbered 161 in 1956. Deleted 1960. 89mm. DC/TP/RT.

No. 100. Lady Penelope's Fab 1 — £135 £40 £25

Pink with firing rocket, silver trim and six wheels. With driver and Lady Penelope figures inside plastic opening hood. Price 15/11d. Issued 1966. Deleted 1977. 147mm. Prices for this model vary according to availability and the model in the cardboard box is worth double the model in the plastic bubble pack.

No. 100A. Lady Penelope's Fab 1 — £500 £100 £40

White. Lady Penelope figure with driver, pink interior, silver trim, wheels etc. Rare colour. Price 15/11d. Issued 1972. 147mm. DC/TP/RT.

	M/B	M/U	G/C

No. 100B. Lady Penelope's Fab 1

£750 £200 £50

Red, with figures and firing rocket.
Rare model. Price 15/11d. Issued
1966. Deleted 1977. 147mm.
DC/TP/RT.

No. 101. Thunderbird 4

£160 £50 £25

Dark green with gold. Space car with
the number '4' in black on its side.
There are stars, numbers and the
word 'Thunderbird 4' in white on the
large model itself. All working parts.
Price 12/11d. Issued 1967. Replaced
in 1974 by No. 106. 143mm. DC/P.

No. 101. Sunbeam Alpine Tourer

£130 £50 £20

Blue or pink, the latter being the rarer
model of the two and worth double.
With civilian driver and no numbers.
Price 3/-. Issued August 1957. Deleted
1960. 94mm.
SW/S/D/WS/DC/TP/P/RT.

No. 102. Joe's Car

£65 £30 £20

Green and grey with red cab interior.
Working parts and rocket. Made from
the TV series Joe 90. With automatic
opening wings and extending tail fins.
With flashing engine, exhaust and
independent super suspension. Price
25/11d. Issued 1969. Deleted 1976.
139mm. DC/TP.

No. 102. Joe's Car

£175 £60 £30

Blue, silver or grey, details otherwise
as previous. Rare colours.

No. 102. M.G. Midget

£150 £45 £20

Yellow or green. With civilian driver
and no numbers. Price 3/-. Issued
September 1957. Deleted 1960.
83mm. SW/S/D/WS/DC/TP/P/RT.

No. 103. Spectrum Patrol Car

£65 £25 £15

Metallic red with white interior, silver
hubs and trim. Model was taken from
the TV series 'Captain Scarlet'. Price
9/11d. Issued 1968. Deleted 1976.
121mm. DC/P.

No. 103. Spectrum Patrol Car

£395 £100 £50

Metallic blue, rare colour, details
otherwise as previous 103.

MODEL	M/B	M/U	G/C

No. 103. Austin Healey 100

	£170	£50	£20

Red or cream. With civilian driver
and no numbers. Price 3/-. Issued
November 1957. Deleted 1960.
85mm. SW/S/D/WS/DC/TP/P/RT.

No. 104. Aston Martin DB3S

	£130	£40	£20

Blue or salmon. With civilian driver
and no numbers. Price 3/-. Issued
September 1957. Deleted 1960.
87mm. SW/S/D/DC/TP/RT.

No. 104. Spectrum Pursuit Vessel

	£95	£50	£25

Blue and white with red interior. All
rocket action. From the TV Series
'Captain Scarlet'. Price 22/11d. Issued
1968. Deleted 1977. 160mm. DC/P.

No. 105. Maximum Security Vehicle

	£95	£40	£20

White with red stripes and red
interior. Opening doors and aerial.
Another model from the 'Captain
Scarlet' series. Price 13/9d. Issued
1968. Deleted 1975. 137mm. DC/P.

No. 105. Maximum Security Vehicle

	£250	£75	£40

Rare colour of grey with black flashes
on sides. Otherwise details as previous
105.

No. 105. Triumph TR2 Sports Tourer

	£170	£50	£20

Yellow or grey. With civilian driver
and no numbers. Price 3/-. Issued
August 1957. Deleted 1960. 84mm.
SW/S/D/WS/DC/TP/P/RT.

MODEL	M/B	M/U	G/C

No. 106. 'The Prisoner' Mini-Moke

	M/B	M/U	G/C
No. 106. 'The Prisoner' Mini-Moke	£45	£20	£10

White with red and white canopy. From the TV series of the same name as model. Opening bonnet and spare wheel. Price 6/9d. Issued 1968. Deleted 1971. 73mm. DC/P.

No. 106. 'The Prisoner' Mini-Moke

	£175	£50	£25

Cream with blue canopy. Rare colour. Otherwise details as previous 106.

No. 106. Thunderbird II

	£95	£40	£20

Blue and white with black marking. Also rare colour in very dark blue with brown and dark yellow, worth double. Price 15/11d. Redesigned 1974. Deleted 1978. 153mm. DC/P.

No. 106. Austin A90 Atlantic

Blue, black or pink and as the values vary because of the colours, I list the three prices. Its original number was 140A. Price 3/-. Renumbered in 1954. Deleted 1958. 95mm. SW/S/DC/TPO/RT.

	M/B	M/U	G/C
Blue	£100	£45	£20
Pink	£110	£50	£20
Black	£130	£50	£20

No. 107. Sunbeam Alpine Competition Finish

	£85	£30	£15

Blue or pink. This model had white circles with racing number. Special competition model. Price 3/11d. Issued November 1955. Deleted 1959. SW/S/D/WS/DC/TP/P/RT.

No. 107. Stripey the Magic Mini

	£70	£30	£15

White, yellow, red and blue with the figures Candy, Andy and the Bearandas. Price 10/9d. Issued 1967. Deleted 1970. 75mm. DC/P.

No. 108. Sam's Car

	£50	£20	£10

This was a beautiful model made in gold with a keyless clockwork motor and automatic drive. Given with the model was a world intelligence network lapel badge. The model had

red interior and was a first of its kind
in the world of diecasts. Price 13/9d.
Issued 1969. Deleted 1975. 111mm.
DC/P.

No. 108. Sam's Car   £350   £250   £100

Metallic green or metallic blue. Also
in red. The red colour was the more
common and either green or blue is
worth three times the price of the red
model. Other details as previous 108.

No. 108. M.G. Midget
Competition Model   £120   £50   £20

Red or white with racing driver and
competition numbers which vary.
Price 3/9d. Issued April 1955. Deleted
1959. 83mm. DC/TP/P/RT.

No. 109. Austin Healey 100   £120   £50   £20

Cream or yellow. Competition
numbers, racing driver and white
circles. Price 3/9d. Issued June 1955.
Deleted 1959. 85mm.
SW/S/D/SW/DC/TP/P/RT.

No. 109. Gabriel's Model T
Ford   £55   £30   £15

Black and yellow with driver. From
an original TV series. Price 7/11d.
Issued 1969. Deleted 1970. 79mm.
DC/P.

No. 109. Gabriel's Model T
Ford   £95   £40   £20

Black, red and white, with black
driver. Rare colour. Details otherwise
as previous 109.

No. 110. Aston Martin DBS   £120   £50   £20

Green or grey with racing driver and
competition numbers, with white

MODEL	M/B	M/U	G/C

circles. Price 3/6d. Issued March 1956. Deleted 1959. 87mm. DC/RT/TP.

No. 110. Aston Martin DBS   £120   £50   £20

Metallic red with black interior, opening bonnet, silver bumpers, radiator and headlights. Price 9/11d. Issued 1965. Deleted 1971. 111mm. DC/P/RT. There is also a metallic blue colour which is very rare and worth treble.

No. 111. Triumph TR2   £80   £30   £15

Pink or turquoise with white circles, racing driver and competition numbers. Price 3/6d. Issued February 1956. Deleted 1959. 84mm. DC/TP/P/RT.

No. 112. Purdey's TR7   £125   £50   £20

Bright yellow or green which is worth double, with silver flashes on doors and sides, black and silver trim with white interior. The black letter 'P' is on bonnet and the model is designed with a double 'V' in silver in front of it. Some models have the full word Purdey and are worth slightly more than the ones with the individual letter. Issued 1978 and although still rarely to be found at the retail price of £2.25p. most of the models are now in the hands of collectors, therefore a collector's price must be paid. 98mm. DC/P.

No. 112. Austin Healey Sprite Mk II   £100   £50   £15

Red. Price 4/-. Issued November 1961. Deleted 1966. 78mm. SW/SS/FTS/S/WS/DC/TP/P/RT.

No. 113. Steed's Special Leyland Jaguar   £650

This model was advertised but never issued on general sale to the public. There were several prototype models handled by salesmen and others which came out of the factory illegally, therefore this model is very rare and worth a good deal of money. In greenish blue or in medium green or medium blue with gold stripes along

each side. The model is also known to
exist with a long orange flash with
silver wheels, bumpers, etc. With
white or fawn interior with the figure
of Steed at the driving seat. Made
from the TV series 'The New
Avengers'. Price 75p. Advertised
1977. 137mm. DC/P.

No. 113. M.G.B.   £80   £20   £10

Off white with several shades. Also in
cream. Price 5/9d. Issued October
1962. Deleted 1969. 85mm. SW/SS/
FTS/SD/WS/OD/DC/TP/P/RT.

No. 114. Triumph Spitfire   £90   £30   £15

Red, silver grey. Gold from 1968 then
purple from 1970. With lady driver
wearing safety belt. Price 6/6d. Issued
September 1963. Deleted 1971.
88mm.
SW/SS/S/D/WS/OB/DC/TP/P/RT.

No. 115. Plymouth Fury
Sports   £65   £30   £15

White or silver grey, which is slightly
scarce and worth double, with driver
and passenger and pull out twin
aerials. Silver trim and red interior
with opening bonnet. Price 7/11d.
Issued 1965. Deleted 1969. 122mm.
DC/P/RT.

No. 116. Volvo 1800S   £55   £25   £10

Red with white or pink interior,
opening bonnet, boot and doors. With
spoked wheels, silver bumper, grille
and headlights. Price 9/11d. Issued
1966. Deleted 1976. 105mm.
DC/RT/P.

No. 116. Volvo 1800S   £55   £25   £10

Red and also in black which is worth
double. Both models have blue or
white interior with opening doors,
boot and bonnet and all silver trim.

Price 9/11d. Issued 1966. Deleted
1976. 105mm. DC/P.

No. 120. Jaguar E Type   £90   £30   £15

Red or blue with black roof. Latter
colour is worth double. With
removable hard top.. Price 6/-. Issued
March 1962. Deleted 1970. 91mm.
DC/TP/P/RT.

No. 122. Volvo 265 DL Estate
Car   £60   £25   £10

Blue with white interior, silver wheels
etc. Price 76p. Issued 1977. Deleted
1979. 141mm. There is also a dark
blue colour or medium blue with
opening rear doors, white interior and
silver trim which was a new model for
1978 and was 128mm. Still available
in some outlets with all plastic
Speediwheels.

Price for second model   £35   £15   £5

No. 123. Princess 2200 HL
Saloon   £55   £25   £10

Metallic gold with white interior. All
silver trim and plastic Speediwheels.
Price 76p. Issued 1977. Deleted 1979.
128mm. DC/P.

No. 123. Princess 2200 HL
Saloon   £45   £20   £10

Rich tan with white interior. Silver
wheels, plastic bumper etc. Price 76p.
Issued 1977 and still found in some
shops at original makers price.
128mm. DC/P.
Collectors will find that they will have
to pay collector's price as most of
these models have been bought up
from all or most model shops.

No. 123. Princess 2200 HL
Saloon   £75   £30   £15

Bronze metallic with black roof and
black bonnet and boot. There are
several plain all metallic gold models
which have white interiors and silver
trims. Keen collectors will have to pay
collector's prices. With black plastic
tyres on metal hubs in place of all

plastic wheels and tyres. Price 89p.
Issued 1978. Deleted 1980. 128mm.

No. 124. Rolls Royce Phantom V

	M/B	M/U	G/C
	£75	£30	£15

Metallic sky-blue with silver tint.
Cream or white interior, silver
bumpers, grille, headlights, etc. with
the number plate 'RR1'. With
opening boot, although the bonnet
does not open on this model. This is a
re-tooled re-issue of No. 152, on
which the bonnet opened. The second
change is the absence of passengers,
but has driver. Price £1.25p. Issued
1977. Deleted 1979. 141mm. DC/P.

No. 124. Rolls Royce Phantom V

	M/B	M/U	G/C
	£55	£25	£10

Medium blue, matt or metallic finish.
With opening boot and doors with
driver. No passengers. Issued 1977.
Deleted 1979.

No. 127. Rolls Royce Silver Cloud III

	M/B	M/U	G/C
	£75	£40	£20

Metallic green, metallic gold, and dark
blue. Price 9/11d. Issued November
1964. Deleted 1972. 124mm.
SW/SS/S/W/OD/OB/TS/DC/P/RT.

No. 128. Mercedes Benz 600

	M/B	M/U	G/C
	£75	£30	£15

Metallic red. With luggage, driver,
and two passengers. With all opening
doors and bonnet and boot. Price
14/11d. Issued October 1964. Deleted
1978. 147mm. DC/P/RT. One of the
longest running models made by
Dinky, but still a good investment.

No. 128. Mercedes Benz 600

	M/B	M/U	G/C
	£80	£20	£10

Metallic blue with white interior,
silver trim, bumpers, etc. This being
the last version has no passengers.
Price 21/-. Issued 1968. Deleted 1979.
147mm. DC/P.

No. 129. M.G. Special American Issue

	M/B	M/U	G/C
	£175	£50	£20

Pink or maroon or red and white, the
rarer colour of the two and worth
double. Equivalent price 5/9d. Issued
1960 with the same casting as 102 and

108 but without any driver. Deleted
1966, although the model had
disappeared from the shops by this
time. The model had a special
presentation box with most of the
early models and is a collector's
dream. 83mm. DC/RT.

No. 129. Volkswagen De Luxe 1300 Sedan

Metallic blue with cream interior,
opening doors, boot and bonnet. With
Speediwheels and silver trim after
1971. Price 8/11d. Issued 1965.
Deleted 1976. 100mm. DC/RT/P.

Price for first type with metal wheels	£65	£25	£10
Price for Speediwheels model	£50	£20	£10

No. 129. Volkswagen 1300 Sedan

	£225	£60	£30

Rare colours of metallic green or
metallic grey. Otherwise details as
before.

No. 130. Ford Consul Corsair

	£55	£30	£15

Metallic red, light or medium blue,
with grey, white, or fawn interior.
With sliding windows and opening
bonnet. Price 5/11d. Issued June
1965. Deleted 1969. 106mm.
DC/P/RT.

No. 130. Ford Consul Corsair

	£60	£40	£25

Metallic emerald green, rare colour,
otherwise details as before.

No. 131. Jaguar 'E' Type 2 + 2

Gold, yellow, metallic tan, mauve,
metallic blue or metallic red. Opening
doors, boot and bonnet, spoked wheels
and silver bumpers, headlights etc.
Speediwheels were introduced in 1971
and deleted in 1978. Price 13/11d.
Issued 1968. Deleted 1975. 112mm.
DC/RT/P.

Spoked wheel version	£55	£25	£10
'Speediwheel' version	£55	£25	£10

Price is for the rare colour of mauve
and white, or purple and white two-
tone, with spoked wheels, white
interior. This model definitely does
exist | £395 |

MODEL	M/B	M/U	G/C

No. 131. Cadillac Eldorado £140 £60 £30

Pink and yellow, also in the rare fawn
livery worth double the normal issues.
Apart from one colour versions there
do exist two-tone colours. Price 4/6d.
Issued June 1956. Deleted 1963.
118mm. DC/TP/RT/P.

Red and yellow, a new colour for
1970 £120 £50 £20

No. 132. Ford 40-RV £95 £50 £25

Silver grey. Also metallic green at a
later date. With opening bonnet,
spoked wheels and suspension details.
Red interior. Price 9/6d. Issued 1967.
Deleted 1970. 100mm. DC/P.

Rare colour of red and yellow £100 £50 £25

No. 132. Packard Convertible £125 £40 £20

Fawn or green. Price 4/6d. Issued
November 1955. Deleted 1961.
112mm.
SW/LHD/WS/S/D/DC/TP/RT/P.

No. 133. Cunningham C5R £80 £40 £20

White with blue stripes, with racing
number '31' in blue. Price 4/3d.
Issued March 1955. Deleted 1960.
99mm.
SW/LHD/S/WS/D/DC/TP/RT/P.

No. 133. Ford Cortina (1965) £65 £30 £15

Gold with white roof, then replaced
by the all yellow livery in 1966.
SW/SS/S/W/OD. With tipping seats,
jewelled headlights and rear lights,
Plus number plates. Price 6/11d.
Issued November 1964. Deleted 1971.
101mm. DC/TP/RT/P.

No. 134. Triumph Vitesse £65 £25 £15

Metallic green with flashes on body
sides in white or dark red, the latter
flash model is worth double. Price
3/11d. Issued February 1964. Deleted
1969. 85mm.
SW/SS/W/DC/TP/RT/P.

No. 134. Triumph Vitesse £275

Metallic blue. Rare colour, otherwise
as before.

MODEL	M/B	M/U	G/C

No. 135. Triumph 2000   £75   £30   £15

Metallic green with white roof, or pale or medium blue with white roof. Also in rare black livery with white roof and red interior. Worth double. With luggage. Price 5/11d. Issued October 1963. Deleted 1969. 105mm. S/W/SS/S/W/OB/OR/DC/RT/P.

No. 136. Vauxhall Viva   £40   £20   £10

Off white, dark blue, medium blue and metallic blue. Also in rare colour of mauve with off white interior. Worth double. Price 4/11d. Issued 1964. Deleted 1973. 93mm. SW/SS/S/W/OB/OR/DC/RT/P.

No. 137. Plymouth Fury Convertible   £110   £40   £15

Metallic grey, green or blue, the latter being worth double as it was quite rare. With removable hard top. Price 5/11d. Issued October 1963. Deleted 1966. 22mm. SW/LHD/SS/FTS/S/WS/OB/DC/TP/RT/P.

No. 138. Hillman Imp   £40   £20   £10

Metallic green or red. With luggage. Price 4/11d. Issued November 1963. Deleted 1973. 85mm. SW/SS/S/W/OB/OR/DC/RT/P.

No. 139. Ford Cortina   £70   £40   £20

First appeared in pale blue, later in metallic and in red metallic which is rare and worth treble the value of the normal model. Price 5/3d. Issued June 1963. Deleted 1964. 102mm. SW/SS/S/W/OD/FS/DC/TP/RT/P.

No. 139A. Ford Fordor Sedan   £90   £20   £10

Red, brown, pale green or yellow and the brown model has matching wheels. Price 2/6d. First issued without an individual box in August 1949. Renumbered 170 in 1954. Deleted 1965. 102mm. DC/TP/RT.

No. 139B. Hudson Commodore Sedan   £95   £40   £15

Maroon, maroon and fawn or fawn and blue, and the first models did not have individual boxes. Price 2/9d.

MODEL	M/B	M/U	G/C

Issued July 1950. Renumbered 171 in
1954. Deleted 1965. 111mm.
DC/RT/TP.

No. 140. Morris 1100	**£80**	**£30**	**£15**

Various shades of blue with red
interior, opening bonnet to reveal
silver engine. Silver bumpers, grille
etc. Price 4/6d. Issued February 1963.
Deleted 1969. 87mm.
SW/SS/S/W/OB/DC/TP/RT/P.

No. 140B. Rover 75 Saloon	**£75**	**£30**	**£15**

Maroon or cream and when first
issued was not individually boxed.
Price 3/2d. Issued April 1951.
Renumbered 156 in 1954. Deleted
1969. 101mm. DC/TP/RT.

No. 141. Vauxhall Victor Estate Car	**£60**	**£30**	**£15**

Yellow or the rare colour of white
which is worth double. Opening rear
door. Price 4/11d. Issued April 1963.
Deleted 1967. 92mm.
SW/SS/S/W/DC/RT/TP/P. Model was
also issued as ambulance No. 278 in
1964 and deleted in 1970.

No. 142. Jaguar Mk. X	**£100**	**£30**	**£15**

Metallic blue from electric to mid-
blue, also in rare metallic green or
metallic dark red, worth double. With
luggage. Price 5/6d. Issued November
1962. Deleted 1969. 106mm.
SW/SS/FTS/S/W/OR RT/P/DC.

No. 143. Ford Capri	**£70**	**£30**	**£15**

Green and white. With luggage. Price
3/11d. Issued August 1962. Deleted
1967. 106mm.
SW/SS/FTS/S/W/OR/DC/P/RT.

No. 144. Volkswagen 1500	**£40**	**£20**	**£10**

White and later in gold from 1965.
Opening bonnet and luggage. Price
4/6d. Issued March 1963. Deleted
1967. 93mm.
SW/LHD/SS/FTS/S/W/DC/TP/RT/P.

No. 145. Singer Vogue	**£50**	**£20**	**£10**

Metallic green and rare colour of
orange, worth double. Price 3/11d.
Issued December 1962. Deleted 1967.
93mm.
SW/SS/FTS/S/W/DC/TP/P/RT.

MODEL	M/B	M/U	G/C

No. 146. Daimler V8 2½ Litre

£75 £30 £15

Metallic green, or metallic blue, worth
double. Price 3/9d. Issued January
1963. Deleted 1967. 95mm.
SW/SS/FTS/S/W/DC/TP/RT/P.

No. 147. Cadillac 62

£100 £50 £20

Metallic green or the rare metallic
red, worth double. Price 4/11d. Issued
October 1962. Deleted 1968. 113mm.
SW/SS/FTS/LHD/S/W/DC/TP/RT/P.

No. 148. Ford Fairlaine

£60 £20 £10

Green and also metallic green, worth
double. Price 4/11d. Issued February
1962. Deleted 1966. 111mm.
SW/SS/FTS/S/W/LHD/DC/TP/RT/P.

No. 149. Citroën Dyane

£75 £30 £15

Gold with black roof. Also in red or
purple with red interior, rare model
and worth treble. With Speediwheels
in plastic. Opening rear door and
bonnet. Price 75p. Issued 1971.
Deleted 1975. 91mm. DC/P.

No. 150. Rolls Royce Silver Wraith

£115 £50 £20

Grey and dark grey with windows and
four wheel suspension. All chromed
parts. Price 5/6d. Issued February
1959. Deleted 1964. 117mm.
DC/TP/RT.

No. 151. Triumph 1800

£65 £25 £10

Blue or brown A renumbering of 40B.
Price 2/2d. Issued 1958. Deleted
1960. 91mm. DC/TP/RT.

No. 151. Vauxhall Victor 101

£55 £20 £10

Lemon or lime green or in metallic
red. Also in cream with white interior,
rare model and worth double. With
opening boot and bonnet and full
silver trim. Price 7/-. Issued 1965.
Deleted 1969. 105mm. DC/TP/RT/P.

MODEL	M/B	M/U	G/C

No. 152. Rolls Royce Phantom V Limousine

	M/B	M/U	G/C
No. 152. Rolls Royce Phantom V Limousine	£80	£40	£20

Black or very deep blue. Also in
metallic dark green, rare colour and
worth double. All opening doors,
bonnet and boot, with fawn interior
with driver. Price 14/11d. Issued
1965. Replaced by 124 in 1977.
Finally deleted 1978. This model was
also issued as Action Kit No. 1001 in
1971 and deleted in 1978. 141mm.
DC/P/RT/TP.

No. 152. Austin Devon   £95   £40   £20

Maroon or blue, or suede green. A
renumbering of 40D. Price 2/2d.
Reissued 1954. Deleted 1956. 86mm.
DC/TP/RT.

No. 152. Austin Devon   £95   £40   £20

Two-tone colours of various shades.
Blue, green, purple and black, the last
colour being rare and worth double.
Also blue and yellow or grey and
cerise. Price 2/6d. Issued August
1956. Deleted 1960. 86mm.
DC/TP/RT.

No. 152c. Austin 7 Car   –   £75   £25

This is the military version of 35d
and should for consistency appear in
the military section as well as this
section. Never issued in an individual
box though it appeared in two boxed
sets, which I will quote a separate
price for. Matt green. With wire
screen and hole in seat for driver.
Price 4d. Issued February 1938.
Deleted 1940. This model was
originally 51mm. approximately, but
metal does expand with age and
several models are between 51mm.
and 55mm. DC/RW.

Price for boxed sets   £60

No. 153. Standard Vanguard   £90   £30   £10

Blue, fawn or cream. With covered
rear wheels similar to those of 40E
with ridged boot. It has large print
baseplate lettering. Price 2/2d. Issued
August 1954. Deleted 1960. 91mm.
DC/TP/RT.

MODEL	M/B	M/U	G/C

No. 153. Aston Martin DB6   £55   £25   £10

Silver blue or metallic green. Also in
rare two-tone green and blue, which is
worth treble. Red interior, opening
boot, bonnet and doors, with spoked
silver wheels, hubs, bumpers etc.
Price 14/11d. Issued 1967. Deleted
1971. 111mm. DC.

No. 154. Hillman Minx   £60   £25   £10

Green or brown. Model was a
renumbering of 40F. Price 2/2d.
Issued May 1954. Deleted 1956.
87mm. DC/TP/RT.

No. 154. Hillman Minx
Two-tone Model   £120   £30   £15

Green and cream, or cerise and blue worth
double. Price 2/6d. Issued September
1956. Deleted 1958. 87mm. DC/TP/RT.

No. 154. Ford Taunus 17M   £75   £35   £15

Yellow, various shades with white
roof and red interior. Opening bonnet
and boot with silver grille etc. Price
9/11d. Issued 1966. Deleted 1976.
110mm. DC/RT/P.

No. 155. Ford Anglia   £50   £20   £10

Green. Price 3/9d. Issued July 1961.
Deleted 1966. 81mm.
SW/SS/S/W/DC/TP.

No. 156. Rover 75   £65   £25   £10

Cream. This model was the
renumbering of 140B. Price 2/5d.
Issued May 1954. Deleted 1956.
101mm. DC/RT/TP.

No. 156. Rover 75 Two-Tone   £100   £40   £20

Blue and cream or two shades of
green, and rare red and black which is
worth treble. Price 3/-. Issued January
1956. Deleted 1960. 101mm.
DC/TP/RT.

No. 156. Saab 96   £65   £30   £15

Red with light fawn or white interior.
Also rare metallic blue livery worth at
least treble. Price 7/-. Issued 1966.
Deleted 1971. 98mm. DC/P/RT.

MODEL	M/B	M/U	G/C

No. 157. Jaguar XK120 — £120 £40 £20

Red or green, with shiny aluminium hubs. It also appears in a 1959/60 and 1961 catalogue in red with shiny wheels. The single and two colour versions were available at various times from 1956 to 1958 when the two colour versions were dropped as they were not very good. There is also a white or yellow version which is rare and worth more. A further range of two-tone colours are worth double, these are cerise and turquoise, grey and yellow and two tone green, the latter being extremely rare. Price 2/5d. Issued March 1956. Deleted 1962. 97mm. DC/TP/RT.

No. 157. BMW 2000 Tilux — £65 £30 £15

Blue and white with flashing indicators. White interior and silver wheels, bumpers etc. Price 13/11d. Issued 1968. Deleted 1973. 121mm. DC/P.

No. 158. Rolls Royce Silver Shadow — £70 £30 £20

Metallic red and later in metallic blue. Four opening doors, opening bonnet and boot, fawn or white interior with silver hubs, bumpers etc. Price 14/11d. Issued 1962. Deleted 1973. 125mm. DC/P.

No. 158. Riley — £100 £30 £15

Blue or cream or pale green. Price 2/2d. Issued March 1954. Deleted 1960. 93mm. DC/TP/RT.

No. 159. Ford Cortina — £65 £35 £15

White with opening doors, bonnet and boot, and red flash on sides. Silver engine, wheels, bumpers etc. Price 9/3d. Issued 1967. Deleted 1970. 105mm. DC/P.

No. 159. Morris Oxford — £75 £35 £20

Renumbering of 40G. Fawn or green. Price 2/2d. Issued March 1954. Deleted January 1956. 97mm. DC/TP/RT.

	M/B	M/U	G/C
No. 159. Morris Oxford Two-Tone	£160	£50	£30

Green and cream or white and red. Price 2/9d. Issued January 1956. Deleted 1960. 97mm. DC/TP/RT.

	M/B	M/U	G/C
No. 160. Austin A30	£65	£25	£15

Fawn or blue. With plastic wheels, either smooth or ridged. Price 2/4d. Issued June 1958. Deleted 1962. 77mm. DC/TP/P.

	M/B	M/U	G/C
No. 160. Mercedes Benz 250SE	£75	£30	£20

Metallic blue with stop lights which work by pressing the car. White interior with silver bumpers and wheels etc. Price 9/3d. Issued 1967. Deleted 1974. 117mm. DC/P.

	M/B	M/U	G/C
No. 161. Ford Mustang Fastback 2 + 2	£65	£30	£15

White and yellow and orange, the latter colour being made from 1970. Red interior, opening doors, boot and bonnet, with silver trim etc. Price 10/9d. Issued 1965. Deleted 1973. 111mm. DC/P.

	M/B	M/U	G/C
No. 161C. Austin Somerset	£100	£35	£20

Blue or red. Price 2/2d. Issued March 1964. Deleted 1970. 89mm. DC/TP/RT..

No. 161D. Austin Somerset Two-Tone

Renumbering of 40J. Black and white or yellow and red. Price 2/6d. Issued August 1956. Deleted 1960. 89mm. DC/TP/RT.

	M/B	M/U	G/C
Black and white	£125	£50	£25
Yellow and red	£125	£50	£25

	M/B	M/U	G/C
No. 162. Ford Zephyr Saloon	£20	£10	£5

Two tone blue, very pale on the upper part, medium or dark on the lower. Silver radiator grille, bumpers and wheels with black tyres. Issued 1957. Deleted 1960. Price 3/-. 96mm. DC/TP/RT.

	M/B	M/U	G/C
No. 162G. Ford Zephyr	£130	£50	£20

Cream and green or two-tone green. Light green and cream is the rarer of

the two and worth double. Price 3/-.
Issued April 1956. Deleted 1960.
96mm. DC/TP/RT.

No. 162H. Triumph 1300

	M/B	M/U	G/C
	£65	£30	£15

Light blue with red interior or with
the red and white interior which is the
rare colour and worth double.
Opening boot and bonnet, all silver
bumpers, headlights, grille and hubs
etc. Price 6/-. Issued 1966. Deleted
1970. 92mm.

No. 163. V.W. 1600 TL Fastback

	£55	£25	£15

Red with fawn interior, opening
doors, bonnet and boot. Silver grille,
bumpers, headlights and wheels, with
spare wheel inside bonnet. Price 9/6d.
Issued 1966. Deleted 1971. 102mm.
DC/P/RT.

No. 163A. Bristol 450

	£65	£30	£15

Green. White circles with racing
number. Price 2/9d. Issued July 1956.
Deleted 1960. 98mm. DC/TP/RT.

No. 164. Ford Zodiac

	£65	£35	£20

Silver with red interior. Also in
bronze which is scarce as it was made
for export only, worth treble. With
opening doors, bonnet and boot, silver
hubs, bumpers, grille and headlights.
Price 13/11d. Issued March 1966.
Deleted 1971. 114mm. DC/P.

No. 164A. Vauxhall Cresta

	£60	£30	£15

Green and grey. The rare grey and
black or maroon and cream worth
double. Price 3/-. Issued March 1957.
Deleted 1960. 96mm. DC/TP/RT.

No. 165. Humber Hawk

	£70	£30	£15

Maroon and cream or green and
black, the former colour being worth
double. With windows and four-
wheel suspension. Price 3/9d. Issued
July 1959. Deleted 1963. 102m m.
DC/TP/P/RT.

No. 165A. Ford Capri

	£75	£40	£20

Green or purple and yellow, with a
metallic finish which is rare and worth
double. There is also a two-tone green
which is valuable and scarce. With red

	M/B	M/U	G/C

ʄ, silver wheels, bumpers etc.
. 6/11d. Issued 1969. Deleted
,6. 102mm. DC/P.

No. 166. Renault R16

| | £55 | £25 | £15 |

Blue. This was a borrowed French
Dinky body casting but chassis made
in England. '1/43' and '65' still cast
into baseplate, French Dinky style.
Numbers indicate scale and year of
introduction. Price 6/11d. Issued
1965. Deleted 1970. 86mm. DC/RT.

No. 166A. Sunbeam Rapier

| | £55 | £25 | £15 |

Cream and orange or two-tone blue,
with windows. Former worth double.
Price 2/11d. Issued June 1958.
Deleted 1963. 89mm. DC/TP/RT/P.

No. 167. A.C. Aceca Coupé

| | £95 | £30 | £15 |

Red and grey, cream and brown, and
cream with maroon roof, a late colour
only seen with shiny aluminium
wheels. Price 2/11d. Issued November
1958. Deleted 1963. 89mm.
DC/TP/RT.

No. 168. Ford Escort

Light blue or metallic red, with cream
or yellow interior. Opening doors,
bonnet and boot. Also in black which
is a rare colour. Also available as a
Dinky Action Kit 1006 with rally
stripes as per Ford Escort Mexico:
1973/78. Price 8/6d. Issued 1968.

Deleted 1977. 97mm. DC/P.	£65	£25	£15
Light blue	£18	£9	£7
Metallic red	£55	£20	£10
Black mint and boxed only	£350		

No. 168A. Singer Gazelle with Windows

| | £70 | £30 | £15 |

Cream and brown, or grey and green.
Former worth double. Price 2/11d.
Issued January 1959. Deleted 1963.
92mm. DC/TP/RT/P.

No. 169. Ford Corsair 2000E

| | £85 | £40 | £20 |

Silver with black roof. Price 5/11d.
Issued 1967. Deleted 1969. 108mm.
DC/P.

No. 169A. Studebaker Golden Hawk

£75 £30 £15

Green and cream, fawn and red, and green and fawn. Red flashes and later cream flashes. With windows. Price 3/5d. Issued November 1958. Deleted 1963. 106mm. DC/TP/P/RT.

No. 170. Ford Fordor

£175 £60 £30

This is a Sedan model in yellow or red, or fawn with red wheels. Price 2/3d. Issued 1954. Renumbered from 139A. Deleted 1956. 102mm. DC/TP/RT.

No. 170. Ford Fordor Two-Tone

£220

Cream and red, or pink and blue. Price 2/11d. Issued March 1956. Deleted 1959. 102mm. DC/TP/RT.

No. 170A. Lincoln Continental

£125 £50 £25

Metallic orange, or medium blue with white roof. There was a series of 1/42nd scale Dinky Toy American cars which were made in Hong Kong in 1965 but this model is not one of them. Both this and the Taunus were marked 'Made in England' on the baseplate, although on the boxes it said 'Made in Hong Kong for Dinky'. With all-chrome parts. Price 14/11d. Issued October 1964. Deleted 1970. 127mm.
LHD/SW/FTS/S/W/OB/DC/RT/P.

No. 170. Granada Ghia

£350 £100 £25

This was a new model for 1978, made in a very limited supply. There was a wooden mock-up for the Dinky stand at the 1979 Exhibition at Earls Court where I was invited as a guest by Mr Hudson, the head of Dinky at Binns Rd, Liverpool. However the 'sit-in' by the workers kept the factory and offices closed, which made it very difficult for the toy firm. This model is very scarce indeed. It was deleted about the same time that it was made. Silver metallic with all silver finish and opening doors. Price £1.50p. 127.5mm. DC/P.

MODEL	M/B	M/U	G/C

No. 171. Hudson Commodore

£150 £50 £25

Maroon and fawn or fawn and blue.
Price 2/8d. Issued 1954. Deleted
1956. 111mm. DC/TP/RT.

No. 171A. Hudson Commodore

£160 £70 £30

Two-tone model, in red and blue or
blue and grey. Price 2/9d. Issued
January 1956. Deleted 1958. 111mm.
DC/TP/RT.

No. 171B. Austin 1800

£80 £40 £10

Blue with red interior, also in red
which is very rare and worth double.
With opening boot and bonnet, silver
trim, with white interior on red
model. Price 7/-. Issued 1965. Deleted
1968. DC/P/RT.

No. 172. Studebaker Land Cruiser

£125 £50 £25

Green or blue. Price 2/8d. Issued
April 1954. Deleted July 1956.
107mm. DC/RT/PT.

No. 172. Studebaker Land Cruiser Two-Tone Model

£125 £50 £25

Maroon and cream or fawn and
brown. Price 2/9d. Issued July 1956.
Deleted 1958. DC/TP/RT.

No. 172. Fiat 2300 Station Wagon

£55 £30 £20

Off white with dark blue roof or green
with white roof, worth double. There
is also a model in light blue with
white roof or blue roof, a very rare
item and worth at least treble normal
price. Opening bonnet and opening
rear doors with full silver trim. Price
7/11d. Issued 1965. Deleted 1969.
108mm. DC/P.

No. 173. Nash Rambler

£75 £30 £15

Pale green with pink and maroon side
flashes or pale pink with blue side
flashes. Also green with purple flashes
or blue with red flashes. Latter is a
rare model and worth treble. Price
3/5d. Issued May 1958. Deleted 1962.
101mm. DC/TP/RT.

No. 173. Pontiac Parisienne

Maroon or metallic blue, also in pink
or purple, and also in red. All models
had pink or white interior, with
retractable aerials and full silver trim.
This model always had Speediwheels
and the first variety made in 1968 had
rubber tyres on metal hubs, the
second variety made in 1970 were
made entirely of plastic. Price 8/11d.
Issued 1968. Deleted 1975. 132mm.
DC/P.

	M/B	M/U	G/C
Price for metal wheels and rubber tyres	£125	£50	£25
Price for all plastic wheel type	£65	£50	£15
No. 174. Hudson Hornet	£95	£40	£25

Red and cream or red and yellow or
yellow and grey. With windows. Price
3/5d. Issued August 1958. Deleted
1963. 111mm. DC/TP/RT/P.

	M/B	M/U	G/C
No. 174A. Ford Mercury Cougar	£80	£30	£15

Metallic blue, metallic sand, metallic
purple and metallic red. Retractable
aerial, silver bumpers and white
interior with opening doors. Price
8/11d. Issued 1960. Deleted 1969.
122mm. DC/P.

	M/B	M/U	G/C
No. 175. Hillman Minx	£80	£30	£15

Green and mustard or pink and green
or grey and blue. With windows.
Price 2/11d. Issued August 1958.
Deleted 1961. 88mm. DC/TP/RT/P.

	M/B	M/U	G/C
No. 175A. Cadillac Eldorado	£95	£50	£25

Mauve with black roof. Also blue
with black roof. In 1969 a new colour
of gold and black appeared. The
former two colours are worth double.
White interior and full silver trim,
bumpers etc. Price 9/6d. Issued 1969.
Deleted 1973. 133mm. DC/P.

	M/B	M/U	G/C
No. 176. Austin A105 Saloon	£95	£30	£15

Grey with red flash and some with
red roof. Cream with blue flash, some
with blue roof and grey with red
flash, some with red roof. Blue with
yellow flash, some with yellow roof,

latter model being rare and worth
double. With windows. Price 3/5d.
Issued April 1958. Deleted 1963.
102mm. DC/TP/RT/P.

No. 176A. N.S.U. RO80   £55   £20   £10

Metallic maroon with or without black
roof; metallic blue with white or fawn
interior. Silver trim, bumpers,
headlights, etc. Luminous seats and
battery operated head and tail lights.
Price 10/6d. Issued 1969. Deleted
1974. 114mm. DC/P.

No. 177. Opel Kapitan   £55   £25   £15

Blue, mid or pale. Price 4/6d. Issued
August 1961. Deleted 1966. 100mm.
SW/LHD/SS/FTS/S/W/DC/TP/RT/P.

No. 178. Plymouth Plaza   £125   £50   £25

Pink and green or two-tone blue.
With windows. Price 3/5d. Issued
January 1959. Deleted 1963. 100mm.
DC/TP/P/RT.

No. 178. Mini Clubman   £45   £25   £10

Metallic bronze with various shades as
years progressed. White or black
interior. Price 75p. Issued 1975.
Deleted 1979.

No. 179. Studebaker President   £115   £50   £25

Blue with blue flash, or yellow with
blue flash, latter being rare and worth
more. With windows. Price 3/5d.
Issued October 1958. Deleted 1963.
108mm. DC/TP/RT/P.

No. 179A. Opel Commodore   £125   £50   £25

This was a borrowed 'French Dinky
Toy' casting. Fitted with
Speediwheels in plastic. Metallic blue
with black roof and metallic green
which is rare and worth double. Price
9/6d. Issued 1971. Deleted 1975.
107mm. DC/P.

No. 180. Packard Clipper   £115   £50   £25

Fawn and pink, or orange and grey.
With windows. Price 3/5d. Issued
September 1958. Deleted 1963.
112mm. DC/TP/RT/P.

MODEL	M/B	M/U	G/C

No. 180. Rover 3500   £75   £40   £20

White with black plastic chassis, black plastic Speediwheels, and on the chassis were the words, 'Made in Hong Kong', the first Dinky Toy to be marked this way since 1965. Price £1.35p. Issued 1978. Deleted 1979/80. 131mm. DC/P.

No. 181. Volkswagen   £60   £30   £15

Grey or pale blue, or grey and sky blue. Green or mid-blue are worth double. Price 2/5d. Issued February 1956. Deleted 1971. 90mm. DC/TP/RT.

No. 182. Porsche 356A Coupé   £90   £40   £20

Blue, cream, or red. With windows. Price 2/10d. Issued September 1958. Deleted 1964. 87mm. DC/TP/RT/P.

No. 183. Fiat 600 Saloon   £60   £20   £10

Red or green with solid plastic wheels. There is a version in red with rubber tyres which is very rare and worth at least four times the normal one. Price 2/3d. Issued May 1958. Deleted 1960. 71mm. DC with plastic wheels or rubber tyres.

No. 183A. Morris Mini Minor Automatic

White body with black roof or red body with black roof. Also blue with darker blue roof, very scarce and worth double. The model had Speediwheels from 1972. Price 7/-. Issued 1966. Deleted 1975. 75mm. DC/P.

Price for metal wheels and rubber tyres	£65	£20	£10
Price for Speediwheels plastic	£50	£20	£10

No. 184. Volvo 122S   £120   £50   £25

Red. Price 4/5d. Issued December 1961. Deleted 1964. 98mm. SW/SS/S/W/DC/TP/RT/P.

MODEL	M/B	M/U	G/C

No. 186. Mercedes Benz 220SE

£50 £20 £10

Pale or mid-blue, and all chromed
parts. Price 5/9d. Issued February
1961. Deleted 1967. 102mm.
LHD/SW/SS/FTS/S/W/DC/TP/RT/P.

No. 187. Volkswagen Karmann Ghia Coupe

£90 £30 £15

Red with black roof and green with
off-white or cream roof. With
windows and four wheel suspension.
Price 3/6d. Issued November 1959.
Deleted 1964. 96mm. DC/TP/RT/P.

No. 187A. De Tomaso Mangusta 5000

£55 £20 £10

Metallic red and white although
shades vary. With opening bonnet and
boot. White interior. Price 10/9d.
Issued 1968. Deleted 1977. 109mm.
DC/P.

No. 188. Jensen FF

£75 £40 £20

This model was mostly in yellow,
although there are the rare colours of
yellow with black roof and cream and
blue, which are worth double. With
metal hubs, rubber tyres and
Speediwheels. With opening doors
and bonnet. Price 10/9d. Issued 1968.
Deleted 1975. 121mm DC/P.

No. 189. Triumph Herald

£65 £20 £10

Green and white, or blue and white.
With windows. Price 3/3d. Issued
May 1959. Deleted 1964. 86mm.
SS/W/DC/TP/RT/P.

No. 189A. Lamborghini Marzal

Green and white with red interior.
Also metallic blue with plastic
Speediwheels and red interior. Dark
green and yellow livery which is also
metallic but quite rare. Also red,
which is very rare. Price 9/6d. Issued
1969. Deleted 1978. 108mm. DC/P.

	M/B	M/U	G/C
Red	£65	£20	£10
Green and yellow	£65	£20	£10
Green and white	£50	£25	£15
Metallic blue	£80	£40	£20
Metallic blue and white	£80	£40	£20

MODEL	M/B	M/U	G/C

No. 190. Monteverdi 375L   £55   £20   £10

Metallic red or metallic maroon with
Speediwheels and rubber tyres, and a
metal hub variety. With pink or white
interior. Price 9/6d. Issued 1971.
Deleted 1974. 116mm. DC/P.

No. 191. Dodge Royal Sedan   £80   £40   £20

Cream with brown flashes and cream
with blue flashes. Also green with
black flashes. With windows. Price
3/5d. Issued March 1959. Deleted
1964. 111mm. DC/TP/RT/P.

No. 192. De-Soto Fireflite   £70   £30   £15

Blue body with orange roof and
orange flashes; grey with red roof;
green with fawn roof; blue with
orange roof and flashes worth treble
and quite rare. Price 3/5d. Issued
December 1958. Deleted 1964.
114mm. DC/TP/RT/P.

No. 192. Range Rover   £65   £30   £15

Gold with pale blue interior. Metallic
bronze with white interior. Also white
or grey, two rare versions worth
double. Model had all plastic
Speediwheels from 1977. Price 10/6d.
Issued 1971. Deleted 1980. 109mm.
DC/P.

No. 193. Rambler Cross Country Station Wagon   £50   £25   £10

Yellow and white, blue and yellow,
this colour being worth double. All
chrome parts. Price 6/3d. Issued 1961.
Deleted 1969. 102mm. DC/TP/RT/P

No. 194. Bentley S Coupé   £95   £40   £15

Grey with red seats and brown plastic
dashboard and grey suited driver.
Later in gold with cream seats. Grey
type is worth double value as it is
now quite scarce. All chromed parts.
Price 6/3d. Issued March 1964.
Deleted 1967. 112mm.
SW/SS/FTS/S/WS/D/DC/RT/TP/P.

No. 195. Alfa Romeo 1900 Sprint   £70   £30   £15

Red or yellow. Price 4/3d. Issued
January 1961. Deleted 1963. 102mm.
SW/LHD/SS/FTS/W/S/DC/TP/RT/P.

MODEL	M/B	M/U	G/C

No. 195. Jaguar 3.4 Litre Saloon

£80 £30 £15

Cream and yellow, grey, maroon, or
dark green, which is worth double.
With window seats, four wheel
suspension and steering wheel. Price
3/11d. Issued August 1960. Deleted
1966. 95mm. DC/TP/RT/P.

No. 195A. Range Rover Fire Chief

£45 £20 £10

Early issue in metallic red and later
plain red. Price 9/6d. Issued 1971.
Deleted 1978. 109mm. DC/P.

No. 196. Holden Special Sedan

£60 £20 £10

Metallic bronze with white roof, also
in light blue with white roof. Also in
black with white roof which is worth
double. This model was not a success
in England but proved a good seller in
the Australian market, parts of
Canada, and the United States of
America. Opening boot and bonnet.
Price 7/-. Issued 1967. Deleted 1970.
108mm. DC.

No. 197. Morris Mini Traveller

£50 £20 £10

Cream or green with imitation wood
panels in brown. Also red which is
worth double. This was a good seller
especially the first model. Price 3/5d.
Issued 1961. Deleted 1970. 72mm.
SW/SS/FTS/S/W/DC/RT/P.

No. 198. Rolls Royce Phantom V

£95 £50 £25

Metallic pale green, cream and grey or
off-white. Also in black and silver
worth treble. All chromed parts. Price
6/11d. Issued November 1962.
Deleted 1965/66. 125mm.
SW/SS/FTS/S/W/D/DC/TP/RT/P.

MODEL	M/B	M/U	G/C

No. 199. Austin 7 Countryman   £50   £20   £10

Originally in pale blue with imitation wood panel in brown at rear. Later in orange. Price 3/5d. Issued May 1961. Deleted 1970. 72mm. SW/SS/FTS/S/W/DC/TP/RT/P.

No. 200. Midget Racer   –   £45   £10

This model never had an individual box, it came in boxes of six. Red or silver. Price 11d. Issued 1954 when it was renumbering of 35B. Deleted 1957. 57mm. DC/RT.

No. 200A. Matra 630   £35   £20   £10

Blue. This was a borrowed French Dinky casting but it was rather spoilt by the small plastic Speediwheels. Price 3/5d. Issued 1971. Deleted 1975. 105mm. DC/P.

No. 201. Stock Car   £35   £20   £10

Dark blue with yellow stickers. This stock car was based on the 278/244 Plymouth casting but with large racing tyres and wheels. Price £2.25p. Issued 1979. Deleted 1980. 134.5mm. DC/P. This model appeared in the Catalogue under 'Meccano & Kits' section.

No. 202. Fiat-Abarth 2000   £35   £20   £10

Red or orange and white. Price 3/5d. Issued 1970, but not released until 1971. Deleted 1975. 91mm. DC/P. This was another borrowed Dinky with the same plastic wheels as 200A.

No. 202. Custom Land Rover   £45   £20   £10

Black with yellow stickers. Limited run and very scarce. Casting was the 344 with racing wheels and large tyres and plastic bumpers. Price £2.25p. Issued 1979. Deleted 1980. 115mm. DC/P.

No. 203. Custom Range Rover   £45   £20   £10

Black body with white plastic chassis. Casting is 192 with racing wheels and large black tyres. Plastic frame with large bumpers front and rear. Price £2.50p. Issued 1979. Deleted 1980. 115mm. DC/P.

MODEL	M/B	M/U	G/C

No. 204. Ferrari 312P   £55   £20   £10

Deep metallic maroon from 1972, but
previously metallic red with white
doors. Also green metallic model with
white doors which is worth double.
Price 4/11d. Issued 1971. Deleted
1975. 99mm. DC/P. Another
borrowed French Dinky.

No. 205. Talbot-Lago   £65   £30   £15

Blue, in a bubble pack container,
which was for the export market only,
although some remained in this
country. Price 3/3d. Issued May 1962.
Deleted 1964. 103mm. DC/TP/RT/P.

No. 205A. Lotus Cortina Rally Car   £55   £20   £10

Cream and red with red flash on sides
and stripes on roof at one side. With
opening boot and bonnet and opening
doors, with yellow squares with a
black '7' on boot, bonnet and doors.
White interior. Chrome bumpers etc.
Speediwheels from approximately
1970. Price 10/9d. Issued 1968.
Deleted 1973. 105mm. DC/P.

No. 206. Maserati   £50   £25   £10

Red. Price 3/3d. Issued May 1962.
Deleted 1964. 94mm. DC/RT/TP/P.
See comments as 204.

No. 206. Customized Corvette Stingray   £55   £20   £10

Bright red with flame flashes in red,
white and yellow, with black chassis
and silver trim. This was the same as
model 221 without opening features, a
last minute effort by Dinky to revive
old moulds. Price £2.25p. Issued
1979. Deleted 1980. 113mm. DC/P.

No. 207. Alfa Romeo   £55   £20   £10

Red. In bubble pack. Price 3/3d.
Issued May 1962. Deleted 1964.
100mm. DC/RT/TP/P. See comments
for 205 Talbot Lago.

No. 207A. Triumph TR7 Rally Car   £50   £20   £10

White with red and purple design on
bonnet. Black interior and '8' on
doors. Price £1.25p. Issued 1978.
Deleted 1980. 98mm. DC/P.

MODEL	M/B	M/U	G/C

No. 208. Cooper Bristol   £50   £20   £10

Green. In bubble pack. Price 3/3d.
Issued May 1962. Deleted 1964.
89mm. DC/TP/RT/P. See comments
for 205 Talbot Lago.

No. 208A. Porsche 914

Yellow with black interior. Metallic
mid-blue with black bonnet and red
interior from 1976. Metallic blue with
white bonnet also from 1976. With
rubber tyres, metal hubs and
Speediwheels. Colours may vary in
various models. Price 75p. Issued
1971. Deleted by 1979. 89mm.
DC/RT/P.

	M/B	M/U	G/C
Yellow	£50	£20	£10
Blue and black	£50	£20	£10
Blue and white	£75	£40	£20

No. 209. Ferrari   £65   £30   £15

Blue and yellow. In bubble pack.
Price 3/3d. Issued May 1962. Deleted
1964. 101mm. DC/RT/TP/P. See
comments for 205 Talbot Lago.

No. 210. Vanwall   £50   £20   £10

Green. In bubble pack. Price 3/3d.
Issued May 1962. Deleted 1964,
95mm. DC/TP/RT/P. See comments
for Talbot Lago 205.

No. 210A. Alfa Romeo 33 Tipo-Le-Mans   £50   £20   £10

Orange with red or white interior
with '36' in white circle on sides and
front. Price 8/6d. Issued 1970.
Deleted 1978. 107mm. DC/P.

No. 211. Triumph TR7 Sports Car   £50   £20   £10

Red with black or white interior and
black plastic chassis with black or grey
plastic bumper. Price £1.20p. Issued
1976. Deleted 1980. 98mm. DC/P.

No. 212. Ford Cortina Rally Car   £75   £30   £15

Cream and black with black bonnet
and black circle with white '8'.
Opening doors, light on roof and
silver trim. Price 7/-. Issued 1965.
Deleted 1970. 102mm. DC/P.

No. 213. Ford Rally Car

Red with black bonnet with white
flash and '20' on opening doors.
Originally issued with rubber tyres
and metal hubs. From 1973 it had all
plastic Speediwheels. Price 70p.
Issued 1970. Deleted 1975. 102mm.
DC/RT/P.

	M/B	M/U	G/C
Metal hubs and rubber wheels	£75	£40	£20
All plastic wheels	£50	£20	£10

No. 214. Hillman Imp Rally Car

£50   £20   £10

Blue with white flash, red interior and
silver trim. With opening boot and
bonnet showing '35' on side. Rally
signs on model. Price 6/-. Issued
1966. Deleted 1969. 86mm. DC/P.

No. 215. Ford GT Racing Car

£75   £40   £20

Cream with red interior and black '7'
on sides. Also in green with red flash.
Opening bonnet at each end to reveal
engine workings. Model was originally
issued with plain silver disc wheels,
later on it had spoked wheels in white
and later still in metallic green. The
plain or spoked wheel model is worth
double the Speediwheel type. Price
8/11d. Issued 1965. Deleted 1974.
96mm. DC/RT/P.

No. 216. Dino Ferrari

£50   £20   £10

Red with opening doors and large
opening rear engine hatch showing a
silver blue racing engine. Blue from
1970. Both colours have stick-on
paper racing numbers, normally '20'.
Some of the red models have gold
spoked wheels and the blue version
had a black engine cover at first and
then changed to a white cover from
1973. Price 8/11d. Issued 1969.
Deleted 1975. 98mm. DC/P.

MODEL	M/B	M/U	G/C

No. 217. Alfa Romeo Scarabeo Osi   £50   £20   £10

Orange with yellow interior, with rubber tyres and metal spoked hubs on Speediwheels on all models no bumpers on the car. Price 7/11d. Issued 1969. Deleted 1974. 90mm. DC/P.

No. 218. Lotus Europa   £80   £30   £10

Dark blue and deep lemon, with orange and black flashes on bonnet and silver wheels. It had metal hubs and rubber tyre Speediwheels from 1969, and all plastic Speediwheels from 1973, The price of the metal early model with rubber tyres is almost double that of the later model. Price 7/11d. Issued 1969. Deleted 1975. 96mm. DC/P.

No. 219. Leyland Jaguar XJ5.3 Coupé   £250   £50   £25

Purple and white with red stripes design. The number '2' is on bonnet and doors. This model was first illustrated in the 1978 catalogue but only a few models were released owing to the sit-in at the factory. Anyone obtaining one of these models has a good investment. Price £1.58p. 137mm. DC/P.

No. 219. The Big Cat Jaguar   £350   £150   £50

Deep purple, also in white, which is the rarer colour of the two, with the face of a Jaguar animal on bonnet and the figure of the same animal in full flight on each side of item. With twin headlights and silver trim. This was another variation of the customized Leyland Jaguar coupé. Price £1.58p. Issued 1978 in a very limited quantity, mostly brought out by reps. during factory sit-in. 137mm. DC/P.

No. 220. Small Open Racing Car   –   £45   £20

Model never issued in an individual box but came in cartons of six. Silver with red flashes and red circles with silver '4' on sides. This was the renumbering of 23A. Price 1/6d. Issued 1954. Deleted 1955. 94mm. DC/RT.

No. 220A. Ferrari P5

Red body and white or cream interior
and opening doors. This model had
metal hubs and rubber tyre
Speediwheels from 1970. Then all
plastic wheels from 1973. Price 7/11d.
Issued 1970. Deleted 1975. 96mm.
DC/P.

	M/B	M/U	G/C
Rubber and metal wheels	£50	£20	£10
All plastic wheels	£40	£15	£10

No. 221. 'Speed of the Wind' Racing Car

	–	£55	£20

Never issued in an individual box but
delivered in cartons of six. Silver with
red trim. Price 2/-. Issued 1954, when
renumbered from 23E. Deleted 1957.
104mm. DC/RT/TP.

No. 221A. Corvette Stingray

	£75	£40	£20

Metallic bronze with swivelling
headlights and speed wheels. Opening
bonnet and doors with off-white or
cream interior, silver bumpers etc.
Rubber tyres and spoked metal hubs
when issued in metallic bronze, it was
later released in metallic orange, with
all plastic Speediwheels, plus a white
version with black bonnet which was
issued from 1976. Metallic bronze
model or orange model is worth
double the white and black. Price
£1.35. Issued 1970. Deleted 1978.
113mm. DC/P.

No. 222. Streamlined Racing Car

	–	£50	£20

Never issued in individual box but
delivered in cartons of six. Silver or
green with red or blue trim. Price
2/4d. Issued 1955 as a renumbering of
23S. Deleted 1957. 126mm.
DC/RT/TP.

No. 222. Hesketh 308E

	£40	£20	£10

Issued 1978 but still available in some
outlets, although like all Dinky models
one will have to pay a collector's
price. With large tyres, silver hubs,
medium blue body with the word
'Olympus' on the rear, front and sides
in yellow. Driver in white and '24' in
orange or yellow on the sides and
bonnet. Price £1.76p. 132mm. DC/P.

No. 223. MacLaren Can Am

First issued in 1970 in blue and white
with metal hubs and rubber tyred
Speediwheels. Then the model
changed to red and white from 1972.
Then metallic green or lime from
1976 with all plastic Speediwheels.
Metallic green was always mottled.
Price 7/11d. Issued 1970. Deleted
1978. 94mm. DC/P.

White and blue or white and red	£50	£20	£10
Metallic green	£40	£10	£5

No. 224. Mercedes Benz CIII

	£50	£20	£10

Metallic maroon; bright red, with
metal hubs and rubber tyres
Speediwheels. With white interior,
opening boot and driver's door. Price
14/11. Issued 1970. Deleted 1977.
192mm. DC/P.

No. 225. Lotus F.1 (No. 7)

Red body with gold nose, and John
Player racing team transfers on sides.
Metallic blue body from 1976. Price
7/6d. Issued 1970. Deleted 1978.
127mm. DC/P.

Red and Gold	£50	£20	£10
Blue	£40	£15	£10

No. 226. Ferrari 312/B2

	£30	£15	£5

Red, and then issued in gold from
1976, with '2' on models. Red model
is worth double. Price 75p. Issued
1972. Deleted 1978. 121mm.

No. 227. Beach Buggy

	£30	£15	£5

Yellow, then later in green with white
interior. White detachable or green
hood. Price 47p. Issued 1975. Deleted
1977. 105mm. DC/P.

No. 228. Super Sprinter

	£30	£15	£5

Blue with metal hubs and rubber
tyred Speediwheels. Price 5/9d. Issued
1970. Deleted 1972. 113mm.

No. 230. Talbot-Lago

	£100	£40	£20

Light blue. This was renumbering of
23K. With yellow '4'. Price 2/5d.
Issued 1954. Deleted 1964. 103mm.
DC/TP/RT.

MODEL	M/B	M/U	G/C

No. 231. Maserati Racer

<table>
<tr><td></td><td>£100</td><td>£40</td><td>£20</td></tr>
</table>

Red with white flash and white '9'. This was renumbering of 23N. Price 2/5d. Issued 1954. Deleted 1964. 94mm. DC/RT/TP.

No. 232. Alfa Romeo Racer

<table>
<tr><td></td><td>£140</td><td>£50</td><td>£25</td></tr>
</table>

Red with white '8' and driver cast in. Renumbering of 23F. Price 2/5d. Issued 1954. Deleted 1964. 100mm. DC/RT/TP.

No. 233. Cooper Bristol Racer

<table>
<tr><td></td><td>£85</td><td>£40</td><td>£20</td></tr>
</table>

Green with driver cast in and white '6'. Renumbering of 23G. Price 2/5d. Issued 1954. Deleted 1964. 89mm. DC/TP/RT.

No. 234. Ferrari Racer

<table>
<tr><td></td><td>£100</td><td>£40</td><td>£20</td></tr>
</table>

There are two varieties of this model, the early one has all the nose in yellow and the later one has a yellow triangle only. Add 50% on to the price for yellow triangle type. Blue with yellow nose and yellow '5', with driver cast in. Renumbering of 23H. Price 2/5d. Issued 1954. Deleted 1964. 101mm. DC/RT/TP.

No. 235. HWM Racer

<table>
<tr><td></td><td>£90</td><td>£40</td><td>£20</td></tr>
</table>

Renumbering of 23J. Green with yellow '7' and driver cast in. Price 2/5d. Issued 1954. Deleted 1960. 99mm. DC/RT/TP.

No. 236. Connaught Racer

<table>
<tr><td></td><td>£80</td><td>£40</td><td>£20</td></tr>
</table>

Green with white number in circle. Price 3/6d. Issued December 1956. Deleted 1959. 96mm. SW/D/DC/RT/TP.

No. 237. Mercedes Benz Racer

<table>
<tr><td></td><td>£65</td><td>£30</td><td>£15</td></tr>
</table>

Some of these models appeared in cream which are worth double. White with red '30'. Price 3/8d. Issued October 1956. Deleted 1969. 98mm. SW/D/DC/RT/TP.

No. 238. Jaguar Type D Racing Car

<table>
<tr><td></td><td>£100</td><td>£40</td><td>£20</td></tr>
</table>

Turquoise. When this model was released, Jaguar had just won the Le Mans for the third year running and it was a great seller. Price 2/11d. Issued September 1957. Deleted 1965. 86mm. SW/D/DC/TP/RT.

MODEL	M/B	M/U	G/C

No. 239. Vanwall Racer

        £110 £40 £20

Green with 'Vanwall' in white on
both sides and white '35'. Price 2/11d.
Issued April 1958. Deleted 1964.
95mm. DC/RT/TPS/WD.

No. 240. Cooper Racing Car

        £40 £10 £5

Blue with white stripes and white
circles with racing number. Cowling
removable to display engine. Price
3/11d. Issued April 1963. Deleted
1970. 83mm.
SW/SS/WS/D/DC/RT/P.

No. 241. Lotus Racing Car

        £40 £10 £5

Green with white circles and racing
number, plus removable cowling to
reveal engine. Price 3/11d. Issued
1963. Deleted 1970. 83mm.
SW/SS/WS/D/DC/RT/P.

No. 242. Ferrari Racing Car

        £40 £10 £5

Red with white circles and racing
number, plus removable cowling to
reveal engine. Price 3/11d. Issued
March 1963. Deleted 1971. 89mm.
DC/RT/P/SW/SS/WS/D.

No. 243. BRM Racing Car

        £40 £10 £5

Metallic green with yellow engine
cover of various shades. Many shades
tend to look like orange. Also blue
model with dark blue engine cover
which is worth double. With
removable cowling to show engine and
white circle with racing number. Price
3/11d. Issued April 1964. Deleted
1971. 83mm.
SW/SS/WS/D/DC/RT/P.

No. 281. Pathé News Car

        £120 £50 £30

Black with opening rear doors and
bonnet, complete with camera man
and camera with stand on roof of car.
Price 9/11d. Issued 1968. Deleted
1970. 108mm. DC/P.

No. 340. Land Rover

        £50 £20 £10

Orange and green with green and
cream interior. Red with green wheels
and green interior plus driver, worth
more. Model had red or yellow plastic
wheels, black plastic steering wheels,

blue plastic driver, seats and matching
wheels most of the time. Price 5/-.
Issued 1967. Deleted 1971. 92mm.
DC/P.

No. 340. Land Rover

	M/B	M/U	G/C
	£50	£20	£10

Red body with any colour wheels.

No. 341. Land Rover Trailer

Orange, green or red. Price 2/11d.
Issued 1967. Deleted 1974. 79mm.
DC/RT/P.

	M/B	M/U	G/C
Orange or green	£30	£15	£5
Red	£40	£20	£10

No. 342. Austin Mini-Moke

	M/B	M/U	G/C
	£35	£20	£10

Green with canopy. Speediwheels
from 1972. Price 5/-. Issued 1966.
Deleted 1975. 73mm DC/P.

No. 344. Estate Car

	M/B	M/U	G/C
	£55	£20	£10

Fawn and brown. The renumbering of
27F. Price 2/11d. Issued 1955.
Deleted 1961. 105mm. DC/RT/TP.

No. 344. Land Rover

Medium blue with all matching colour
in back interior. Cream or white
interior of cab. Opening doors.
Bonnet opens to reveal silver engine.
Metallic red models started in 1973.
There is a rare two-tone green model
which is priced separately. Price
7/11d. Issued 1970. Deleted 1978.
108mm.

	M/B	M/U	G/C
Blue	£50	£25	£15
Red	£40	£20	£10
Green	£60	£30	£15
Two-tone green	£125	£50	£20

No. 350. Tiny's Mini Moke

	M/B	M/U	G/C
	£100	£30	£20

Red and yellow with hole in canopy
for the giraffe driver to put his head
through. From the TV series 'The
Enchanted House'. Price 4/6d. Issued
1970. Deleted 1973. 73mm. DC/P.

No. 475. Model T Ford

£225   £100   £30

Medium blue and sky blue with yellow wheels, black chassis and mudguard. Gold headlights with radiator, grille and starting handle. One plastic male and one plastic female figure, with red interior seats. There is also a rare model with a red body, which is worth treble. Price 8/11d. Issued 1965. Deleted 1968. 79mm. DC/P.

No. 476. 1913 Morris Oxford

£225   £100   £30

Yellow with blue chassis and also with rare colour of black body and dark blue chassis which is worth treble. Complete with canopy and driver. Red or black wheels. Price 8/11d. Issued 1965. Deleted 1970. 92mm. DC/P.

No. 477. Parsley's Car

£175   £75   £30

Green and black, with the friendly lion driver in plastic, created from the TV series 'The Herbs'. Price 11/3d. Issued 1970. Deleted 1973. 92mm. DC/P.

No. 485. Model T Ford with Santa Claus

£175   £75   £8

Red and white with green, Xmas motifs on doors, Santa Claus figure, sack of presents and tree. Price 9/11d. Issued October 1964. Deleted 1968. 83mm. DC/RT/P.

No. 486. Dinky Beats Car £175 £70 £30

Blue chassis with white or cream body
and red wheels, with three figures in
black, one with harmonica and the
other two with guitars. Words like
'Kinky Gear' on sides. Price 9/11d.
Issued 1965. Deleted 1970. 92mm.
D/DC/P.

No. 518. Renault £65 £30 £15

Brown French Dinky toy imported
into England for a few years. First
issued in France in 1961. Available
from 1962 until 1965, though toy was
made in France until 1972, when
grille was changed for a later one.
There is nothing to distinguish the
one imported into England except the
price, if it is written on the box, from
those available in France. This applies
to all French Dinkies imported into
England. Price 5/11d. Issued July
1962. Deleted 1965. 85mm.
SW/LHD/SS/FTS/S/W/DC/RT/TP/P.

No. 524. Panhard 24C

Another French Dinky imported into
England between 1965 and 1968,
although made in France and sold
between 1964 and 1970. Only
available in England in metallic grey
with red interior and shiny metal
wheels. Issued in France in pale blue
or white. With headlights and winding
windows. Price 7/-. 100mm. DC/P.

	M/B	M/U	G/C
Metallic grey version	£125	£50	£25
Pale blue or white	£175	£100	£40

MODEL	M/B	M/U	G/C

No. 535. 2 C.V. Citroën   £125   £50   £25

Blue, also in maroon with grey
imitation canvas roof or very dark
grey roof. Model was made in France
from 1955 to 1965; then imported
into England from July 1962. On sale
in England for almost four years.
Price 3/11d. Deleted 1968. 88mm.
DC/TP/RT.

No. 550. Chrysler Saratoga   £175   £60   £30

Pink and white. Another model made
in France from 1962 to 1965, and
imported into England. There were
models on sale in France in 1961, but
the model was only in a limited
supply until the following year when
supplies were made for England. Price
7/8d. Deleted 1968. 129mm.
SW/LHD/SS/FTS/S/W/DC/RT/TP/P.

No. 553. Peugeot 404   £75   £40   £10

Light green. Made in France from
1961 until 1969. Price 7/11d.
Imported July 1962. Deleted 1967.
102mm.
SW/LHD/SS/FTS/S/W/DC/RT/TP/P.

No. 555. Ford Thunderbird Convertible   £95   £60   £25

White or red, Made in France 1961 to
1969. Price 7/8d. Imported 1962.
Deleted 1967. 121mm.
SW/LHD/D/SS/FTS/S/WS/DC/
TP/RT/P.

POLICE, BANKS, FIRE SERVICE AND SECURITY

No. 243. Volvo Police Car   £50   £20   £10

White with broad orange flash. Blue
or black edge on each side, opening
door at rear, black mudguards and
'Police' roof sign. Price £2.25p. Issued
1978. Deleted 1980. 141mm. DC/P.

MODEL	M/B	M/U	G/C

No. 244. Plymouth Police Car   £150   £50   £25

Black and white, with light and
transfer details on sides and on rear of
model. Price £2.25p. Issued 1978.
Deleted 1980. 161mm. DC/P.

No. 250. Police Mini Cooper S   £55   £20   £10

White with 'Police' sign and dummy
light plus aerial on roof, opening
doors and bonnet. Silver bumpers etc.
Price 8/3d. Issued 1968. Deleted
1976. 75mm. DC/P.

No. 251. Pontiac Parisienne
U.S.A. Police Car   £150   £50   £25

Authentic colours, designs etc. White
with black roof. Driver. Price 9/6d.
Issued 1973. Deleted 1975. 132mm.
DC/P.

No. 252. R.C.M.P. Police Car
Pontiac Parisienne   £175   £100   £50

Dark blue and white. With two
policemen, roof light, twin aerials.
Price 9/6d. Issued 1969. Deleted
1975. 132mm. DC/P.

No. 254. Police Range Rover   £65   £30   £10

White with orange stripe with black
border around each side. Opening
doors at side and rear with 'Police'
roof sign. Blue interior. Silver
bumpers, wheels etc. From 1976 car
had plastic Speediwheels and for the
early model one should add 50% to
price given. Price 9/11d. Issued 1971.
Deleted 1978. 109mm. DC/P.

No. 255. Ford Zodiac   £65   £30   £15

Authentic police colours. Opening
doors, boot and bonnet. Driver. Price
16/-. Issued 1967. Deleted 1972.
114mm. DC/P.

No. 255. Police Mini Clubman   £65   £30   £15

Pale blue with white doors, police
roof sign and the word 'Police' on
each door. Price £1.25p. Issued 1977.
Deleted 1980. 82mm. DC/P.

No. 255. Mersey Tunnel Police
Van Special   £2500 (Mint & Boxed only)

Red with matching wheels and
black tyres. Silver bumper, grille
and radiator. With 'Mersey Tunnel'

MODEL	M/B	M/U	G/C

in yellow or gold lettering on sides
and also Police sign in white
lettering with black background on
roof. Issued 1955. Deleted 1960.
Price 2/11d. 73mm. DC/RT/TP.

No. 256. Police Patrol Car	£65	£30	£15

Black. This is a Humber Hawk model
with 'Police' on roof in white letters.
Driver and passenger. Price 5/3d.
Issued December 1960. Deleted 1964.
102mm. DC/RT/TP/P.

No. 257. Canadian Fire Chief's Car	£65	£30	£15

Red. Nash Rambler model with the
words 'Fire Chief' on sides with
dummy red roof-light. Price 3/5d.
Issued November 1961. Deleted 1969.
102mm. DC/TP/RT/P.

No. 258. U.S.A. Police Car

Black with white doors, Police badge
and wording. Price 4/11d. Four
models in production ran from
October 1960 until July 1969.
Cadillac came into production in
1966. 114mm. DC/TP/RT/P.

De-Soto model	£125	£50	£25
Dodge model	£125	£50	£25
Ford model	£100	£40	£20
Cadillac model	£100	£40	£20

No. 260. V.W. Deutsche Bundespost	£175	£50	£25

Yellow. Model of the late V.W. with
opening bonnet, boot, and doors.
Issued for sale only in Germany
although a few were found in shops in
England. Price £1.45p. Issued 1971.
Deleted 1976. 100mm. DC/P.

No. 261. Ford Taunus 'Polizei' Car	£75	£40	£20

White and green with police
markings. Released as No. 154 for the
German market. 'Polizei' is German
for Police. Very scarce in England.
Equivalent price 7/11d. Issued 1967.
Deleted 1978. 110mm. DC/P.

No. 262. V.W. Swiss Post

Yellow and black with jewelled lights.
This No. 262 was used for two

	M/B	M/U	G/C

versions of the V.W. Swiss Post. The
first came from a Dinky 181 casting
and was issued in Switzerland from
1961 until 1966. Then from the
Dinky 129 casting with opening boot,
bonnet and doors with jewelled
headlights from 1966 to approx. 1975.
There were plastic Speediwheels on
the later version from approx. 1973.
Price 7/11d. 100mm. DC/P.

	M/B	M/U	G/C
First version	£150	£60	£30
Second version Model A metal	£95	£40	£20
Model B plastic SW's	£75	£30	£15

No. 264. R.C.M.P. Patrol Car

Dark blue with white doors. First type
is Ford Fairlane 111mm. Second
model is Cadillac 62. Price 6/6d. First
date for models 1962, and finally
deleted 1969. 113mm.DC/TP/RT/P.

	M/B	M/U	G/C
Ford Fairlane	£130	£50	£25
Cadillac	£115	£40	£20

No. 264. Police Rover 3500

	M/B	M/U	G/C
	£75	£30	£15

White with orange stripes edged in
blue or black and the word 'Police' at
rear. Same casting as 180. With
opening boot and doors. Silver hubs
etc. Price £2.50p. Issued 1978 and
still found in the odd shop but mainly
found in the special collector-
fleamarkets etc. 131mm. DC/P.

No. 269. Jaguar Motorway Police Car

	M/B	M/U	G/C
	£100	£40	£20

White. With two policemen, dummy
roof light, aerial, and the word
'Police' on boot. Price 5/6d. Issued
April 1962. Deleted June 1966.
95mm.
SW/SS/FTS/S/W/DC/TP/RT/P.

No. 270. Ford Panda Police Car

£65   £20   £10

Blue and white with opening doors, bonnet and boot. The model had plastic Speediwheels from 1975. Price 8/11d. Issued 1969. Deleted 1977. 97mm. DC/P Ford Escort casting as per no. 168.

No. 275. Brinks Armoured Van

£125   £50   £25

Grey with the words 'Brinks Security Since 1895' on each side with blue chassis. Blue defence guard complete with gold bars and opening doors. Price 12/11d. Issued 1964. Deleted 1970. 121mm. DC/P.

No. 277. Police Land Rover

£65   £20   £10

Dark blue or medium blue with white top and part of sides. The word 'Police' in white letters on black base on front and sides. There is also a blue base and roof light. Opening doors and bonnet. Price £2.25p. Issued 1978. Deleted 1980. 110mm. DC/P.

No. 280. Mobile Midland Bank Van

£150   £50   £25

Light blue, silver and white, with opening doors. With the words 'Midland Bank Ltd' on sides and front. Model body is mounted on a long chassis. With silver grille, bumpers, headlights etc. With hubs and roof-light. Price 9/11d. Issued 1966. Deleted 1969. 124mm. DC/P.

No. 269. Ford Transit Accident Unit

£95   £40   £10

White with wide orange flash and the words 'Police' and 'Accident Unit' on sides. Opening doors at side and rear,

complete with signs, cones etc. Silver
wheels and bumpers. Price £2.25p.
Issued 1978. Deleted 1980. 113mm.
DC/P.

No. 272. Ford Transit Police Accident Unit

      £95   £40   £10

White and red. Redesign of model
No. 287. With one piece opening rear
door. Driver's door does not open.
This was a second grille type. Price
£2.35p. Issued 1975. Deleted 1978.
129mm. DC/P.

No. 287. Police Accident Unit   £125 £50 £25

Orange and cream motorway colours,
with 'Police' wording, badges etc.
With safety cones and barriers, signs
etc., and opening doors at front and
rear. Roof light and sign. With driver
and other officer. First grille type.
Price 13/11d. Issued 1967. Replaced
by 272 in 1975/6. Deleted 1978.
122mm. DC/P/RT.

No. 297. Police Vehicle Set   £150 £60 £30

White and pale pink. With opening
doors, signs, cones and drivers etc.
This set contained 250, 255 and 287.
Price 37/11d. Issued 1967. Changed
to 294 in 1973. Deleted 1980. Overall
length 300/306mm. DC/P.

SPECIALIZED MODELS FROM TV, SPACE, ETC.

Please Note: Some models also in the Sports Car and Saloon
Section.

No. 267. Paramedic Truck   £150 £60 £30

Red with the figures of De-Soto and
Gage from the TV series 'Emergency'.
Price £2.25p. Issued 1978. Deleted
1980. 119mm. DC/P.

No. 281. Pathé News Camera Car

      £120 £50 £30

Black with the words in white 'Pathé
News' on sides. With red interior,
opening bonnet and rear door. With
cameraman on roof. Price 9/11d. Issued
1968. Deleted 1970. 108mm. DC/P.

MODEL	M/B	M/U	G/C

No. 351. U.F.O. Interceptor   £125   £50   £25

Lime green, orange, silver and black, with red tipped cap firing rocket. Taken from Gerry Anderson's U.F.O. TV programme. Price 14/11d. Issued 1971. Deleted 1979. 194mm. P.

No. 352. Ed Straker's Car   £125   £50   £25

Metallic bronze or gold with lemon or off-white interior. Model was known as the keyless clockwork motor. Silver hubs. Price 7/6d. Issued 1971. Deleted 1975. 124mm. DC/P.

No. 353. Shado 2 Mobile   £100   £40   £20

All action model in green, orange and silver, with the word 'Shado' and the figure '2' in white on sides, with twelve wheels and heavy tracks, white interior and firing rocket on roof. Another model taken from Gerry Anderson's U.F.O. TV programme. Price 17/11d. Issued 1971. Deleted 1979. 145mm. DC/P.

No. 354. Pink Panther   £275   £100   £50

There is no doubt that this model came to the rescue of a firm which was on the verge of bankruptcy. This same model was rejected by Corgi and the Dinky firm made it as a gimmick because of the television series of the same name and it sold by the thousands, not only in England but also in America. Pink, with the figure of the panther with black markings etc. The model tears alongs under its own dynamic power. It has a central gyroscopic road wheel with a pull through track rod. Price £1.75p. Issued 1972. Deleted 1977. 175mm. DC/P.

No. 355. Lunar Roving Vehicle   £150   £60   £30

Blue and red with thick black plastic wheels and knobby treads with two white spacemen. The front and rear wheels are steered by pivoting a central control column. With model astronauts and simulated solar energy cells. Price 14/11d. Issued 1972. Deleted 1975. 114mm. DC/P.

No. 357. Klingon Battle Cruiser

| | £150 | £60 | £30 |

Blue and silver. Taken direct from TV series 'Star Trek'. Price £1.55p. Issued 1977. Deleted 1979. 220mm. DC/P.

No. 358. U.S.S. Enterprise

| | £150 | £60 | £30 |

Silver and orange, with black lettering. Taken from TV series 'Star Trek'. The model fires photon torpedoes and doors open for access to shuttlecraft. Price £2.25p. Issued 1976. Deleted 1979. 234mm. DC/P.

No. 359. Eagle Transporter

| | £150 | £60 | £30 |

Lime green, red, white and silver. Model from the TV series 'Space 1999'. All working components, adjustable feet etc. Price £2.50p. Issued 1975. Deleted 1979. 222mm. DC/P.

No. 360. Eagle Freighter

| | £100 | £50 | £25 |

Another model from 'Space 1999' programme. All silver body with red, orange and purple parts, with adjustable feet. Price £2.50p. Issued 1975. Deleted 1979. 222mm. DC/P.

No. 361. Galactic War Chariot

| | £125 | £50 | £25 |

Lime green or yellow green. Silver rocket attachments, wheels and six large tyres. Complete with two astronauts in white and orange or bright yellow. Price £2.50p. Issued 1978. Deleted 1980. 126mm. DC/P.

No. 362. Trident Star Fighter

| | £45 | £20 | £10 |

Dark brown or chocolate, with dark orange and yellow markings on wings, tail and nose. Complete with rocket which fires by pressing the centre of the fighter. Price £1.47p. Issued 1978. Deleted 1980. 170mm. DC/P.

MODEL	M/B	M/U	G/C

No. 364. Space Shuttle

£250 £150 £50

This is a model of the famous American Nasa Shuttlecraft. White and dark blue with American flag markings on sides. Price £4.35p. Issued 1978. Deleted 1980. 186mm. DC/P.

No. 367. Space Battle Cruiser

£175 £100 £40

White with blue engine and cockpit interior, with spaceman pilot. With firing rockets and opening clear plastic hatch, rockets have black tips and rocket holders have orange or deep red circles around them. Price £3.25p. Issued 1978. Deleted 1980. 187mm. DC/P.

No. 370. Dragster Set

£100 £60 £20

Yellow, silver with red stripes, with driver. This was another first ever idea. The model had the new Speediwheels and proved a great success and was also sold as a single item apart from a dragster set. Price 17/11d. Issued 1969. Deleted 1976. 113mm. DC/P.

No. 370. The Dragster

£75 £30 £15

Yellow, silver, and pink and white striped engine cover. With large racing wheels. Price 14/11d. Issued 1969. Deleted 1975/76. 113mm. DC/P.

No. 602. Armoured Command Car

£125 £50 £25

Metallic dark blue or green with black wheels. Model designed by Gerry Anderson of Thunderbird TV fame. With tracer-projector and super radar scanner powered by its own clockwork motor. Price £2.95p. Issued 1976. Deleted 1978. DC/P.

No. 755. Harpoon for Fab 1

£5 – –

These came in packets of six as spare harpoons for No. 100, produced between 1966 and 1977, which being realistic can only be bought as mint. You would never find six loose harpoons. Price 6d. per packet.

MODEL	M/B	M/U	G/C
No. 756. Rocket for Fab Car	£5	£3	£1

Made as a spare for Dinky No. 100
between 1966 and 1977. Price 6d.

	M/B	M/U	G/C
No. 967. B.B.C. Mobile Control Room	£150	£100	£40

Green with white flash and the words
'BBC Television Services' in yellow
or gold. With windows. Price 8/3d.
Issued July 1959. Deleted 1964/65.
151mm. DC/TP/RT/P.

	M/B	M/U	G/C
No. 968. BBC Roving Eye Vehicle	£175	£100	£50

Green with white flash to match 967
and the word 'TV Roving Eye' and
BBC badge on sides. With TV aerial
and revolving camera and operator on
roof. Price 8/3d. Issued May 1959.
Deleted 1964. 110mm. DC/RT/TP/P.

	M/B	M/U	G/C
No. 969. BBC Extending Mast Vehicle	£175	£100	£50

Green with white flash to go with 967
and 968. With extending mast and
badge on sides. Price 13/6d. Issued
October 1959. Deleted 1964. 195mm.
DC/TP/RT/P.

	M/B	M/U	G/C
No. 987. ABC Mobile Control Room	£125	£70	£20

Blue and grey with all authentic
markings. Model has red flash. The
words 'ABC Television' on front and
sides with camera and operator on
roof. Price 12/6d. Issued July 1962.
Deleted 1970. 151mm. DC/TP/RT/P.

	M/B	M/U	G/C
No. 988. ABC TV Transmitter Van	£175	£100	£40

Matching blue and grey with red flash
like No. 987. With 'ABC' on front
and rotating aerial on roof. Price 7/9d.
Issued May 1962. Deleted 1970.
111mm. DC/TP/RT/P.

DINKY ACTION KITS

MODEL	M/B	M/U	G/C
No. 1001. Rolls Royce Phantom V Limousine	£75	–	–

This was the first of a range of Dinky toys to be called 'Action Kits' in unpainted form with a tiny holder of paint. The colours usually differ from the normal models and also many collectors bought other paints and did a range of colours. However, in good condition and perfectly constructed these models are worth a lot of money to the real enthusiast. I will mention the correct colours if I am positive about them, as it is very important to note the kit colours from the standard models. Made up models should always be regarded as 'Re-paints' as it will not be a factory job. Prices for these models can vary all according to the quality of the work done to the model. I will set out the number of the regular Dinky model from which the kit derived, if it had one. Above model was based on Dinky toy No. 152. Colours: black; royal blue; maroon or silver grey. Jewelled headlights, opening doors, boot and bonnet. Price £1.45p. Issued 1971. Deleted 1978.

No. 1002. Volvo 1800 S Coupé	£50	–	–

From Dinky model No. 116. Colours: lemon or lime green. All opening doors, boot, bonnet and folding seats. Price £1.25p. Issued 1971. Deleted 1975.

No. 1003. Volkswagen 1300	£50	–	–

Colours: red and white. Opening doors, bonnet, boot and jewelled headlights. Price £1.25p. Issued 1971. Deleted 1975.

No. 1004. Ford Escort Police Panda Car	£75	–	–

From Dinky No. 270. Blue and white paint and authentic police transfers. Opening doors, bonnet, boot and folding seats. Colour on all models by Humbrol. Price £1.25p. Issued 1971. Deleted 1977.

MODEL	M/B	M/U	G/C

No. 1005. Peugeot 504 Cabriolet Kit

£50 – –

Made from French Dinky No. 1423 which was never released. Very rare model in green or black. Price £1.50p. Issued 1971. Deleted 1978. Note: Only a few models were given to private collectors by reps. or work staff.

No. 1006. Ford Escort Mexico Kit

£50 – –

Made from Dinky model No. 168. In red colours, with transfer Mexico stripes. Price £1.50p. Issued 1973. Deleted 1978.

No. 1007. Jensen FF

£50 – –

Made from Dinky model 188. Colours: blue, dark green or silver. Opening doors and bonnet. Price £1.50p. Issued 1971. Deleted 1975.

No. 1008. Mercedes Benz 600

£50 – –

Made from Dinky model No. 128. Colours: dark green or lemon. Price £1.35p. Issued 1973. Deleted 1977.

No. 1009. Lotus F.1

£50 – –

Made from Dinky model 225. Red paint and gold, white and red, also in green colours. John Player racing team transfers. With detailed rear engine and racing driver. Price £1.76p. Issued 1971. Deleted 1975.

No. 1012. Ferrari 213-B2

£50 – –

Made from Dinky toy No. 226. With transfers in red and white with red paint and black '9' in white circle. Price £1.25p. Issued 1973. Deleted 1975.

No. 1013. Matra Simca M.530

£50 – –

A few of these models were made but never released on sale to the general public. Made from French Dinky 1403. See comments for No. 1005.

No. 1014. Beach Buggy

£50 – –

Made from Dinky model 227. Colours: mid blue with dark red band down bonnet and silver grey top. Red, white and blue star transfers. Price 95p. Issued 1975. Deleted 1977.

No. 1017. Routemaster London Bus

£75   –   –

Made from Dinky model No. 289. With Esso advert transfers and red paint. Other transfers are known to exist with same model. Price 75p. Issued 1971. Deleted 1977.

No. 1018. Leyland Atlantean Bus

Made from Dinky model 295. Price £1.25p. Issued 1973. Deleted 1977. Issued with several paints and I will list the prices given for the various transfers.

National emblems and white paint   £75   –   –

With silver paint and 'Silver Jubilee' transfers   £125   –   –

Red with 'See London by Night' transfers   £125   –   –

Dark blue and 'Fly by British Airways' transfers   £150   –   –

Other transfers in good make up condition worth between £50 and £75 mint.

No. 1023. AEC Merlin Single Decker Bus

£75   –   –

Made from Dinky model 283 and issued with green paint and Green-Line Bus transfers. Also with green paint and white and red markings. Watch for unusual transfers and colours on this model as worth double normal livery. With auto/doors, button bell and moulded seats. Price £1.25p. Issued 1972. Deleted 1977.

No. 1025. Ford Transit Van

£50   –   –

Made from Dinky model No. 407. Red paint and 'Avis' transfers. With sliding door, opening rear doors, opening side door. Again this model was made up by several firms as a promotional gimmick. Many of these are worth between £10 and £50, although I advise caution and the advice of an expert. Price £1.25p. Issued 1971. Deleted 1976.

No. 1027. Lunar Rover Kit

£50   –   –

Made from Dinky model No. 355. Blue and white. Front and rear wheels steered by pivoting central control

MODEL	M/B	M/U	G/C

column. With model astronauts and
simulated energy cells. Price 75p.
Issued 1972. Deleted 1975.

No. 1029. Ford D.800 Tipper Truck
£50 – –

Made from Dinky model 438. Issued
with red paint for cab and yellow
paint for tipper with opening doors, a
tip-up body and opening tail-board.
Also in green and grey, worth double.
Price 99p. Issued 1971. Deleted 1977.

No. 1030. Land Rover Breakdown Truck
£50 – –

Made from Dinky model 442. Red
and white paint. Price £1.25p. Issued
1974. Deleted 1977.

No. 1032. Army Land Rover
£40 – –

Made from Dinky model 344. Green
army livery and transfers. Price 75p.
Issued 1977.

No. 1033. U.S.A. Army Jeep
£40 – –

Made from Dinky model 615. U.S.
stars and lime green or mustard paint.
Extra large model with driver, spare
wheel and radio aerial etc. Price
£1.75p. Issued 1971. Deleted 1977.

No. 1034. Mobile Gun
£25 – –

Made from Dinky model 654.
Military green paint. Price 55p.
Issued 1974. Deleted 1977.

No. 1035. Striker Anti-Tank Vehicle
£40 – –

Made from Dinky No. 691. Army
livery and complete with military
transfers. Price £1.35p. Issued 1975.
Deleted 1975.

No. 1036. Leopard Tank
£50 – –

Made from Dinky model 692. With
military livery and transfers. Price
£2.25p. Issued 1974. Deleted 1977.

No. 1037. Chieftain Tank
£50 – –

Made from Dinky model 683. With
full army transfers and army livery.
Price £2.25p. Issued 1974. Deleted
1977.

MODEL	M/B	M/U	G/C

No. 1038. Scorpion Tank   £50   –   –

Made from Dinky model No. 690.
With military transfers and military
paint. Price £2.25p. Issued 1975.
Deleted 1977.

No. 1039. Leopard Recovery Tank   £50   –   –

Made from Dinky model 699. With
military transfers and paint. Price
£1.75p. Issued 1975. Deleted 1977.

No. 1040. Sea King Helicopter   £35   –   –

Made from Dinky model 724. White
and orange with red stripes with
battery operated main rotor, finger
operated lifting gear, and moulded
seats. Price £1.25p. Issued 1971.
Deleted 1977.

No. 1041. Hawker Hurricane Mk 11C   £30   –   –

Made from Dinky model 718. With
RAF transfers and paint for
camouflage. Price 75p. Issued 1973.
Deleted 1976.

No. 1042. Spitfire Mk 11   £30   –   –

Made from Dinky model 719. With
RAF transfers and livery paint. Price
75p. Issued 1971. Deleted 1977.

No. 1043. S.E.P.E.C.A.T. Plane   £30   –   –

Made from Dinky model 731. Dark
green and blue. With transfers and
livery. Price 75p. Issued 1973.
Deleted 1976.

No. 1044. Messerschmitt BF 109E   £30   –   –

Made from Dinky model 726. With
transfers and brown or bronze and
blue paint. Price 75p. Issued 1972.
Deleted 1976.

No. 1045. Multi-Role Combat Aircraft   £30   –   –

Made from Dinky model 729. With
transfers and livery. Price 75p. Issued
1973. Deleted 1976.

No. 1050. Motor Patrol Boat   £45   £3   £1

Made from Dinky model 675. With
transfer and white and blue paint.
Price £1.00. Issued 1975. Deleted
1977.

No. C1. Motor Car Outfit   £350   £200   £100

A range of super cars can be built
with this set. Parts supplied can build
four cars in a colour combination of
red and light blue. Powerful
clockwork motor included in set. Price
10/-. Issued 1935. Deleted 1940.

No. C2. Motor Car Outfit   £550   –   –

Larger models of a superior type can
be built with this gift set. Colours
including: red, light blue, and black.
With enough parts to build six sports
cars and two racing cars. With two
powerful clockwork motors, each
giving a run of more than 150 ft. on
one winding. Price 20/-. Issued 1936.
Deleted 1940.

No. C3. Two-Seater Sports Car (non-constructional)   £450   £300   £150

This is a realistic model of a two-
seater sports car, beautifully made and
finished by factory craftsmen, fitted
with a strong clockwork motor. With
blue body, black chassis and cream
mudguards. Price 6/6d. Issued 1936.
Deleted 1940. Length 234mm. Width
95mm. Depth 57mm.

No. C4. Clockwork Sports Car   £600   £400   £200

Red body with cream mudguards,
blue interior. Seats and silver
headlights. Bumpers and black grille.
Solid red wheels and white rubber
tyres, with spare wheel on rear.
Sidelights and reflector on rear. Price
7/6d. Issued 1937. Deleted 1940.
Length 236mm. Width 96mm. Depth
59mm.

No. C5. Sports Tourer with Hood   £600   £400   £200

Red and cream with black outline and
black hood. With black mudguards
and running board, with long running
clockwork motor and cream interior.
Price 9/6d. Issued 1937. Deleted
1940. Length 240mm. Width 99mm.
Depth 59mm.

MODEL	M/B	M/U	G/C

No. C6. Road Racer No. 1   £400   £250   £150

Red and blue with black chassis and
black seats with white driver (tin-
plate). With long running clockwork
motor and '1' in black on sides and on
nose. Price 1/3d. Issued 1937. Deleted
1940. Length 117mm. Width 91mm.
Depth 53mm.

No. C7. Saloon Coupé   £500   £400   £200

Red with blue interior and cream
mudguards. With long running
clockwork motor. Tin-plate driver.
Bumpers and headlights and sidelights
and tail light and also sounding horn,
all work with battery. Price 10/-.
Issued 1938. Deleted 1940. Length
240mm. Width 99mm. Depth 101mm.

No. C8. Sports Tourer   £500   £300   £100

Red, light blue or cream. With long
running clockwork motor, headlights,
sidelights and tail light, plus horn all
working with battery. With opening
doors and a dicky seat in the rear.
Price 9/-. Issued 1938. Deleted 1940.
Length 240mm. Width 99mm. Depth
59mm.

No. C10. Road Racer Special   £500   £300   £100

Red body and light blue interior.
With '10' on black discs on sides, rear
and nose. With long running
clockwork motor. With tin-plate driver
in black suit, red helmet and goggles.
Price 9/-. Issued 1939. Deleted 1940.
Length 235mm. Width 97mm. Depth
56mm.

No. C11. Motor Van with no adverts   £750   £400   £200

Red body and light blue mudguards.
With running board and long running
clockwork motor. Opening doors at
rear and opening cab doors. With
black steering wheel. Thick grey tyres,
rear light and horn and strong bumper
bars and black grille. Price 15/-.
Issued 1939. Deleted 1940. Length
300mm. Width 99mm. Depth 76mm.

No. C12. Dinky Garage and Car

£500   £400   £250

Cream garage with red doors and black workbench with vice. Containing blue sports car with cream mudguards and seats with black steering wheel. With long running clockwork motor. Lights and horn worked by battery. With white tyres. Price 4/11d. Issued 1938. Deleted 1940. Garage height 115mm. Length 132mm. Width 102mm. Car length 117mm. Width 91mm. Depth 53mm.

MOTOR CYCLES

No. 37a. Civilian Model

–   £45   £10

Many of these models never had individual boxes as they were packed in either half-dozens or in dozens. Green or brown rider on black cycle with white wheels. Price 6d. Issued June 1938. Deleted 1940. 46mm. DC/RW.

No. 37A. Civilian Model

–   £35   £10

Grey or green rider. Cycle with black or white wheels. Many post-war models have white solid rubber wheels and are only distinguishable from pre-war models by the better detailed paint finish. The pre-war models have more details picked out in silver. Price 1/9d. Issued 1946. Deleted 1948. 45mm. DC/RW.

MODEL	M/B	M/U	G/C

No. 37b. Police Motor Patrolman

| | – | £35 | £10 |

Blue rider on black cycle with white wheels. Price 6d. Issued June 1938. Deleted 1940. 46mm. DC/RW.

No. 37B. Police Patrolman

| | – | £25 | £10 |

Blue rider on black machine with black or white wheels. Price 1/9d. Issued 1946. Deleted 1948. 45mm. DC/RW.

No. 37e. Royal Corps of Signals Rider

| | – | £45 | £10 |

Khaki rider on green motor cycle. Rider has blue and white armband. White rubber wheels, but black from 1939. Price 6d. Issued June 1938. Deleted 1940/41. 45mm. DC/RW. Never reissued post-war.

No. 42b. Police Motor Cycle Patrol

| | – | £45 | £10 |

Very dark blue police livery, much darker than post-war. White rubber wheels. Dark blue bike and figures with dark green sidecar. Price 10d. Issued August 1936. Deleted 1940. 47mm. DC/RW.

No. 42B. Police Motor Patrol

| | – | £35 | £10 |

Blue bike with green sidecar and black wheels. Price 1/9d. Issued 1948. Deleted 1956. 47mm. DC/RW.

No. 43b. RAC Patrol Bike

| | – | £45 | £10 |

Blue rider with black cycle and blue sidecar. Driver has white shirt, black tie and red sash painted on. White or black solid rubber wheels. Price 9d. Issued October 1935. Deleted 1940. 46mm. DC/RW.

No. 43B. RAC Motor Patrol Bike

| | – | £35 | £10 |

This model has two or three different shades of blue. Driver has plain blue uniform and the model has black wheels and black or blue sidecar. Price 2/6d. Issued 1946. Deleted 1950. 45mm. DC/RW.

MODEL	M/B	M/U	G/C

No. 44b. AA Motor Patrol

		M/U	G/C
	–	£55	£15

The pre-war and early post-war AA
bikes have a small 'AA' transfer on
the sidecar and later ones and 270
have larger ones. Driver has shirt and
tie with blue painted sash. White
wheels. Price 9d. Issued October
1935. Deleted 1940. DC.

No. 44B. AA Motor Cycle Patrol

	–	£45	£10

Black cycle with yellow sidecar and
AA badge on sidecar. Driver painted
plain. Model with black wheels. Price
2/11d., Issued 1946. Deleted 1949.
45mm. DC/RW.

No. 270. AA Motor Cycle Patrol

£45	£20	£10

This model was a reissue of 44B after
a gap of 10 years and was only issued
with grey plastic wheels and in an
individual box. The wheels were as
those used in the Hornby Dinky
Dublo models 064, 066 and 073. The
early models were in boxes of six, but
later the first individual boxes were
issued. Authentic AA livery with rider
with pink face. Badge on sidecar.
Price 2/2d. Issued February 1959.
Deleted 1962.

No. 271. 'Touring Secours' Motor Cycle Patrol

£125	£60	£30

Yellow with grey plastic wheels and
'T.S.' badge. This was an identical
270 model made in special livery for
the Belgian market. Equivalent price
2/6d. Issued 1962. Deleted 1966.
46mm. DC/RW.

No. 272. 'A.N.W.B.' Patrol Bike

£125	£60	£30

Dark yellow with 'A.N.W.B.' badge
and markings. With plastic wheels.
Identical model to 270. Equivalent
price 2/6d. Issued for Dutch market
1962. Deleted 1966. 46mm. DC/RT.

GARAGES, PUMPS, TYRES AND BOXES

MODEL	M/B	M/U	G/C
No. 42a. Police Box	–	£45	£10

Very dark blue police colours (much darker then the post-war variety) with the word 'Police' on the sides. These models never had individual boxes but were sold single, unwrapped, or in a set with 42B, 42C, and 42D. Should any person find any sets for any Dinky models of the pre-war period they should write to me for separate valuation. Price 6d. Issued August 1936. Deleted 1940. DC

Price of set	£125		
No. 42A. Police Box	–	£35	£10

Blue police colours, with the word 'Police' on sides. Not individually boxed but sold in boxes of six at the price of 5/-. Issued 1948. Renumbered 751 in 1954/55. Deleted 1960. Height 66mm. DC

Price for box of six in mint condition	£75		
No. 43a. RAC Box	–	£55	£15

Blue with RAC badge on sides. Never had individual box but sold unwrapped singly, or in a set with 43B, 43C, and 43D. Price 6d. Issued October 1935. Deleted 1940. Height 81mm. TP.

Price of set	£175		
No. 44a. AA Box	–	£55	£15

Black and yellow with AA badge and three sign posts on top. Not individually boxed. Price 8d. Issued October 1935. Deleted 1940. Height 81mm. TP.

Price of set.	£175		
No. 45. Garage	£175	£100	£50

With opening double doors. Price 1/6d. Issued December 1935. Deleted 1940. TP.

No. 48. Garage and Service Station	£175	£100	£50

Pink or maroon. With the words 'Filling and Service Station . . . Petrol, Oil, Air, Tyres, and Spares'. Price 1/6d. Issued June 1935. Deleted 1940. TP. Garage 145mm x 45mm. Height 97mm.

MODEL	M/B	M/U	G/C

No. 49. Set of Petrol and Oil Pumps

£500 – –

Price 1/6d. Issued June 1935. Deleted 1940. As with all sets it is well to note that the price given is for mint and boxed only, as after this the set must split up and become separate items, and therefore subject to an agreed price between buyer and seller.

No. 49. Set of Petrol and Oil Pumps

£125 – –

Price 5/-. Issued 1948. Deleted 1953. DC. Price for set mint and boxed only.

No. 49a. Bowser Petrol Pump

– £35 £10

Green with rubber pipe. Price 4d. Issued 1935. Deleted 1940. Height 46mm. DC. Not individually boxed. Only boxed with set 49.

No. 49A. Bowser Petrol Pump

– £20 £5

Green with plastic pipe. Price 1/-. Issued 1948. Deleted 1953. 46mm. Not individually boxed.

No. 49b. Wayne Petrol Pump

– £35 £10

Blue with rubber pipe. Price 4d. Issued June 1935. Deleted 1940. 39mm. DC. Not individually boxed.

No. 49B. Petrol Pump

– £20 £5

Blue with plastic hose. Price 1/-. Issued 1948. Deleted 1953. 39mm. DC. Not individually boxed.

No. 49c. Theo Petrol Pump

– £35 £10

Royal blue with rubber pipe. Price 4d. Issued June 1935. Deleted 1940. 58mm. DC. Not individually boxed.

No. 49C. Petrol Pump

– £20 £5

Brown with plastic hose. Price 1/-. Issued 1948. Deleted 1953. 53mm. DC. Not individually boxed.

No. 49d. Shell Petrol Pump

– £35 £10

Red with white top to pump. With rubber pipe. Price 4d. Issued June 1935. Deleted 1940. 58mm. DC. Not individually boxed.

No. 49D. Shell Petrol Pump

– £20 £5

Red with plastic hose. Price 1/-. Issued 1948. Deleted 1953. 53mm. DC. Not individually boxed.

MODEL	M/B	M/U	G/C

No. 49e. Pratts Oil Bin
| | – | £35 | £10 |

Yellow with words 'Pratts Motor Oil'.
Front hinges to show three red oil
dispensers. Price 3d. Issued June
1935. Deleted 1940. 32mm. DC. Not
individually boxed.

No. 49E. Oil Bin
| | – | £20 | £5 |

Post-war casting identical to pre-war.
Post-war version had no transfer as
Pratts no longer existed, only Shell
survived the war. Price 10d. Issued
1948. Deleted 1953. 32mm. DC/TP.
Not individually boxed.

No. 502. Garage
| | £30 | £15 | £5 |

Light blue and grey. With automatic
opening doors. This was a French
imported Dinky Toy. Price 8/7d.
Issued September 1961. Deleted 1963.
272mm. Plastic.

No. 12c. Telephone Box
Cream with silver windows. Red from
1946 to 1954 when it was renumbered
750. Price 4d. Post-war price 10d.
Issued 1936. Deleted 1940. Came in
boxes of six.

Pre-war	–	£45	£10
Post-war	–	£25	£7

MODEL	M/B	M/U	G/C

No. 750. Telephone Box

		£15	£5

Post Office red. Price 10d. Issued 1954. Deleted 1962. Height 58mm. DC. Model was sold in boxes of 6 and the casting is the same as 12C.

Box of 6 in mint condition	£100	–	–

No. 751. Police Box

		£15	£5

Blue. Renumbering of 42A. Price 1/9d. Issued 1954. Deleted 1960. Height 66mm. DC. Not in individual box, but in boxes of 6.

Box of 6 in mint condition	£100	–	–

No. 781. Esso Petrol Pump Station

	£25	£10	£5

Brown, with cream and red etc. Pale grey base is rare and worth double. Price 4/11d. Issued July 1955. Deleted 1966. Length 114mm. With plastic hoses.

No. 782. Shell Petrol Station

	£35	£15	£10

Brown or grey base with red and yellow pumps which are metal, while sign is plastic. Plastic kiosk and plastic hoses on pumps. Four pumps. Price 7/6d. Issued November 1960. Deleted 1971. 203mm. DC/P.

No. 783. BP Petrol Station

	£35	£15	£10

Grey, green and yellow. BP plastic sign and kiosk. Price 7/6d. Issued November 1960. Deleted 1971. 203mm. DC/P.

No. 785. Service Station

	£35	£15	£10

Yellow and black. With garage opening door. Price 27/6d. Issued June 1960. Deleted 1964. 335mm x 185mm. P.

No. 786. Tyre Rack and Tyres

		£20	£5

Green with twenty-one tyres of various sizes. Four white and the rest black. Dunlop trade mark tyres. not individually boxed. Price 2/11d. Issued June 1960. Deleted 1967. 52mm. DC/RT.

SETS OF TYRES IN BOXES OF 12

Prices are for Mint/Boxed and good condition. Tyres are in demand owing to increasing numbers of collectors and the fact that Dinky no longer make any models or tyres and parts etc. Any original parts, such as tyres, are often worth more than many collector dealers are telling customers. No model is worth a high price unless it is in good condition and complete with correct tyres etc.

On the last few pages of this section I will quote all correct numbers and colours, values etc. and any collector wishing to have private valuations should write to me c/o the publishers and enclosed a stamped addressed envelope for reply.

Please Note: Only genuine Dinky products are priced in this section. In no way are prices quoted for mock-up tyres or imitation items.

MODEL	M/B	M/U	G/C
No. 097. Rubber Wheel	£10		

These were issued for the 35 series and motor cycles respectively. In boxes of 12. Price 1/6d. Issued late 1940. Stopped through war. Reissued 1948/49. Deleted 1962. 13/32".

No. 097. Rubber Wheel	£10		

Price 1/6d. Issued 1948. Deleted 1962. 7/16".

No. 020. Black Tyres	£5		

Price 2/-. Issued 1962. Deleted 1977. 16mm. Rubber.

No. 080. Black Tyres	£10		

Price 5/-. Issued 1962. Deleted 1976. 38mm. Rubber.

No. 081. White Tyres	£5		

Price 1/6d. Issued 1962. Deleted 1976. 14mm.

No. 082. Black Tyres	£5		

Price 2/-. Issued 1962. Deleted 1976. 20mm.

No. 083. Grey Tyres	£20		

Price 2/-. Issued 1963. Deleted 1969. 20mm.

No. 084. Black Tyres	£10		

Price 1/6d. Issued 1963. Deleted 1976. 18mm.

MODEL	M/B	M/U	G/C

No. 085. White Tyres   £10

Price 1/6d. Issued 1963. Deleted
1976. 15mm.

No. 086. Black Tyres   £10

Price 2/-. Issued 1963. Deleted 1976.
16mm.

No. 087. Black Tyres   £15

Price 4/6d. Issued 1963. Deleted
1976. 35mm.

No. 088. Black Tyres   £10

Price 2/-. Issued 1963. Deleted 1976.
25mm.

No. 089. Black Tyres   £10

Price 2/-. Issued 1963. Deleted 1976.
19mm.

No. 090. Black Tyres   £10

Price 1/6d. Issued 1964. Deleted
1976. 14mm.

No. 091. Black Tyres   £10

Price 1/6d. Issued 1964. Deleted
1976. 13mm.

No. 092. Black Tyres   £10

Price per doz. 2/-. Issued 1964.
Deleted 1976. 15mm.

No. 093. Black Tyres   £15

Price 3/6d. Issued 1964. Deleted
1976. 27mm.

No. 094. Black Tyres   £10

Price 2/-. Issued 1963. Deleted 1976.
20mm.

No. 095. Black Tyres   £10

Price 1/6d. Issued 1963. Deleted
1976. 18mm.

No. 096. Black Tyres   £15

Price 2/-. Issued 1963. Deleted 1976.
24mm.

No. 097. Black Tyres   £15

Price 3/6d. Issued 1964. Deleted
1976. 32mm.

No. 098. Black Tyres   £10
Price 2/-. Issued 1963. Deleted 1976.
17mm.

No. 099. Black Tyres   £15
Price 2/-. Issued 1963. Deleted 1976.
20mm.

No. 6677. Engraved Tyres   £25
Set of 12. Price 1/3d. Issued 1963.
Deleted 1968. 24mm.

No. 10253. Engraved Tyres (black)   £25
Set of 12. Price 1/3d. Issued 1963.
Deleted 1966. 32mm.

No. 14094. Engraved Tyres (black)   £25
Set of 12. Price 1/3d. Issued 1963.
Deleted 1966. 25mm.

No. 14095. Engraved Tyres (white)   £10
Set of 12. Price 1/3d. Issued 1963.
Deleted 1966. 13mm.

No. 60036. Engraved Tyres (black)   £15
Set of 12. Price 1/3d. Issued 1963.
Deleted 1966. 13mm.

No. 030. Set of Tracks (Black)   £15
For model No. 104. Price 2/-. Issued
1964. Deleted 1976.

No. 031. Set of Tracks   £10
Made for models 619, 622, and 690.
Also for models 694 and 984. Price
30p. Issued 1975. Deleted 1979.

No. 032. Set of Tracks   £7
Made for models 353 and 977. Price
45p. Issued 1965. Deleted 1979.

No. 033. Set of Tracks   £7
Made for models 654 and 683. Price
45p. Issued 1965. Deleted 1979.

No. 13978. Set of Engraved Tyres   £15
Price 2/6d. Issued 1962. Deleted
1965. 32mm.

GARDEN TOOLS

Many of the following models never had individual boxes and were sold in either boxes of six or sometimes twelve. Therefore many of the items will be priced as in mint/unboxed, and good condition. I will also give them for mint and boxed in sixes.

MODEL	M/B	M/U	G/C

No. 105A. Garden Roller

Green and red. Price 1/-. Issued June 1948. Renumbered 381 in 1954. Deleted 1958. 66mm. DC.

	M/B	M/U	G/C
Box of 6	£125		
Singles		£8	£5

No. 105B. Wheelbarrow

Brown with red interior. Metal wheel. Price 1/2d. Issued June 1949. Deleted 1958. Renumbered 382 in 1954. 82mm. DC.

	M/B	M/U	G/C
Box of 6	£125		
Singles		£8	£5

No. 105C. Four-Wheel Hand Truck

Green and also in blue. Four wheels with a front swivel. With extended handle. Price 1/11d. Issued June 1949. Deleted 1958. Renumbered 383 in 1954. DC. 126mm.

	M/B	M/U	G/C
Box of 6	£125		
Singles		£8	£5

No. 105E. Grass Cutter

Red, green or yellow. With rotating wheels and blade. Price 1/8d. Issued November 1949. Deleted 1958. Renumbered 384 in 1954. 73mm. DC.

	M/B	M/U	G/C
Box of 6	£250		
Singles		£8	£5

MODEL	M/B	M/U	G/C

No. 381. Garden Roller

Red and green. Also brown and yellow which is very rare and worth double or even more. Price 1/-. Issued July 1954. Deleted 1958. 67mm. DC.

	M/B	M/U	G/C
Box of 6	£150		
Singles		£15	£8

No. 382. Wheelbarrow

Brown with red interior. Also found in black, and green with red interior. Latter models are worth at least double. Renumbering of 105B. Metal wheels. Price 1/3d. Issued June 1954. Deleted 1958. 82mm. DC.

	M/B	M/U	G/C
Box of 6	£150		
Singles		£15	£8

No. 383. Four-Wheeled Hand Truck

Blue, green, or brown, latter being worth double. Price 2/-. Issued 1954 renumbering of 105C. Deleted 1958. 128mm. DC.

	M/B	M/U	G/C
Box of 6	£150		
Singles		£15	£8

No. 384. Grasscutter

Red, green or yellow. With rotating wheels and blade. Price 1/4d. Issued 1954 renumbering of 105E. Deleted 1958. 73mm. DC.

	M/B	M/U	G/C
Box of 6	£150		
Singles		£15	£8

No. 385. Sack Truck

Blue with black wheels. Price 1/-. Issued 1954. Deleted 1960. Packed in boxes of 6. 63mm. DC.

	M/B	M/U	G/C
Box of six	£150		
Singles		£15	£8

	M/B	M/U	G/C
### No. 386. Lawn Mower	£75	£30	£15

Green or red. First model in this range to have an individual box. Full working blades. Price 5/6d. Issued 1954 renumbering of 751. Deleted 1958. 140mm. DC.

	M/B	M/U	G/C
### No. 751. Lawn Mower	£75	£30	£15

Green and red with full working blades. Price 5/-. Issued June 1949, and renumbered 386 in 1954. Deleted 1978. 140mm. DC.

THE FRENCH DINKIES

Introduction

The French Dinky models have always been widely sought after by collectors from many parts of the world. I hope that the following information will help people who have written to me over the past few years. I have chosen what I consider to be the best models from a French company that really never liked to associate themselves with their English counterparts although they had the greatest respect for Frank Hornby and his team of brilliant experts at the Binns Road, Liverpool factory.

I have read the books 'Histoire Des Dinky-Toys Français' By Jean-Michel-Roulet and also the 'French Meccano Trains Hornby-Dinky-Toys Marques Deposées' and the 'Dinky Toys-E.T.-Dinky Supertoys Fabriqués-En-France Par Meccano Paris' by Jean Masse, but I found no guide lines at all as to what the prices were in the collector's market. This book should prove the ideal guide to the models and trains which are now in the hands of some very fortunate people.

25 Series Trucks

This commercial series was roughly equivalent to the English 25 Series in the very early era from 1935 up to 1949. The castings were almost identical, although very different in many of the details, especially with the French cast bumpers as front parts of the chassis. The major castings on the Fords manufactured between 1949 and 1957 had two chassis lengths and two wheelbase lengths, one short and the other long. The 'short' models had an integral cab and a separate rear body casting and the 'long' chassis had integral body one piece castings. The very early models had more protruding grilles and lamps and could be recognised by the cast 'tow-hooks' at the back end. These were made between 1949–1951, while the later models had tin-plate tow hooks from 1951 until 1955. The very early models were fitted with all-metal wheels and some had normal wheels with rubber tyres. The models which followed this series all had rubber tyres fitted.

From 1950 until 1955/56 the short chassis versions all had rubber tyres fitted to the wheels. All castings were the same with no variations.

The Studebakers

These models also had two variations. From 1949 to 1950 they had smaller windows with a rather thick centre bonnet strip. From 1951 until 1954 there was a raised rectangular line which indicated a toolbox on each side of the cab directly under the doors. However, on the much earlier type the casting had a larger raised rectangular blob under the right-hand door. The 25K Studebaker model in the early series had no toolbox moulding at either side of the cab and it was in red and blue and had all metal wheels. This model is not rare but still a nice item to have in one's French collection. The 25K was a Market Gardens Truck and was always in two colours, mainly red and blue, green and red, red and yellow, or any combination. Grey and black was rare.

The 25M Studebaker Tipping Wagon had a dark green cab with a metallic grey body complete with spare wheel and tow hook. Roulet says it had no spare wheel or tow hook but I have seen one in a fine collection and I assure readers that my information is authentic. In fact it is one of the nicest in the 25 series.

Another nice model was the 25O Studebaker Milk Wagon. Early models had Nestlés stamped on them and the later models used transfers. There are also models showing no printing whatsoever and these were used to advertise certain local milk firms and private European farmers.

Of all the pick-up trucks produced I think that the 25P Studebaker was one of the best. Both cab types were used. The earlier models had an extra H shape to strengthen their bodies, like a kind of a brace underneath. Later ones were quite flat. The livery was always yellow with a red body. Another nice pick-up with a tilt was the 25Q Studebaker which was the 25P complete with a tin tilt. It had a green cab and tilt with the body showing a prominent red or yellow. Some of the models looked rather brown and this was owing to the brown tilt coming from 25T to a 25P.

The Studebaker 25R breakdown truck actually was a 25P model with a red livery and a tin plate crane fixed at the rear with the words 'Dinky Service' stamped on the side in white lettering. Both cab types were produced.

The Fords

The 25A was a Cattle Truck in light metallic blue or metallic grey. Shades could vary. This model has a short chassis. The 25H Ford Beverage Truck had the long chassis with a cast hook and crane in the following colours: red, brown, blue, grey green and yellow. One or two of these had rubber tyres and a tinplate tailboard.

The 25I Wagon was available in a wide range of colours with a long chassis, and the 25I Covered Wagon, with a tin tilt, became 25J in the colours of brown, gold, blue, red with green or cream or brown tilt.

Adverts and names always mean money and a good example of this is 25JB which has printed on the cover, 'Societé Nationale Des Chemins De Fer Français' or the 25JV Covered Wagon with the words 'Grands Moulins De Paris'–quite rare as an early cab series in grey livery with black tilt. These models will bring anything from £250 up to £500, but also remember there is always the chance of an even higher price being paid for something that is termed as a 'one off'.

25M Ford Tipping Wagon has exactly the same body as the 25M Studebaker Tipping Wagon but only on a much shorter chassis with identical livery. Again with the spare wheel and tow hook. The 250 Ford Milk Wagon with its short chassis was produced in a limited number in the early part of 1950 with the main production line coming along between 1954 and 1955. This model has a light blue cab with a white body and the word 'Nestlé' on the side. At a later date this model had the Nestlé transfers with hollow letters.

The 25R Ford breakdown truck was introduced in 1954. You will find that it has quite a smooth tailboard with the words 'Dinky Service' again stamped in white lettering. A much later version has chrome wheels showing no printing on the rear at all.

Small Vans

Once again I must emphasize the importance the importance of advertisements which were the forerunners of the promotional models of today. Some of the outstanding names were the following: '25B Peugeot D3A' which were first issued in 1953 with the words 'Lampe Mazda' and 'Postes' in grey or blue livery. Then in late 1953 this was superseded by the yellow and green version and in 1954 replaced by the green model, and given the catalogue number 25BV. At a still later stage it became 560. In the beginning the word 'Postes' was engraved on the side. Several different decals were used at a later stage. There also can be found a few odd colours on this same casting which were possibly done by artistic collectors, again, which is a common practice now. Both the genuine factory produced models and also those designed by an individual have a high priced collectable value.

25C Citroën 1200kg Van is a large corrugated iron type which was typical of the kind which could be seen all over France in the pre-war and post-war years. The model itself was identical to its large counterpart in four main liveries of grey, green, red and blue. The first model which was made in 1954 had no advertisements and was in metallic grey.

In 1957 the 25C was superseded by 25CG Citroen 1200kg 'CH. Gervais' which was in cream with a green, blue and white decal. After being renumbered to 561 it was deleted in 1959. Then along came the 25CG Citroen 1200kg 'Cibie' issued in 1959 in a very attractive blue livery with yellow, red and black decals. This model was also renumbered in 561 about the middle of 1960 and then finally deleted in 1963.

The 561 Citroen 1200kg 'Glaces Gervais' was the final version. Issued in 1963 and deleted in 1966. Painted in white at the top and blue on the lower half, it made a very attractive two tone model with decals painted in red and blue. Another very fine model which, I may add, is very rare indeed is the 'Baroclem Citroen' 1200kg. There was a combination of workmanship and skills both by the French Dinky Company and the firm of Baroclem themselves. It was produced by Dinky and decalled in blue and white by Baroclem. It came out in 1964 and was deleted almost at once. I am not sure of the production run but it must have been small as the last model of this type I saw being sold reached a price of £750.

Apart from the large vans there were some small attractive models, four of which stand out. The first was the 'Citröen 2cv' which was a small mobile corrugated iron garden shed. There was the 'Paris Fire Service' issued in 1958 in red, renumbered 562 in 1959 and finally deleted in 1964. Then there was the 560 'P.T.T.' issued in 1963 in very attractive yellow livery with blue decals and deleted in 1970. Finally, I must mention the 'Wegenwacht' made especially for the Dutch market and issued between 1965 and 1968 in another attractive yellow livery with jet black decals.

More Wagon Variants

Apart from the models which I have set out in this special section, of French Dinkies, I know the following information makes very good reading to the collector of this much sought after series. The following are facts which I am pleased to say were given to me from a very reliable source. It would be impossible to name everyone who helped me but I would like to just say thanks at this point.

Petrol tankers remain favourites regardless of what make they happen to be. Models such as the '25U Ford Petrol Tanker' which was made with a later type cab with a one piece casting, have always appealed to collectors. The much earlier models had a support bracket and a hook cast at the rear, underneath the body, while the later ones had not. They were always in red when the Esso sign was on the sides and rear. In 1957 there was another very attractive Esso Tanker, the 32C 'Tracteur Panhard', very much sought after. Some attractive refuse trucks were produced like the '25V Ford Refuse Truck' with its short chassis, tipping body and opening tailgate. It had tin plate centre sections at the top of the body, which could slide neatly apart, and a favourite colour was dark green.

I must also mention the 25S and 25T Trailers which were actually pick up bodies fitted with tin plate chassis. One was painted red, yellow or green without the tilt while with the tilt the livery was shown as yellow and brown or red and green. These fine models became part of one of the most valuable diecast series and certainly one of the best investments.

MODEL	M/B	M/U	G/C
No. 22a. Roadster	–	£550	£250

Red or blue. Silver with red wings, or green with yellow wings. There could be other colours, all valued at a high price. Completely different casting from the English 22a. One-piece body/wings, and casting with separate windscreen. Cast dashboard and steering wheel. Cast in lead with solid metal wheels or with smooth hubs and Dunlop tyres. Issued 1933. Deleted 1939.

No. 22A. Maserati Sport 2000	£80	£15	£10

Red with white driver. Silver wheels, grille, lights and screen. Black tyres. Issued 1958. Deleted 1966. 88mm. DC/P.

No. 22b. Sports Coupé	–	£550	£250

Again very different from the English version. Dates, price and colours as 22a.

No. 22c. Roadster Sports	–	£550	£250

Details and casting as 22a. Royal blue with yellow wings. Also cream with red wings. Issued 1933. Deleted 1939.

No. 22d. Sports Coupé 2	–	£550	£250

Details and castings etc, as 22a. Colours etc as 22a. Issued 1933. Deleted 1939.

1st No. 23a. M.G. Model	–	£175	£75

Blue and white or silver stripes, orange and white or green stripes, cream and greenish blue or red stripes. Cast in lead always with a driver (compare first English release). With four exhaust stubs but no exhaust pipe. White rubber tyres with

'Dunlop' stamped upon them. Issued
1934. Deleted 1940. Never had
individual box.

2nd No. 23a. M.G. Model

–	£150	£50

Cast in Zamac always with driver and
with six branch exhaust pipe, white
Dunlop tyres. Issued 1935. Deleted
1939.

3rd No. 23a. M.G. Model

–	£125	£40

As No. 2, but with solid Zamac
wheels. Issued 1939. Deleted 1940.
Reissued again in identical form after
the war in 1949. Deleted 1958.

1st No. 23b. Renault Record Car

This first model was not really a
racing car but rather a private
businessman's invention. Specifically
French casting, never issued in
England. First issued 1935. Deleted
1940. There are at least 14 colour
schemes attached to this model. These
are not really important as all colours
are very much sought after. The
model is so scarce that a good price
will be paid by any Dinky enthusiast.
Model was reissued after the war in
1947. Deleted 1956. 97mm. Never
had individual box.

Pre-war	–	£550	£250
Post-war	–	£100	£65

2nd No. 23b. Hotchkiss Racing Car

From 1939 to 1940 pre-war car was
produced. Post-war version made from
1946 to 1954, along with Renault
Record Car. Car was in every way
identical to the English model, only it
was marked 'Made in France'. It had
French wheels with smooth hubs and
white coloured tyres. Some of the
tyres were coloured and later replaced
with solid metal wheels. Post-war
model had ribbed hubs with black 'M'
tyres, also with a range of colour
schemes connected with the car itself.
Any colour will bring a good price in

MODEL	M/B	M/U	G/C

this range. Red with silver flash etc.
Length 95mm.

Pre-war	–	£125	£50
Post-war	–	£40	£25

No. 23c. Mercedes Racing Car

	–	£150	£50

Silver with red grille and exhaust
pipe. Solid metal wheels on post-
war model only. With ribbed hubs
and black 'M' tyres. With number
'2' on sides. Issued 1949. Deleted
1956. 92mm. DC/TP. Never
individually boxed.

No. 23. Auto Union Racing Car

	–	£125	£50

Red or silver, or pale green with red
number and silver radiator and grille.
Driver slotted into body. Issued 1950.
Deleted 1954. 100mm. DC/TP.

No. 23H. Auto De Course Talbot Lago

	£125	£100	£50

Blue with white driver. Blue wheels
and large ribbed racing tyres. Silver
grille and exhausts. Number '6' in
orange or yellow on sides. Issued
1950. Deleted 1966. 83mm.

No. 23J. Auto De Course Ferrari

	£150	£100	£50

Red with white driver. Silver
wheels, grille and exhausts. Black
ribbed tyres and the Number '1' on
sides. Also with red exhausts. Issued
1950. Deleted 1966. 102mm.

No. 23m. Thunderbolt Record Car

	£275	£175	£75

Silver or dark blue. Imported into
France from England. Driver cast into
body. Issued 1938. Deleted 1940.
126mm. DC/RT/TP. One of the first
Dinky models to be boxed
individually.

No. 24a. Ambulance

Model was never issued in France
although it had 'Made in France'
marked on the model. Off-white or
cream colour with French wheels and
smooth hubs, plus white or coloured
Dunlop tyres. This car had the same
body style and features as its English
counterpart of the 24 series. Issued

MODEL	M/B	M/U	G/C
1934. Deleted 1939. Reissued 1945 and deleted in 1952.			
Pre-war	–	£175	£75
Post-war	–	£75	£60

No. 24A. Chrysler 'New Yorker'

Yellow with green interior or red with
white interior. Silver grille, bumpers,
screen, lights, radiator and wheels.
White tyres and silver trim. Issued
1950. Deleted 1968. 112mm. DC/P.

Yellow	£175	£75	£35
Red	£145	£65	£25

No. 24b. Limousine   –   £250   £100

Red with red chassis; yellow with
black chassis; yellow with red chassis;
red with grey chassis, and many
others. With criss-cross chassis and
horizontal bonnet louvres. Issued
1934. Deleted 1939. 98mm. DC/RT.
Never individually boxed.

No. 24B. 403 Peugeot   £150   £75   £40

Grey, worth double, also in blue.
Silver wheels, grille, lights, radiator
and bumpers. White tyres and off-
white interior. Issued 1952. Deleted
1968. 104mm. DC/P.

No. 24c. Town Sedan

Another model that was never issued
in France but had 'Made in France'
marked on the model. In various
colours, with French white or
coloured tyres marked 'Dunlop'. With
the same features and body style as
English 24 series. English model.
Issued 1934. Deleted 1939. Reissued
1946. Deleted 1952.

Pre-war	–	£250	£100
Post-war	–	£125	£75

No. 24C. DS 19 Citroën   £125   £75   £45

Light or dark green. Also in lime
green with white roof. Silver
bumpers, grille, wheels etc, and
white tyres. With windscreen,
windows and headlights. Issued
1952. Deleted 1968. 112mm. DC/P.

No. 24CP. DS 19 Citroën   £125   £75   £45

Golden lemon body with white roof.
Rare. Silver wheels, grille, bumpers,
etc. White tyres. Issued 1953.
Deleted 1963. 112mm.

No. 24d. Vogue Saloon

Dark blue; blue with black chassis; green with red chassis; grey with red chassis, and various others. First issued with spare wheel and later without spare wheel. Wheel variant issued concurrently with presence or absence of spare wheel. Issued 1935. Deleted 1939. Reissued 1947. Deleted 1952. 107mm. DC/RT.

	M/B	M/U	G/C
Pre-war	–	£150	£80
Post-war	–	£125	£65

No. 24D. Plymouth 'Belvedere.'   £100   £75   £45

Green with black roof and side panels. Silver grille, bumpers, wheels, trim. etc. White tyres. Issued 1953. Deleted 1968. 110mm. DC/P.

No. 24e. Super Streamlined Saloon

Red and dark red with black chassis; green with red chassis, and others. Comments as 24B. Never had spare wheel. 97mm. DC/RT.

	M/B	M/U	G/C
Pre-war	–	£150	£75
Post-war	–	£100	£60

No. 24E. Renault 'Dauphine'   £125   £75   £45

Maroon or orange. Silver trim, grille, wheels, bumpers etc, and black tyres. Issued 1957. Deleted 1968. 92mm. DC/P.

No. 24f. Sportsman Coupé

Yellow with brown chassis; green with yellow chassis; yellow with red chassis. Issued with or without spare wheel. Issued 1937. Deleted 1939. Reissued 1947. Deleted 1952. 100mm. DC/RT.

	M/B	M/U	G/C
Pre-war	–	£150	£75
Post-war	–	£125	£65

No. 24F. Peugeot. Familiale 403   £125   £75   £35

Pale or medium blue with silver trim, wheels, grille, bumpers, radiator and lights. Made in 1957. Deleted 1968. 107mm. DC/P.

MODEL	M/B	M/U	G/C

No. 24g. Four-Seater Sports Tourer

Blue body with brown or black chassis; green with red chassis. Was issued with full spare wheel on the boot or later, concurrently with introduction of solid metal wheels, with a simulated spare-wheel cover cast on boot. Open screen. Issued 1936. Deleted 1939. Reissued 1946. Deleted 1952. 98mm. DC/RT.

	M/B	M/U	G/C
Pre-war	–	£150	£75
Post-war	–	£125	£65

No. 24h. Two-Seater Sports Tourer

Red body with green chassis; green with blue chassis; green with red chassis. Comments as 24 g. 98mm. DC/TP.

	M/B	M/U	G/C
Pre-war	–	£125	£65
Post-war	£100	£60	£35
No. 24H. Mercedes 190 SL.	£15	£8	£6

Silver grey with purple or blue roof. Silver wheels, grille, bumpers, lights etc. White tyres. Issued 1957. Deleted 1968. 99mm. DC/P.

	M/B	M/U	G/C
No. 224J. Alfa Romeo 1900 Sprint	£75	£35	£15

Red with silver grille, bumpers, headlights and wheels. Black tyres. Issued 1957/58 deleted 1968. 99mm. DC/P.

No. 24k. Peugeot

This was a model of Peugeot 402. Dark maroon, grey blue, maroon, white, green, red. Black wheels and black or white tyres. Smooth hubs and Dunlop tyres. Issued 1939. Deleted 1940. Then from 1948 to 1950 with solid metal wheels. 95mm. DC/TP/RT.

	M/B	M/U	G/C
Pre-war	–	£395	£250
Post-war	–	£150	£75

No. 24l. Peugeot Taxi

No driver and two-tone finish of various colours with yellow side panels, black roof and wings. Black wheels with black or white tyres. Paris markings. Issued 1939. Deleted 1940.

MODEL	M/B	M/U	G/C
Reissued 1948 to 1950 with solid metal wheels.			
Pre-war	–	£395	£250
Post-war	–	£150	£75

No. 24N. Citroën II B.L. —

Never issued pre-war. Grey or blue, or black. It first appeared in 1949, the modernised version with boot in place of spare wheel cover came in 1953.

	M/B	M/U	G/C
First version	–	£150	£75
Second version	–	£100	£50

No. 24N. Citroën II BL
	M/B	M/U	G/C
	£125	£75	£35

Silver grey body with matching or red wheels and silver headlights and white tyres. Issued 1955. Deleted 1968. 96mm. DC/P.

No. 24R. Peugeot 203
	M/B	M/U	G/C
	£100	£50	£25

Light or medium grey with white tyres. Silver bumpers, wheels, grille, trim, etc. Issued 1953. Deleted 1968. 100mm. DC/P.

No. 24S. Simca 8 Sport
	M/B	M/U	G/C
	£60	£30	£15

Grey body with black roof and tyres. Yellow or silver wheels. Silver grey bumpers, grille, etc. Issued 1954. Deleted 1968. 88mm. DC/P.

No. 24U. Simca 'Aronde'

Medium or dark blue. Also off-white or light grey with green roof. Silver wheels, grille, radiator, bumpers and lights. White tyres. Issued 1954. Deleted 1968. 95mm. DC/P.

	M/B	M/U	G/C
Price for blue body.	£40	£20	£15
Price for two-colour	£50	£30	£20

MODEL	M/B	M/U	G/C
No. 24UT. Taxi 'Aronde'	**£45**	**£20**	**£15**

Two-tone red with blue roof and
red and white 'Taxi' sign. Silver
grille and bumpers. Red wheels and
white tyres. Issued 1955. Deleted
1965. 95mm. DC/P.

	M/B	M/U	G/C
No. 24XT. Taxi 'Vedette'	**£100**	**£50**	**£35**

Royal blue with white, fawn, or
cream roof. Silver wheels, bumpers,
grille and white tyres. White and
red taxi sign on roof. Issued 1956.
Deleted 1966. 105mm. DC/P.

	M/B	M/U	G/C
No. 24V. Buick 'Roadmaster'	**£130**	**£75**	**£35**

Sky-blue, medium blue, or dark
blue with yellow or cream, or fawn
roof. Silver grille, lights, bumpers,
and white tyres. Silver or blue
wheels. Issued 1956. Deleted 1968.
112mm. DC/P.

	M/B	M/U	G/C
No. 24. Simca Vedette	**£83**	**£45**	**£30**

Dark blue, white tyres, black wheels,
silver bumpers and headlights.
Possibly in other colours. Issued
1956/57. Deleted 1968. 105mm.
DC/P.

	M/B	M/U	G/C
No. 24Y. Studebaker 'Commander'	**£100**	**£75**	**£35**

Bright orange with mustard or fawn
roof. Silver trim, grille, wheels,
bumpers, radiator and lights. White
tyres. Issued 1956. Deleted 1968.
109mm. DC/P.

	M/B	M/U	G/C
No. 24Z. Simca 'Versailles'	**£95**	**£55**	**£35**

Buttercup or dull yellow body with
black roof. Silver wheels, grille,
radiator, bumpers, and lights etc.
White tyres. Issued 1957. Deleted
1968. 105mm. DC/P.

	M/B	M/U	G/C
No. 25a. A Generic 'Lorry'	–	**£175**	**£65**

This lorry of the 1930s is the same as
far as description is concerned as 25d.
With no advertising.

	M/B	M/U	G/C
No. 25b. Citroën Covered Wagon	–	**£175**	**£65**

Comments etc, as 25a, and prices as
25d. With no advertising.

MODEL	M/B	M/U	G/C

No. 25B Lampe Mazda Peugeot Van

£325 £150 £75

Two two lime green top and yellow lower body. Green wheels with black tyres, silver grille, lights and bumpers. Words 'Lampe Mazda' on sides in black on yellow background: Issued 1954/55. Deleted 1968. Rare model. DC/P 90mm.

No. 25BV. Fourgon Postal Van

£175 £75 £35

Medium, light or dark green with the word 'Postes' and a middle line in orange or golden yellow. Matching green wheels and black tyres. Silver, black or green grille, radiator and lights. Issued 1954. Deleted 1968. 90mm. DC/P.

No. 25c. Citroën Flat Truck

– £250 £125

Red or green. Comments and details as 25a. With no advertising.

No. 25CG. Camionette Citroën 'Gervais'

£125 £75 £35

This van is in fawn or light mustard with a decorative design in blue and green with the word 'Gervais' in white lettering. Ribbed sides and roof. Silver wheels, grille, radiator and black tyres. Issued 1954. Deleted 1968. 90mm. DC/P.

Dark red body and gold lettering. Otherwise as above. (Rare colour.).   £250 £150 £75

No. 25d. Petrol Tanker

Model has completely different profile to that of English version, in fact all the 25 series differ. The French 25 series were made between 1935 and 1939, when deleted. Then they reappeared between 1945/46 and 1950, when they were deleted. This is the description for all tankers. In 1935, they had smooth hubs with white Dunlop tyres, and front bumpers cast on. From 1939 to 1940 they had solid metal wheels. After the war the models appeared without livery or with 'Standard', 'Essolube', 'Esso' or 'Mobiloil' advertising. 108mm. RT/DC/TP.

MODEL	M/B	M/U	G/C
Pre-war with no advertising	–	£250	£100
Pre-war with advertising	–	£350	£175
Post-war with no advertising	–	£150	£75
Post-war with advertising	–	£175	£75

No. 25D. Fourgonnette Incendie 2 CV Citroën

	M/B	M/U	G/C
No. 25D. Fourgonnette Incendie 2 CV Citroën	£50	£30	£20

Red ribbed body with curved roof. Silver grille, radiator, lights. Red wheels with black tyres. Shield emblem in green and gold on doors. Issued 1957. Deleted 1968. 84mm. DC/P.

Blue body. Otherwise as above apart from matching blue wheels. £100 £75 £35

No. 25e. Tipping Wagon

Numerous colour schemes, all worth money. Blue with green chassis; yellow with blue rear and black chassis; maroon, yellow, or fawn etc. Price and comments as 25d.

No. 25f. Citroën Dropside Truck

	M/B	M/U	G/C
No. 25f. Citroën Dropside Truck	–	£175	£75

Green, red, or fawn. The 25f is the French version of the Market Gardeners Wagon (Stake Truck). Comments as 25d. With no advertising.

No. 25g. Trailer

Marked 'Made in France' W. with tin-plate hook. Smooth hubs with Dunlop tyres (1935–1939). Cast metal wheels (1939–1940 and 1946–1948). Ribbed hubs and black 'M' tyres from 1948 to 1952. Made for use with the 25 Ford, and Studebaker series. Otherwise comment and prices as 25d. 69mm. DC/RT.

No. 25h. Fire Engine

Red. Issued in France, marked 'Made in England'. An identical model to English version. Price and comments dealt with in the Fire Engines section. section.

No. 29b. Streamlined Coach

Never issued as a French Dinky, although many people thought it was. This was an imported model and

English models appeared in France before the war. Details of this model and number had already been dealt with in the Buses section.

No. 29d. Panhard Paris Autobus

Dark green with off-white roof. The lower part of the model is in diecast Zamac while the roof and windscreen are tin-plate. Smooth metal hubs and Dunlop tyres from 1939 to 1940. Then solid metal wheels from 1940 to 1949. Then ribbed metal hubs and 'M' tyres from 1950 to 1952. Deleted 1960.

	M/B	M/U	G/C
Pre-war	–	£295	£150
Post-war	–	£150	£100

No. 29D. Panhard Paris Autobus

	M/B	M/U	G/C
	£95	£50	£30

Two-tone green lower and cream on the upper. Gold or silver radiator, bumpers, and lights. Green wheels and black tyres. Issued 1954. Deleted 1968. 143mm. DC.

No. 29F. Autocar Chausson

	M/B	M/U	G/C
	£100	£65	£30

A fine streamline coach with cream top, and red on lower. Silver or yellow ribs. Red wheels and white tyres. Silver or gold grille, radiator, etc. Issued 1955. Deleted 1968. 154mm. DC P.

Rare blue lower livery with matching blue wheels. Otherwise as above.

	M/B	M/U	G/C
	£115	£75	£30

No. 30a. Chrysler Airflow Saloon

	M/B	M/U	G/C
	–	£275	£125

Green or cream. Issued pre-war in France with smooth hubs and Dunlop tyres. Model was assembled in France, but still marked 'Made in England'. Issued June 1935. Deleted 1936/37. 103mm. DC/RT.

No. 30b. Rolls Royce

	M/B	M/U	G/C
	–	£495	£250

Very dark green or dark grey with black chassis. One of the very rare models issued in France in 1936. Deleted 1940. 101mm. DC/RT.

MODEL	M/B	M/U	G/C

No. 30e. Breakdown Car

	—	£175	£75

Dark red with black chassis, also in dark green or very dark grey. This French Dinky was totally different to the English version. This was in fact one of the 25 series Trucks. With the cast metal crane from a French Dinky Train set. Issued 1935. Deleted 1939. 120mm.

No. 32AB. Panhard Artic. S.N.C.F.

	£180	£75	£45

Blue cab with matching box trailer body with the words, 'Societé Nationale Des Chemins de Fer Français', in gold or yellow lettering. Also with a green square with white line border, and the letters 'S.N.C.F.' in black on sides. Matching blue wheels. Silver grille, bumpers and lights. Issued 1955. Deleted 1968. 165mm. DC/P.

No. 32C. Panhard Esso Tanker

	£180	£130	£75

This articulated tanker is in red with white lines and the word 'Esso' in white circle and black wings in red lettering. Red wheels, black tyres. Silver radiator grille, bumper and lights. Issued 1955. Deleted 1968. 178mm. DC P.

No. 32D. Fire Engine

	£130	£75	£35

This fine fire engine is in red with white or silver extending ladder on red winch. Red wheels and white tyres. Silver grille, radiator and windscreen. Issued 1954, Deleted 1968. 120mm. DC P.

No. 32E. Berliet Fire Engine

	£150	£75	£35

Another fine fire fighting machine in red with silver or white ladder. Red wheels and white tyres. Silver grille, radiator and bumpers. The ladder is removable. The hose pipe reels are in a separate trailer. Issued 1955. Deleted 1968. 105mm. Overall length (with the hose pipe reels): 118mm. DC/P.

MODEL	M/B	M/U	G/C

No. 33AN. Simca Cargo Removal Van   £70   £30   £25

Yellow ribbed body with off white or cream roof, matching yellow wheels and black tyres. Silver grille, radiator, bumper and trim. The words 'Bailly Demenagements Garde Meubles' in thick yellow on black base. Issued 1955. Deleted 1968. 133mm. DC/P.

No. 33B. Simca Cargo Tipper Lorry   £70   £35   £25

Lime green cab and chassis with grey tipper body and tail board. Matching green wheels and black tyres. Silver grille and radiator. Issued 1955. Deleted 1968. 127mm. DC/P.

No. 33C. Simca Cargo Glass Carrier   £120   £80   £30

Yellow cab and chassis with green flat trailer back. Matching yellow wheels and rear frame work for mirror glass. With the word 'Miroitier' in red lettering on rear. Silver radiator and grille. Issued 1956. Deleted 1968. 129mm. DC/P.

No. 34A. Berliet Tipper Lorry   £70   £40   £30

Blue cab and chassis with matching wheels and black tyres. Mustard or yellow tipper body with silver grille and radiator. Issued 1956. Deleted 1968. 128mm. DC/P.

No. 34B. Berliet Container Lorry   £140   £100   £55

Red cab and chassis with matching red wheels and black tyres. Grey rear with black box container. Silver grille and radiator. Issued 1956. Deleted 1968. 125mm. DC/P.

No. 35A. Citroën Breakdown Van   £80   £40   £25

All red body and cab with matching wheels. Silver grille, bumper and radiator. Spare wheel and black crane with silver hook on rear.

Matching red wheels and black
tyres. With the words 'Dinky
Service' in gold lettering on sides.
Issued 1956. Deleted 1958. 125mm.
DC/P.

No. 36A. Willeme Artic. with Log Trailer

	M/B	M/U	G/C
No. 36A. Willeme Artic. with Log Trailer	£150	£80	£55

Orange cab and chassis with yellow
or orange trailer carrying log load.
Yellow wheels and black tyres.
Silver grille, radiator and bumpers.
Spare wheel at rear of cab. Issued
1955. Deleted 1968. 235mm. DC/P.

No. 36B. Willeme Artic. and Tarpaulined Trailer

	M/B	M/U	G/C
No. 36B. Willeme Artic. and Tarpaulined Trailer	£120	£60	£35

Red cab and chassis with matching
red wheels. Orange and red trailer
body with green tarpaulin cover.
Silver bumper, grille and radiator,
grey tyres and spare wheel. Issued
1958. Deleted 1969. Overall length
267mm. DC/P.

No. 38A. Camion Unic Multibenne Marrel

	M/B	M/U	G/C
No. 38A. Camion Unic Multibenne Marrel	£175	£100	£55

The first issue of this model had an
all grey cab with matching bucket
and wheels, with orange or dark
fawn bucket holder. Issued 1957.
Deleted 1968. 132mm. DC/P. When
fully extended 197mm.

The second issue in 1958 had a grey
cab with yellow mudguards and
matching bucket holder body with
yellow wheels. Otherwise as above.

	M/B	M/U	G/C
	£135	£75	£45

No. 39A. Artic. Car Transporter

	M/B	M/U	G/C
No. 39A. Artic. Car Transporter	£275	£125	£75

An exceptional car transporter in
silver blue livery with matching
wheels and black tyres. Silver
bumper, grille, radiator and trim.
With the words 'Dinky Toys
Service Livraison' in black lettering.
Issued 1957. Deleted 1968. Overall
length 325mm. DC/P.

MODEL	M/B	M/U	G/C

No. 45D. Esso Petrol Pumps Set — £75

Blue and white, and red and white pumps on grey stand with red and white Esso sign and the words "Esso" in oval advert. Made in early part of 1950's. Deleted 1968.

No. 60A. Mystère IV A (Marcel Dassault) — £45 £25 £15

This was the first of a compact aeroplane super toy series in silver with orange, blue and yellow decals. Issued 1955. Deleted 1968. Length 68mm. Wing span 59mm. DC/P.

No. 60B. Vautour (Sud Aviation) — £45 £25 £15

Silver body with blue, orange and yellow decals on wings. Issued 1955. Deleted 1968. Length 92mm. Wing span 80mm. DC/P.

No. 60C. Lockheed Super G Constellation — £120 £55 £30

Silver, blue and white with Air France decals in black. Issued 1957. Deleted 1968. Length 181mm. Wing span 197mm. DC/P.

No. 60D. Sikorsky S 58. Helicopter — £45 £25 £15

Silver, blue and white with black blades with orange tips. Issued 1956. Deleted 1968. Length 80mm. Rotor span 87mm. DC/P.

No. 60E. Vickers Viscount — £35 £15 £10

Silver, blue and white with black decals and lettering on wings. Issued 1957. Deleted 1968. Length 132mm. Wing span 150mm. DC/P.

No. 60F. Caravelle Air France Airliner — £175 £95 £35

Silver, black and yellow with authentic Air France decals. Issued 1957/58. Deleted 1968. Length approx. 181mm. wing span 197mm. DC/P.

MODEL	M/B	M/U	G/C

No. 50. Salev Crane

£95 £45 £15

Red and silver grey with matching
crane and wheels with black tyres,
blue driver. Two levers control the
movement of the crane. Issued 1957.
Deleted 1968. Length 89mm.
Overall length (crane horizontal)
156mm. DC/P.

No. 70. Four Wheeled Covered Trailer

£30 £15 £10

Red trailer body and chassis with
matching wheels and smooth black
tyres. Green canopy and silver tow
bar. The cover is removable. The
trailer fixes on to lorries equipped
with hooks. Issued 1957. Deleted
1968. Length 111mm. DC/P.

No. 80A. Panhard Armoured Reconnaissance Car

£50 £25 £10

French military green. Revolving
gun turret. Black tyres and
displaying the Army decals. Issued
1958. Deleted 1968. 103mm. DC/P.

No. 80B. Jeep Hotchkiss-Willys

£45 £20 £10

Military green with black tyres and
spare wheel on rear. Issued 1958.
Deleted 1968. Length 66mm. DC/P.

No. 80C. A.M.X. 13 Tonnes Tank

£45 £25 £10

Military green with revolving gun
turret and rubber tracks. Army
decals. Issued 1958. Deleted 1968.
108mm. DC/P.

No. 80D. Berliet Cross Country Military Lorry (Removable Cover)

£125 £65 £35

Military green with large ribbed
black wheels, and spare wheel.
Issued Sept. 1958. Deleted 1968.
144mm. DC/P.

No. 80E. 155 A.B.S. Howitzer

£45 £20 £10

Military green. The gun is
adjustable. Issued 1958. Deleted
1968. Overall length 146mm. DC/P.

No. 90A. Richier Steam Roller £95 £55 £25

Golden yellow with red and grey wheels. Driver in dark uniform. Issued 1957/58. Deleted 1968. 96mm. DC/T.

No. 152a. Light Tank £75 £45 £24

Matt green with aerial and rotating turret and full French Army squadron markings. With chains. Imported into France 1938. Deleted 1940. 68mm. DC.

No. 161. Anti Aircraft Unit £75 £55 £25

Matt green. With French squadron markings. Issued in France 1939. Deleted 1940. 115mm. DC/TP/RT.

No. 162. Anti Tank Gun £45 £25 £10

Matt green with full French squadron markings. Made and issued in France 1939. Deleted 1940. 78mm. DC/RT.

No. 151a. Medium Tank £135 £75 £35

Green with French Army squadron markings. With rotating turret and aerial. Issued in France 1938. Deleted 1940. 92mm. DC/TP. With chains.

No. 972. Coles Crane Lorry £165 £100 £50

Orange, yellow and black, complete with two drivers in blue. Yellow wheels and black tyres. Silver grille and bumpers. Two levers control the crane. The crane pivots on a lorry. Issued 1958. Deleted 1968. Length of lorry 163mm. Overall length (crane lowered) 240mm. DC/P.

No. 14. Three-Wheeled Carrier

Grey or brown. Made in 1935 with smooth hubs and Dunlop tyres. From 1939 to 1940 the model had solid metal wheels. The model was reissued in 1949 and deleted in 1952, in red with green driver or yellow with blue driver, also grey with yellow driver. Imported into England pre-war dates only. Never individually boxed.

With Dunlop tyres	–	£75	£35
With solid metal wheels	–	£55	£25
With 'M' tyres	–	£45	£25

MODEL	M/B	M/U	G/C

No. 268. Renault Dauphine — £125, £75, £35

Red with silver wheels, bumpers, lights and grille. Issued 1958. Deleted 1968. 92mm. DC P.

No. 514. Alfa Romeo Giulia 1600 — £95, £55, £25

White. Silver wheels, bumpers, grille and lights. Issued 1961. Deleted 1963. 102mm.

No. 520. Fiat 600 D — £115, £75, £35

Cream with red interior. Silver wheels, grille, lights and bumpers. Black tyres. Issued 1958. Deleted 1960. 71mm.

No. 529. Vespa 2CV — £65, £25, £10

Mid or dark blue. Black roof, silver wheels, bumpers, grille and lights. Issued 1957. Deleted 1965. 88mm.

No. 531. Fiat Grande Vue — £125, £75, £35

Cream with grey roof. Gold or silver wheels and black tyres. Silver grille, bumpers and lights. Issued 1960. Deleted 1964. 91mm.

No. 532. Lincoln Premier — £250, £100, £50

Blue body, shades vary. Silver roof, wheels, bumpers and lights. White wall tyres. Issued 1957. Deleted 1965. 112mm.

No. 533. Mercedes Benz — £95, £45, £15

Metallic blue body. Also in red. With silver wheels, grille, bumpers and lights. White or fawn interior. Black tyres. Issued 1954. Deleted 1978. 147mm.

No. 536. Renault 16 — £65, £35, £15

Light blue. Silver wheels, grille, bumper and lights. Black tyres. Issued 1957. Deleted 1965. 92mm.

No. 539. Citroen ID 19 Estate — £75, £65, £25

Fawn with white roof. Red interior. Silver bumpers, grille and lights. White wall tyres. Issued 1957. Deleted 1965. 112mm.

MODEL	M/B	M/U	G/C

No. 542. Simca Aronde Taxi   £125   £75   £35

Dark blue or black. White interior,
red roof, with Taxi sign in red and
grey. Silver wheels, bumpers, grille
and lights. White wall tyres. Issued
1957. Deleted 1963. 95mm.

No. 543. Renault Floride   £85   £35   £15

Metallic fawn or light brown. Silver
wheels, grille and bumpers. White
wall tyres. Also in purple, which is
worth treble. Issued 1957. Deleted
1965. 92mm.

No. 546 Austin Healey 100   £175   £100   £45

White body with red interior and
blue driver. Silver wheels, grille and
bumpers. Black tyres. Watch for
colour variants which could be worth
more. Issued 1957. Deleted 1960.
85mm.

No. 547 Panhard PL 17   £125   £75   £35

Purple. Silver wheels, grille, bumpers
and lights. Black tyres. Issued 1957.
Deleted 1968. 100mm.

No. 548 Fiat 1800 Estate   £65   £35   £15

Cream with dark brown roof and red
interior. Silver wheels, grille,
bumpers and lights. White wall tyres.
Issued 1957. Deleted 1965.

No. 533. Peugeot 404   £65   £35   £15

White or grey with red interior.
Silver wheels, bumpers, grille and
lights. White wall tyres. Issued 1957.
Deleted 1960. 100mm.

No. 561 Citroen 'Cibie' Van   £175   £95   £55

Blue or bluey green with yellow
wheels and black tyres. Silver grille
and bumpers. Word 'Cibie' in red
letters on yellow background on sides.
Issued 1952. Deleted 1968. 90mm.

No. 575. Panhard 'S.N.C.F.'
**   Artic. Lorry**   £180   £95   £65

Dark blue with matching mudguards
etc. Decals and lettering in gold,
white and blue on sides. Issued 1963.
Deleted 1968. 220mm.

MODEL	M/B	M/U	G/C

No. 811. Caravan £45 £25 £10

Golden yellow with red lines and
white roof. Issued 1960. Deleted
1968. 118mm.

**No. 814. AML Panhard
 Armoured Car** £95 £55 £25

French military colours. Issued 1960.
Deleted 1968. 80mm.

No. 815. E.B.R. Panhard Tank £85 £45 £15

French military colours. Issued 1960.
Deleted 1968. 132mm.

No. 817 AMX 13 tonne Tank £95 £55 £25

French military colours. Issued 1960.
Deleted 1968. 134mm.

**No. 820. Renault Army
 Ambulance** £95 £55 £25

Military green with large red cross on
white background on roof and sides.
Issued 1960. Deleted 1968. 110mm.

**No. 821. Mercedes Unimog
 Army Truck** £95 £45 £25

French military green with fawn
cover. Issued 1962. Deleted 1964.
118mm.

No. 822. Half Track M3 £95 £45 £25

French military green with decals.
Issued 1962. Deleted 1964. 122mm.

No. 884. Brockway Bridge Layer £255 £125 £55

French military green. Issued 1962.
Deleted 1964. 181mm. Rare model.

**No. 886. Richier Road Level
 Machine** £145 £75 £35

Yellow body with red wheels. Black
tyres and blue driver. Issued 1960.
Deleted 1964. 122mm.

**No. 893. Articulated Pipe
 Carrier** £155 £75 £45

Light fawn body with matching
wheels and black tyres. Black pipe
load. Issued 1963. Deleted 1965.
132mm.

MODEL	M/B	M/U	G/C
No. 899. Turntable Fire Escape	£275	£125	£55

Red body with matching wheels.
White tyres. Silver grille and
extending ladder. Issued 1964.
Deleted 1967. 121mm.

	M/B	M/U	G/C
No. 1411. Alpine Renault A310	£75	£35	£15

Red. Metal wheels. Black tyres. Silver
grille. White interior. Issued 1965.
Deleted 1968. 89mm.

	M/B	M/U	G/C
No. 1421. Opel GT 1900	£75	£35	£15

One of the early Super Speedy wheels
models "Super Rapide". Blue. Silver
wheels, bumpers, lights and grille.
Silver luggage carrier on rear, red
interior. Issued 1965. Deleted 1968
92mm.

	M/B	M/U	G/C
No. 1453. Renault 6	£65	£25	£10

Red or rose pink. Silver wheels,
bumpers, lights and grille. Silver trim
with white interior. Black tyres.
Issued 1964. Deleted 1967. 86mm.

GIFT SETS

MODEL	M/B	M/U	G/C
No. 10. Railway Miniatures Set	£65		

Station Master, Mechanic,
Controller, Greaser, Lamp Lighter.
Issued 1956. Deleted 1968.

	M/B	M/U	G/C
No. 11. Travellers Miniatures Set	£65		

Campers, Skier, Lady Traveller,
Porter with luggage. Issued 1956.
Deleted 1968.

	M/B	M/U	G/C
No. 24/58. Gift Box Tourisme 1958	£350		

This is a unique French Dinky Set
which consists of five cars. Issued
1958. Deleted 1968.

	M/B	M/U	G/C
No. 40. Road Signs Set	£65		

Six road signs in yellow box. Issued
1955. Deleted 1968.

No. 41. Road Signs Set   £65

Six more road signs in a special box.
Issued 1955. Deleted 1968.

No. 49D. Service Station   £50

Set of Esso pumps with station flag
in red, white and blue livery on
grey stand. Issued 1955. Deleted
1968. Length 90mm. Total height
92mm.

No. 60. Air Gift Box Set   £50

This neatly boxed set is another
worthwhile investment. Vickers
Viscount Mystère IV A, SO 4050
Vautour, Sikorsky S 58. Issued
1958. Deleted 1968.

No. 64. French Factory   £2200
Aeroplanes Set

Contains 61a Dewoitine, 64b Bloch
200, 64a amiot 370, 64d Potez 662,
64c Potez 63. Issued 1937.(?). Deleted
1940(?)

Meccano Set (Box) No. 0   £75

This fine set would make 30
Meccano models. Instruction
booklet contained. Box 0A
transforms box 0 into box 1. Issued
1952. Deleted 1968. Price for
Mint Boxed only.

Meccano Set (Box) No. 1   £95

This fine set will make 62 Meccano
models. Instruction booklet
contained. Box 1A transforms box 1
into box 2. Issued 1952. Deleted
1968. Price for Mint Boxed only.

Meccano Set (Box) No. 2   £275

Will make 84 Meccano models.
Instruction booklet contained. Box
2A transforms box 2 into box 3.
Issued 1953. Deleted 1968. Price for
Mint Boxed only.

Meccano Set (Box) No. 3   £295

Will also make 84 Meccano models
although contents are different from
Set No. 2 Larger models can be
made. Instruction booklet
contained. Box 3A transforms box 3
into box 4. Issued 1953. Deleted
1968. Price for Mint/Boxed only.

Meccano Set (Box) No. 4   £310

We now come to the start of the really large sets. This one can make 94 large Meccano models. A really solid investment if kept in Mint condition. Instruction booklet contained. Box 4A transforms box 4 into box 5. Issued 1954. Deleted 1968. Price for Mint/Boxed only.

Meccano Set (Box) No. 5   £350

Another magnificent set which if in perfect Mint/Boxed condition is worth a great deal. Makes 105 super models. Instruction booklet contained. Box 5A transforms box 5 into box 6. Issued 1954. Deleted 1968.

Meccano Set (Box) No. 6   £295

Will make 115 models of a large size and super quality. Instruction booklet contained. Box 6A transforms box 6 into box 7. Issued 1954. Deleted 1968.

Meccano Set (Box) No. 7   £350

The time had come in 1955 for the company to introduce this very strong box container with even larger sets to make 136 models. Instruction booklet contained. Box 7A transforms box 7 into box 8. Issued 1955. Deleted 1968.

Meccano Set (Box) No. 8   £375

Another super large box with enough parts to make 157 models. Instruction booklet contained. Box 8A transforms box 8 into box 9. Issued 1955. Deleted 1968.

Meccano Set (Box) No. 9   £400

With this fine set one could make a large bulldozer or a hydraulic press. In a new three-tier box beautifully illustrated on box cover. Altogether one could build 177 models. Instruction booklet contained. Box 9A transforms box 9 into box 10. Issued 1955. Deleted 1968.

MODEL	M/B	M/U	G/C

Meccano Set (Box) No. 10   £450

As a result of the growing demand for more parts and even bigger sets after a nationwide poll in model shops in France, Holland, Germany, and Italy, the firm decided to excel themselves and put out a large Meccano set in a wooden case with handles both inside and out. The trays were a treasure to behold and should any person own such a set they are very lucky indeed. This set enables collectors to build over 200 models. Instruction booklet contained. Issued 1956. Deleted 1966.

RAILWAYS

Apart from cars and Meccano, the French Dinky company made some unique train sets and some fine coaches, wagons, and buildings to go with them. I enclose a list of fine investments from authentic catalogues and leaflets.

The mechanical Hornby trains are extremely well made and are guaranteed a long life. They are particularly successful due to their excellent presentation and the remarkable performance of their locomotives. And don't forget that the track can be added to with more straight or curved rails, points or crossings. Each train has a rail operated by a lever which enables the train to stop automatically. Prices for boxed sets only in trains.

MODEL	M/B	M/U	G/C

BUFFERS

Buffer No. 1   £25   £10   £5

Sprung stoppers. Can be adapted for use on all electric and mechanical Hornby rails. Place for standard lighting. Issued 1955. Deleted 1968.

MODEL	M/B	M/U	G/C

CARRIAGES

	M/B	M/U	G/C
Mixed Passenger/Baggage Car	£55	£35	£15

With sliding doors. Issued 1956.
Deleted 1968. Length 25cm.

	M/B	M/U	G/C
Pullman Salon Car	£55	£35	£15

Issued 1958. Deleted 1968. Length
25cm.

	M/B	M/U	G/C
Restaurant Car	£55	£35	£15

Issued 1958. Deleted 1968. Length
25cm.

CONTROL PANELS

	M/B	M/U	G/C
Control Panel	£25	£10	£5

Supplies current for the running of
five accessories. Book with
instructions for the wiring of the
transformer. Issued 1955. Deleted
1968.

EXPRESS TRAINS

	M/B
Express Train 1	£55

This train consists of a locomotive,
tender and car. The curved rails of
the track form a circle of 60cm in
diameter. Length of train — 33cm.
Issued 1953. Deleted 1968.

	M/B
Express Train 2	£65

Same composition as Express Train
1, but with 2 cars instead of one.
Length of train — 45cm.

	M/B
Express Train 3	£75

As well as the locomotive, tender,
and 2 carriages, this set contains an
attractively decorated metal siding.
In addition, the rail track is more
important than that of Express
Trains 1 and 2, consisting of 6
curved sections of rail, and 2
straight, to form an oval of 86 ×
60cm. Issued 1955. Deleted 1968.

FOOTBRIDGES

	M/B	M/U	G/C
Metallic Footbridge	£45	£25	£10

Equipped with two semaphores.
Can span two tracks. Issued 1954.
Deleted 1968.

MODEL	M/B	M/U	G/C

LEVEL CROSSINGS
Level Crossing No. 1 £45 £25 £10

With signalman's box. In two
separate parts, allowing the passage
of one or more tracks. Working
barriers. Place for standard lighting.
Issued 1956. Deleted 1968.

Level Crossing M £25 £15 £10

In two separate parts. Working
barrier. Place for standard lighting.
Issued 1955. Deleted 1968.

LOADING BAYS
Loading Bay £65 £45 £15

Equipped with a working crane
which pivots. Height 155cm, length
58cm. Width 14cm. Issued 1955.
Deleted 1968.

POINTS
Electric Points £35 £15 £10

Radio-controlled points. Issued
1955. Deleted 1968.

SIGNAL BOXES
Automatic Signal Box £50 £30 £15

Red and green lights. Can be used
on any electric Hornby track.
Controls the arrival and departure
of trains. (With instruction booklet
and wiring instructions). Issued
1954. Deleted 1968.

Signal Box £35 £15 £10

Can be dismantled. With Plexiglass
cabin. Issued 1957. Deleted 1968.
Height 15cm, Length 29cm, Width
28cm.

Round Signal £25 £15 £10

Lever for red signal. Place provided
for standard electric lighting. Issued
1955. Deleted 1968.

STATIONS
Station No. 20 £75 £45 £25

Can be dismantled. Crossing over
the track to the interior of the

MODEL	M/B	M/U	G/C

station. Issued 1957. Deleted 1968.
Height 17cm, Length 43cm, Width
29cm.

Station No. 21

£95 £55 £25

Can be dismantled. With Plexiglass.
Crossing over two tracks to the
station interior. Issued 1957.
Deleted 1968. Height 22cm, Length
52cm, Width 28cm.

TRAIN SETS

Electric Autorail Train Set

£195

Bugatti type with two cars. Same
motor as the O.BB locomotive, two
lights, automatic coupling. Issued
1957. Deleted 1968.

Mechanical Autorail Train Set

£125

2 Bugatti type autorail cars with
automatic coupling devices,
allowing the coupling of Hornby
wagons. Same engine as M series.
Length of locomotive: 42cm.
Curved rail sections forming a circle
of 60cm in diameter. Possible to buy
the autorails separately. Issued 1955.
Deleted 1968.

The 'M' Series

This robust train consists of a
locomotive, the movement of which
is protected from dust and shocks.
The wagons come complete with
automatic coupling devices and a
standard railway track. This layout
can be completed with straight or
curved rails, points and crossings.
Each track has an automatic
stopping lever. Each set comes with
a guarantee leaflet.

Train Set M5

£135

An electric BB-M type locomotive
with 2 passenger cars with opening
windows. 6 curved and 2 straight
rail sections form an oval of 86 ×

60cm. The locomotive can be purchased separately. Issued 1955. Deleted 1968.

Train Set M6 £135

An electric BB-M type locomotive with 2 tip cart wagons. Same rail track as the M5 train. Issued 1956. Deleted 1968.

Train Set M7 £150

Same train and rail track as M5, with the addition of a station, siding, signal box, and 2 signals. All the accessories are in finely decorated metal. Issued 1956. Deleted 1968.

MO Train Set £135

An electric BB-M type locomotive with 2 passenger cars with slit windows. Six curved rail sections and two straight forming an oval of 86 × 60cm. Locomotive can be bought separately. Issued 1955. Deleted 1968.

Electric Series 0-20 volts — 32mm Gauge

It is possible to change the direction of the locomotives or autorails of the O Series. Each train has an O transformer, 12 curved rail sections forming a circle of 120cm in diameter, and 2 pamphlets containing a guarantee and explanations on how the Hornby trains work.

OB-BM Train Set 'Le Bourguignon' £150

An O.BB locomotive, a refrigeration car with sliding doors and a wagon with detachable tarpaulin. Issued 1956. Deleted 1968.

Train Set OV-AM 'Le Breton' £175

An O.VA steam locomotive with tender, a refrigeration car with sliding doors, and wagon with opening doors. Issued 1956. Deleted 1968.

MODEL	M/B	M/U	G/C

Train Set OB-BV 'Le Mistral' £150

An O.BB locomotive, passenger car
with bogies, and mixed car
(passengers and baggage) with
bogies and opening doors. Issued
1956. Deleted 1968.

T Series — Novelty (Total Security) £225

These two remote control trains are
equipped with a new locomotive
and transformer ensuring total
safety. The transformer can be
connected to currents of either 110
or 220 volts and controls from a
distance the speed and direction of
the T-BB locomotive. This
locomotive is equipped with special
tyres and has exceptional track and
traction holding which allows the
train to start smoothly with its 20
wagons and bogies. Each train in
the Hornby ST Series comes with 2
brochures containing a guarantee
and instructions on the use of the
radio controlled train. All the parts
which go with these trains can be
bought separately.

TB-BV Train Set 'Le Drapeau' £155

This is an exceptional set in the
authentic livery of the 'Le
Drapeau'. A T-BB locomotive,
Pullman car, Restaurant car, ST
transfo, twelve curved rail sections
forming a circle of 120cm in
diameter. Issued 1956. Deleted 1968.

TB-BM Train Set 'Le Provençal' £135

A T-BB locomotive, a car, a low-
sided car, an ST transfo, twelve-
curved rail sections forming a circle
of 120cm in diameter. Issued 1958.
Deleted 1968.

The T-BB Loco £125 £75 £35

Apart from the sets, one can
purchase the Loco separately boxed,
and for this I have given the three
prices. Motor with a permanent
magnet. Rubber tyres (Four
wheels). New hinged pantographs.

MODEL	M/B	M/U	G/C

Stoppers, automatic coupling,
headlights. Issued 1958. Deleted
1968.

TRANSFORMERS

O Transformer   £55

Three speed, hand controlled. 20v
debit. Supplied with a plug to light
up the accessories, which is able to
function when the train is
stationary. Fused for safety. Issued
1955. Deleted 1968.

ST. Transformer   £55

Power up to 40v. It is protected on
the circuit by a self righting system.
There was a special price for the
speed control (introduced in 1958)
which allows separate control of the
speed and direction of the two
locomotives on the same track, or
on two different tracks, as well as
the possibility of a wide range of
manoeuvres. A single hand control
with a potentiometric rheostat
reverser controls the speed and
direction of the locomotives. Issued
1958. Deleted 1968.

TUNNELS

Tunnel   £35   £15   £10

Can be dismantled. Issued 1955.
Deleted 1968. Height 19cm, Length
29cm, Width 28cm.

WAGONS

'Arbel' Wagon   £55   £35   £15

With Arbel decals on sides. For
transporting coal and ore. Issued
1957. Deleted 1968. Length 235cm.

Cattle Wagon No. 2   £55   £35   £15

With opening doors. Issued 1956.
Deleted 1968. Length 23.5cm.

Novelty Covered Wagon   £55   £35   £15

With two sliding doors. Issued 1967.
Deleted 1968. Length 235cm.

Crane Wagon No 1   £35   £15   £10

Functioning crane with pivot.
Issued 1954. Deleted 1968. Length
155cm.

MODEL	M/B	M/U	G/C
Double Bolt Wagon	£35	£15	£10

Issued 1952. Deleted 1968. Length 155cm.

IS Wagon	£55	£35	£15

With 2 sliding doors. Issued 1956. Deleted 1968. Length 18cm.

Low-Sided Wagon	£55	£35	£15

Ideal for transporting Dinky Toys. Issued 1957. Deleted 1968. Length 23.5cm.

Passenger Wagon	£65	£45	£25

Issued 1957. Deleted 1968. Length 25cm.

Relief Wagon With Crane	£55	£35	£15

Working crane with pivot. Two sliding doors. Issued 1958. Deleted 1968. Length 23.5cm.

'Stef' Refrigerated Wagon	£50	£25	£10

Two sliding doors. Issued 1953. Deleted 1968. Length 18cm.

'Azur' Tanker Wagon	£65	£35	£15

With 'Azur' decals on side. Issued 1958. Deleted 1968. Length 23.5cm.

'Esso' Tanker Wagon	£65	£35	£15

Aluminium paintwork. Issued 1954. Deleted 1968. Length 15.5cm.

'Primagaz' Tanker Wagon	£65	£35	£10

White paintwork. With 'Primagaz Le Butane Français' decals on the sides. Issued 1955. Deleted 1968. Length 15.5cm.

Tarpaulin Wagon	£45	£25	£10

The hoops and tarpaulin are removable. Issued 1953. Deleted 1968. Length 15.5cm.

Timber Wagon	£65	£35	£15

For transporting tree trunks. Issued 1957. Deleted 1968. Length 23.5cm.

Tip Wagon	£45	£25	£15

The wagon tips one way or the other. Issued 1955. Deleted 1968. Length 15.5cm.

MODEL	M/B	M/U	G/C
Tip Cart Wagon With Look-Out Seat	£35	£15	£10

Issued 1954. Deleted 1968. Length
15.5cm.

DUBLO DINKYS

The Dublo Dinky models were first made with the railway
enthusiast in mind. In no way were the little toys copied from
the Matchbox series, as believed by many people. Frank
Hornby had thought of tiny pocket toys long before the
Matchbox range had been conceived. It so happened that
plans were found by the takeover firm of Lines Bros and the
Dublo Dinky was born. They had a two year production and
the run was very successful. Today the models are always in
constant demand by collectors, and in fact, very hard to come
by. To me these little items were special, especially the No.
068, The Royal Mail Van. They are equally special to
thousands of collectors in many parts of the world and will be
a real investment to anyone who has the set mint and boxed.

MODEL	M/B	M/U	G/C
No. 060. Milk Wagon	£1250	£200	£100

Very rare model, possibly pre-war.
Reported but not verified in dark
brown or cream.

	M/B	M/U	G/C
No. 061. Ford Prefect	£65	£20	£10

Fawn or grey. Latter worth at least
three times more. With smooth grey
plastic wheels and tyres. Price 1/6d.
Issued March 1958. Deleted 1960.
58mm. DC/TP/PW.

	M/B	M/U	G/C
No. 062. Singer Roadster	£65	£20	£10

Orange with red seats. Also fawn with
red seats, worth double. Smooth grey
plastic wheels and tyres. Price 1/6d.
Issued 1958. Deleted 1960. 50mm.
DC/PW.

	M/B	M/U	G/C
No. 063. Commer Van	£95	£30	£15

Blue with plastic wheels. Price 1/6d.
Issued March 1958. Deleted 1960.
53mm. DC/TP.

MODEL	M/B	M/U	G/C

No. 064. Austin Lorry — £75 £30 £15

Green, with smooth grey or ribbed black plastic wheels and tyres. Price 1/6d. Issued December 1957. Deleted 1962. 64mm. DC/PW.

No. 065. Morris Pick-up — £55 £20 £10

Red with smooth grey plastic wheels and tyres. Price 1/9d. Issued December 1957. Deleted 1960. 54mm. DC/PW.

No. 066. Bedford Flat Truck — £65 £20 £10

Grey. Also in brown, worth at least treble. With smooth grey plastic wheels and tyres. Price 1/11d. Issued December 1957. Deleted 1960. 107mm. DC/PW.

No. 067. Austin Taxi — £95 £30 £15

Blue and cream with ribbed grey or black plastic wheels. One of the more sought after models. This is a good investment buy. Price 2/5d. Issued March 1959. Deleted 1967. 60mm. DC/PW.

No. 068. Royal Mail Van — £95 £30 £15

Red, with the words 'Royal Mail' and 'E2R' on the side. I consider this to be the best investment of all the Dublo range. With plastic windows and ribbed black plastic wheels and tyres. Price 2/2d. Issued April 1959. Deleted 1964. 48mm. DC.

No. 069. Massey Harris Ferguson Tractor — £55 £30 £15

Various shades of blue. Also rare model in black which definitely exists. With grey ribbed plastic wheels, and hook. There is also a driver in some of these models though, surprisingly, it is quite rare as the hole in the seat was meant specifically for this purpose. Price 1/6d. Issued September 1959. Deleted 1965. 37mm. DC.

No. 070. A.E.C. Shell Tanker — £75 £40 £25

Red and green. With black ribbed plastic wheels. Windows. Words 'Shell Petroleum Products BP' on sides. Price 2/6d. Issued October 1959. Deleted 1964. 91mm. DC/TP/PW.

No. 071. V.W. Delivery Van   £55   £20   £10

Yellow with the words 'Hornby
Dublo' on sides. With black ribbed
plastic wheels. Windows. Price 2/-.
Issued March 1960. Deleted 1967.
54mm. DC/TP/PW.

No. 072. Bedford Artic. Truck   £55   £20   £10

Orange cab and red trailer. Windows.
Price 2/6d. Issued June 1959. Deleted
1964. Overall length 116mm.
DC/TW.

No. 073. Land Rover and
Trailer   £55   £20   £10

Green Land Rover with windows and
orange trailer with black plastic door.
Smooth grey or ribbed black plastic
wheels and tyres. With tin baseplate.
Price 4/3d. Issued 1960. Deleted
1967. Overall length 103mm. DC.

No. 076. Lansing Bagnall   £65   £25   £15

Maroon. Tractor has a driver and
hook. Hook also on trailer. Price 2/9d.
Issued June 1960. Deleted 1964.
Overall length 75mm. DC/TP/PW.

MODEL	M/B	M/U	G/C

No. 078. Lansing Bagnall   £55   £20   £10

This is for the trailer only and for
some unknown reason, this item
remained in the catalogues until 1971.
Price 1/4d. Issued June 1960.
Officially deleted in 1964. 49mm.
DC/TP/PW.

GIFT SETS

Ever since the first diecast models were made people have
been interested in collecting sets as a means of making sure
that they did not miss any particular number as they were
manufactured. I have set out the full list of all the sets made
by the Dinky firm from the beginning.

I have set out the prices as mint and boxed only, for once
the box is lost the models become individual items. The very
first sets had plain boxes, and later the name of the firm was
added, plus the drawings or photographs of the particular
models in question.

MODEL	M/B	M/U	G/C

The 1st Set. 22 Series   £3000

Contains: an Army Tank; a Sports
Coupé; a Farm Tractor; a Motor
Truck; a Sports Car and a Delivery
Van. Price 3/11d. This was advertised
in the 1933 'Meccano Magazine' but
officially did not appear until 1934,
and was then deleted in 1940.

The 2nd Set. 24 Series   £3000

Contains: 24a Ambulance; 24b
Limousine; 24c Town Sedan; 24d
Vogue Saloon; 24l Super Streamlined
Saloon; 24f Sportsman Coupé; 24g
Four-Seater Sports Tourer; 24h Two-
Seater Sports Tourer. Fitted with
rubber tyres and silver plated
radiators. Price 6/6d. Issued 1934.
Deleted 1940.

The 3rd Set. 25 Series   £3000

Contains: 25a Wagon; 25b Covered
Wagon; 25c Flat Truck; 25d Petrol
Tank Wagon; 25e Tipping Wagon

and 25f Market Gardener's Van.
Square type vans with no rear wheel
covers. Price 4/6d. Issued 1934.
Deleted 1940.

The 4th Set. 28/1 Series   £3000

Contains: 28a Hornby trains Van; 28b
Pickford's Removal Van; 28c
Manchester Guardian Van; 28d Oxo
Van; 28l Ensign Cameras van and 28f
Palethorpe's Sausages Van. Square
type vans with no rear wheel covers.
Price 4/6d, reduced to 3/- at a later
date. Issued August to October 1934.
Deleted 1940.

The 5th Set. 28/2 Series   £3000

Contains: 28g Kodak Cameras Van;
28h Sharps Toffees Van; 28i
Crawford's Biscuit Van; 28m
Wakefield's Oil Van; 28n Marsh and
Baxter's Sausages Van and 22d
Meccano Van. Price 3/-. Issued
September/November 1934. Deleted
1940.

The 6th Set. 30 Series   £2500

Contains: 30a Chrysler Airflow
Saloon; 30b Rolls Royce Car; 30c
Daimler Car; 30d Vauxhall Car; 30e
Breakdown Car and 30f Ambulance
in grey and red. Fitted with rubber
tyres and silver plated radiators. Price
4/6d. Issued 1935. Deleted 1940.

The 7th Set. 28/1 Revised Set   £2650

Contains: 28a Hornby Trains Van;
28b Pickford's Removal Van; 28c
Manchester Guardian Van; 28e
Firestone Tyres Van; 28f Palethorpe's
Sausages Van and 28n Atco Lawn
Mowers Van. Price 4/6d. Issued 1935.
Deleted 1940.

The 8th Set. 28/2 Revised Set   £2600

Contains: 28d Oxo Van; 28g Kodak
Cameras Van; 28h Dunlop Van; 28k
Marsh and Baxter's Sausages Van and
28p Crawford's Biscuits Van. Price
4/6d. Issued 1935. Deleted 1940.

The 9th Set. 33 Series £2500

Contains: 33a Mechanical Horse; 33b
Flat Truck; 33c Open Wagon; 33d
Box Van; 33l Dust Wagon and 33f
Petrol Tanker. Price 3/6. Issued 1935.
Deleted 1940.

The 10th Set. Petrol Pumps
Set £1250

Contains: 49a Bowser Pump; Wayne
Pump; Theo Pump; Shell Pump; and
one Pratt's Oil Bin. These were fitted
with thin rubber hose pipes and a
metal nozzle which hooked onto the
pump body. Price 1/6d. Issued 1935.
Deleted 1940.

The 11th Set. 43 Series RAC
Set £1000

Contains: 43a RAC Hut; 43b RAC
Motor Cycle Patrol; 43c RAC Guide
Directing Traffic; 43d RAC Guide
Saluting. Price 2/3d. Issued 1935.
Deleted 1940.

The 12th Set. 44 Series AA Set £2000

Contains: 44a AA Hut; 44b AA
Motor Cycle Patrol; 44c AA Guide
Directing Traffic; 44d AA Guide
Saluting. Price 2/3. Issued 1935.
Deleted 1940.

The 13th Set. 28/3 Series £2000

Contains: 28r Swan's Van; 28s Fry's
Van; 28t Ovaltine Van; 28w Osram
Van; 28x Hovis Van; 28y Exide/
Drydex Van. Price 4/6. Issued 1936.
Deleted 1940.

The 14th Set. 42 Series Police
Set £600

Contains: 42a Police Box; 42b Motor
Cycle Patrol; 42c Point Duty
Policeman in white coat and 42d
Point Duty Policeman. Price 1/11d.
Issued 1936. Deleted 1940.

The 15th Set. 280 Series £4000

Contains: 280a Viyella Van; 280b
Lyons Van; 280c Shredded Wheat
Van; 280d Bisto Van; 280e Ekco Van
and 280f Mackintosh's Van. Price
4/6d. Mackintosh's Van. Issued 1937.
Deleted 1940.

The 16th Set. 151 Series Royal Tank Corps Medium Tank Set

£850

Contains: 151a Medium Tank (12 tons, 90 h.p.); 151b 3 ton Transport Wagon; 151c Cooker Trailer with jack stand; 151d Water Tank trailer; 151d Driver. Price 3/6d. Issued 1938. Deleted 1940.

The 17th Set. 152 Series Royal Tank Corps Light Tank Set

£850

152a Light Tank; 152b Reconnaissance Car; 152c Austin 7 Car; 150d Driver. Price 2/6d. Issued 1938. Deleted 1940.

The 18th Set. 150 Series Royal Tank Corps Personnel Set

£250

Contains: 150a Officer; 150b Private in sitting position; 150c Private in standing position; 150e NCO. Price 10d. Issued 1938. Deleted 1940.

The 19th Set. 12 Series Postal Set

£1000

Contains: 12a Pillar Box GPO; 12b Pillar Box Airmail; 12c Telephone Call Box; 12d Telegraph Messenger; 12e Postman; 34b Royal Mail Van. Price 2/3d. Issued 1938. Deleted 1940.

The 20th Set. 37 Series Cyclist Set

£350

Contains: 37a Civilian Motor Cyclist; 37b Police Motor Cyclist; 37c Royal Corps of Signals Despatch Rider. This set had an intricate casting with driver cast in and solid white rubber wheels. Price 1/6d. Issued 1938. Deleted 1940.

The 21st Set. 36 Series Motor Vehicle Set

£4750

Contains: 36a Armstrong Siddeley Limousine with driver and footman; 36b Two-Seater Bentley Sports Coupé with driver and passenger; 36c Humber Vogue Saloon with driver and footman; 36d Streamlined Rover

Saloon with driver and passenger; 36e
Two-Seater British Salmson Sports
Car with driver and 36e Four-Seater
British Salmson Sports model with
driver. A very unusual set comprising
cars, drivers and passengers etc.
Fitted with detachable rubber tyres
and silver plated radiators. Price 5/6d.
Issued 1938. Deleted 1940.

The 22nd Set. 161 Series
Mobile Anti Aircraft Unit   £300

Contains: 161a Lorry with
Searchlight and 161b Anti Aircraft
Gun on mobile platform. Price 3/-.
Issued 1939. Deleted 1940.

The 23rd Set. 162 Series
Field Gun Set   £400

Contains: 162a Light Dragon Motor
Tractor; 162b Trailer and 162c Gun.
Price 2/-. Issued 1939. Deleted 1940.

The 24th Set. 38 Series
Sports Car Set   £6000

Contains: 38a Frazer Nash BMW
Sports Car; 38b Sunbeam Talbot
Sports Car; 38c Lagonda Sports Car;
38d Alvis Sorts Tourer; 38e triumph
Dolomite Sports Coupé and 38f SS
Jaguar Sports Car. All fitted with
detachable rubber tyres. Price 5/-.
Issued 1939. Deleted 1940.

The 25th Set. 39 Series
Sedans and Coupés Set   £6000

Contains: 39a Packard Super 8
Touring Sedan Car; 39b Oldsmobile
6 Sedan Car; 39c Lincoln Zephyr
Coupé; 39d Buick Viceroy Saloon
Car; 39e Chrysler Royal Sedan and
39f Studebaker State Commander
Saloon Car. All fitted with detachable
rubber tyres. Price 5/-. Issued 1939.
Deleted 1940.

The 26th Set. 160 Series
Royal Artillery Personnel   £75

Contains: 16a NCO; 160b Gunner
Sitting; two figures; 160c Gun Layer
and 160d Standing Gunner. These
models were intended for use on the
guns of the 161 and 162 Sets. Price
10d. Issued 1939. Deleted 1940.

The 27th Set. 156 Series Mechanised Army Set

£1500

This was a special combined set in a special box consisting of the four army sets numbers 151, 152, 161 and 162. Price 12/6. Issued 1939. Deleted 1940.

The 28th Set. 23 Series Racing Car Set

£4500

Contains: 232J HWM; 23H Ferrari Racing Car; 23F Alfa Romeo; 23N Maserati; 23R Talbot Lago; 23G Cooper Bristol Racing Car. Price 12/6. Issued 1953. Deleted 1966.

Military Gift Set No. 1

£2500

Contains: 621 3 Ton Army Wagon; 641 1 Ton Army Cargo Truck; 674 Austin Champ and 676 Armoured Personnel Carrier. Price 12/6d. Issued March 1955. Deleted 1968.

No. 695. Howitzer and Tractor Gift Set

£250

Contains: 689 and 693. Price 13/11d. Issued 1962. Deleted 1966.

No. 697. 25 Pounder Field Gun Set

£250

Contains: 688 Field Artillery Tractor and driver; 687 Trailer and 686 Gun. Price 10/9. Issued 1957. Deleted 1972.

No. 698. Tank Transporter Set

£450

Contains: 660 Tank Transporter carrying 651 Tank. Price 21/11d. Issued 1957. Deleted 1964.

No. 699. Military Vehicles Set

£350

Contains: 621; 641; 674 and 676. Green. Price 17/6d. Issued March 1955. Deleted 1964.

Farmyard Equipment Gift Set No. 1

£350

Contains: 27A; 27B; 27C; 27G and 27H. Price 17/3d. Issued December 1952. Deleted 1954. Renumbered 398. Deleted 1976.

MODEL	M/B	M/U	G/C

Commercial Vehicles Gift Set No. 2   £750

Contains: 27D; 25M; 30N; 30P and 30S. Price 17/9d. Issued December 1952. Deleted 1966.

Passenger Cars Gift Set No. 3   £750

Contains: 27F; 30H; 40E; 40G; 40H and 140B. Price 15/-. Issued November 1952. Deleted 1976.

Racing Cars Gift Set No. 4   £750

Contains: 23F; 23G; 23H; 23J and 23N. Price 12/6d. Issued October 1953. Deleted 1971. Renumbered 249 in 1954. Deleted 1960.

Tow-Away Glider Gift Set No. 118   £150

Contains: 135 Triumph 2000 in metallic green with white roof and red interior. The words 'Southdown Gliding Club' in red letters. Glider set is also in blue, worth double. Price 15/3d. Issued 1965. Deleted 1966. Overall length 289mm.

No. 121. Goodwood Racing Set   £400

Contains: 112; 113; 120; 182 and nine figures. Price 22/11d. Issued 1963. Deleted 1966.

No. 122. Touring Set   £300

Contains: 188; 193; 195; 270; 295 and 796. Price 25/11d. Issued 1963. Deleted 1965.

No. 123. Mayfair Gift Set   £500

Contains: 142; 150; 186; 194; 198 and 199, plus four civilians from set 009. Price 35/11d. Issued 1963. Deleted 1965.

MODEL	M/B	M/U	G/C

No. 124. Holiday Gift Set   £300

Contains: 952; 137; 142 and 796.
Price 35/11d. Issued 1964. Deleted
1967.

No. 125. Fun Ahoy Set   £150

Contains: 130 in pale blue and 796.
Price 9/11d. Issued July 1964. Deleted
1969.

No. 126. Motor Show Set   £300

Contains: 171; 133; 127 and 151.
Price 21/-. Issued 1965/66. Deleted
1969.

No. 149. Sports Models   £750

Contains: 107; 108; 110 and 111.
Price 15/-. Issued September 1958.
Deleted 1961.

No. 201. Racing Car Set   £200

Contains: 240 Cooper racing car and
BRM racer. Price 9/6d. Issued
1965/66. Deleted 1969.

No. 237. Dinky Way Set   £350

Contains four Dinky diecast vehicles:
AA Service Van (Bedford); Triumph
TR7; Police Mini; Dumper Truck
and twenty feet of scale model roads
and two traffic signs. Price £4.55p.
Issued 1978. Deleted 1980.

No. 245. Superfast Set   £350

Contains: 131 Jaguar E Type; 153
Aston Martin and 188 Jensen FF.
Price 38/11d. Issued 1969. Deleted
1973.

No. 246. International Set   £250

Contains: 187 De-Tomaso 5000; 215
Ford and 216 Dino Ferrari. Price
32/6d. Issued 1969. Deleted 1973.

No. 249. Racing Cars Gift Set   £550

A renumbering of Gift Set No. 4.
Contains: 231; 232; 233; 234 and 235.
Price 12/6d. Issued 1956. Deleted
1960.

No. 249A. Racing Cars Gift Set   £400

Contains: 230; 231; 232; 233 and 234.
Talbot Lago replaced the H.W.M.
which was deleted 1960. Price 14/11d.
Issued 1960. Deleted 1964.

MODEL	M/B	M/U	G/C

No. 297. Police Vehicles Set   £300

Contains: 250; 254; 287 and 255.
Ford Zodiac Police Car replaced by
the Police Range Rover. Price 14/6d.
Issued 1967. Replaced by 294 in
1967. 294 deleted 1970.

No. 294   £150

No. 298. Emergency Services
Gift Set   £300

Contains: 258; 263; 276 and 277.
With figures in plastic. Price 36/11d.
Issued 1963. Deleted 1966.

No. 299. Police Crash Squad
Set   £200

Contains: 244 Plymouth Police Car;
732 Bell Police Helicopter and some
bollards and signs. U.S.A. models.
Price £2.75p. Issued 1978. Deleted
1980.

No. 299. Post Office Services
Set   £550

Contains: 260; 261; 750 plus a
messenger and a postman. Price
9/11d. Issued 1957. Deleted 1960.

No. 299. Motorway Services
Set   £500

Contains: 257; 263; 269; 276 and 434.
Price 53/11d. Issued 1963. Deleted
1967.

No. 300. London Scene Gift
Set   £250

Contains: London Taxi and London
Routemaster Bus. Price £2.99p. Issued
1978. Deleted 1980.

No. 302. Emergency Squad Set   £350

Contains: Paramedic Truck; Cadillac
Ambulance and two figures. Price
£2.99p. Issued 1978. Deleted 1980.

No. 303. Special Commando
Squad Set   £200

Contains: Army Truck; Armoured
Car and Army Helicopter. Price
£2.25p. Issued 1978. Deleted 1980.

No. 304. Fire Rescue Gift Set   £300

Contains: 384 Convoy Fire Rescue
Truck; 282 Land Rover Fire

Appliance and 195 Range Rover Fire Chief's Car. Price £2.55p. Issued 1978. Deleted 1980.

No. 307. New Avengers Gift Set £950

Not officially released but some reps did bring out a few of these in the very early part of 1978. Contains. Purdey's TR7 Car and Steed's Special Leyland Jaguar, featuring a novel fly-off assailant. Very rare set indeed. Price £3.75. Issued and deleted 1978.

No. 309. Star Trek Gift Set £750

Contains: U.S.S. Enterprise and the Klingon Battle Cruiser. Price £3.75p. Issued 1978. Deleted 1980.

No. 387. Farm Equipment Set £200

Contains: 300; 320; 321; 322 and 324. This was the renumbering of Gift Set No. 1. Price 21/-. Issued 1954. Deleted 1968.

No. 399. Convoy Gift Set £150

Contains: 380; 381 and 382. Colour liveries varied a great deal in this set. Price £4.50p. Issued 1978. Deleted 1980.

No. 784. Dinky Goods Train Set £100

Contains a blue engine, a fawn trailer, and a red tank wagon. The measurements for the three vehicles in correct order: engine 115mm; fawn wagon 92mm and tanker wagon 92mm. Price £2.25p. Issued 1972. Deleted 1975.

No. 900. Building Site Gift Set £200

Contains: 437; 960; 962 and 965. Price 57/11d. Issued 1963. Deleted 1970.

No. 957. Fire Services Gift Set £300

Contains: 257; 955 and 956. Price 23/6d. Issued 1959. Deleted 1966.

No. 990. Car Transporter Set £750

Contains: 982 Transporter; and cars 154, 156, 161 and 162. Price 28/11d. Issued 1955. Deleted 1960.

MODEL	M/B	M/U	G/C

No. 23 Series. Racing Car Set   £2550

Contains: 23C Mercedes Benz Racing
Car; 23D Auto-Union Racing Car and
23E Speed of the Wind Racing Car.
Fitted with driver and detachable
racing tyres. Price 1/11d. Issued 1934.
Deleted 1940.

No. 47. Road Signs Set   £200

Contains: 47E; 47F; 47G; 47H; 47K;
47M; 47N; 47P; 47Q; 47R; 47S; 37T.
Price 1/6d for set of 12. Issued 1935.
Deleted 1940.

No. 50. Ships of the British Navy Set   £500

Contains: 50A Battle Cruiser Hood;
50B Battleships Nelson (two models);
50C Cruiser Effingham; 50D Cruiser
York; 50E Cruiser Delhi; 50F three
model Broke Class Destroyers; 50G
Submarine K Class; three Amazon
Class Destroyers (50H) and one 50K
Submarine X Class. Price for set of 14
pieces 3/6d. Issued 1935. Deleted
1940.

No. 51. Famous Liners Set   £400

Contains: 51B Europa; 51C Rex; 51D
Empress of Britain; 51E Strathaird;
51F Queen of Bermuda and 51G
Britannic. Price 3/6d. Issued 1934.
Deleted 1940. DC.

No. 60. Aeroplanes Set   £1500

Contains: 60A Imperial Airways
Liner; 60B Leopard Moth D.H.; 60C
Percival Gull; 60D Low Wing
Monoplane; 60E General Monospar
and 60F Cierva Autogiro. Price set of
six models 3/-. Issued 1935. Deleted
1940.

No. 61. R.A.F. Aeroplanes Set   £700

Contains 60h Singapore Flying Boat,
2 60n Fairey Battle Bombers, 2 60p
Gloster Gladiator Biplanes. Issued
1937. Deleted 1940.

No. 68. Camouflaged Aeroplanes Set   £6500

Contains 60t Armstrong Whitworth
Whitley Bomber, 68b Frobisher
Liner, 3 62h Hawker Hurricane
fighters, 3 62e Vickers Supermarine

Spitfire Fighters, 68a Armstrong
Whitworth Ensign Liners, 2 62d
Bristol Blenheim Bombers, 2 60s
Fairey Battle Bombers. Issued 1938.
Deleted 1940.

No. 1. Station Staff Set   £100

Contains: 1A Stationmaster; 1B
Guard; 1C Ticket Collector; 1D
Driver; 1E Porter with bags and 1F
Porter. Price 1/6d. Issued 1935.
Deleted 1940.

No. 2. Farmyard Animals Set   £75

Contains: two 2A Horses; two 2B
Cows; 2C Pig; 3D Sheep. Price for
set of six pieces 1/6d. Issued 1934.
Deleted 1940.

No. 3. Passengers Set   £75

Contains: 3A Woman and Child; 3B
Businessman; 3C Male Hiker; 3D
Female Hiker; 3E Newsboy and 3F
Woman. Price 1/6d. Issued 1935.
Deleted 1940.

No. 4. Engineering Staff Set   £75

Contains: 4A, 4B, 4C and 4E. There
are two of 4B. Price 1/6d. Issued
1935. Deleted 1940.

No. 5. Train and Hotel Staff Set   £75

Contains: 5A Pullman Car Conductor;
two Pullman Car No. B Waiters and
two 5C Hotel Porters. Price 1/3d.
Issued 1935. Deleted 1940.

No. 6. Shepherd Set   £125

Contains: 6a Shepherd; 6d Sheepdog
and four 2d Sheep. Price set of six 1/-.
Issued 1934. Deleted 1940.

No. 16. Silver Jubilee Set   £350

Price 1/6d. Issued 1935. Deleted 1940.

No. 17. Diecast Passenger
Train Set   £300

Contains: miniature diecast model
17A Locomotive; 17B Tender; 20A
Coach and 20B Guard's Van. Price
2/3d. Issued 1935/36. Deleted 1940.

No. 18. Diecast Goods Train
Set   £75

Contains: 21A Tank Locomotive and
three No. 21B Wagons. Price 1/9d.
Issued 1935. Deleted 1940.

No. 19. Diecast Mixed Goods Set

£350

Contains: 21A Tank Locomotive; 21B Wagon; 21D Petrol Tanker and 21E Lumber Wagon. Price 1/11d. Issued 1935. Deleted 1940.

No. 20. Diecast Passenger Train Set

£500

Contains: 21A Tank Locomotive; two No. 20A Coaches and 20B Guard's Van. Price 2/6d. Issued 1935. Deleted 1940.

No. 33R. Mechanical Horse and Trailer Set

£950

Contains: 33RA Railway Mechanical Horse and 33RD, complete with detachable rubber tyres. L.M.S.R., L.N.E.R., G.W.R. or S.R. livery. With the words 'Express Parcels Traffic' on sides. Price 1/6d. Issued 1935. Deleted 1940.

No. 35. Small Cars Set

£650

Contains: 35A Saloon Car; 35B Racer and 35C M.G. Sports Model. Price 9d. Issued 1934/35. Deleted 1940.

DINKY FIGURES

No. 12D. Telegraph Messenger

£75

Blue. Price 3d. Issued 1939. Deleted 1940. 35mm. Never individually boxed. Delivered to shops in boxes of 6.

No. 12E. Postman

£75

Blue with bag and badge. Price 3d. Issued 1938. Deleted 1940. 35mm. DC. Box of 6.

No. 42C. Point Duty Policeman in White Coat

£75

Price 3d. Issued August 1936. Deleted 1940. 42mm. DC. Box of 6.

No. 42D. Point Duty Policeman in Blue Uniform

£75

Price 4d. Issued August 1936. Deleted 1940. 40mm. DC. Box of 6.

MODEL	M/B	M/U	G/C

No. 43C. RAC Guide Directing Traffic — £75

With red sash etc. Price 3d. Issued October 1935. Deleted 1940. 37mm. DC. Box of 6.

No. 43D. RAC Guide Saluting — £75

With red sash etc. Price 3d. Issued October 1935. Deleted 1940. 36mm. DC. Box of 6.

No. 44C. AA Guide Directing Traffic — £75

With blue sash etc. Price 3d. Issued October 1935. Deleted 1940. Box of 6.

No. 44D. AA Guide Saluting — £75

With blue sash etc. Price 3d. Issued October 1935. Deleted 1940. 36mm. DC. Box of 6.

No. 007. Set of Two Petrol Pump Attendants — £15 £8 £4

Male and female with white coats. Price 10d. Issued October 1960. Deleted 1967. Plastic. Average height 35mm.

No. 008. Fire Station Personnel — £25 £10 £5

Set of six figures in blue uniforms. Complete with length of hose. Price 3/-. Issued April. Deleted 1964. 35mm. Plastic.

No. 009. Service Station Personnel — £35 £15 £10

Set of eight figures mainly in white. Price 3/9d. Issued June 1962. Deleted 1967. Average height 35mm. Plastic.

No. 010. Road Maintenance Set — £15 £10 £5

Set of six figures in various colours with set of road signs etc. Price 5/-. Issued May 1962. Deleted 1964. Average height 35mm.

No. 012. Postman — £75

Blue with bag and badge etc. Price 9d. Issued April 1952. Deleted 1960. Average height 35mm. DC. Box of 6.

MODEL	M/B	M/U	G/C

Set No. 1. Station Staff £75

Six figures in set. Price 1/6d. Issued
1934. Deleted 1940. Pre-war only.

Set No. 2. Farmyard
**   Animals** £75 – –

Set of six figures. Price 2/-. Issued
1934. Deleted 1940. Reissued 1948.
Deleted 1956.

Set No. 3. Passengers £50 – –

Price 1/-. Issued 1934. Deleted 1940.
Pre-war set only.

Set No. 4. Engineering Staff £50 – –

Set of six figures. Price 1/6d. Issued
1934. Deleted 1940. Pre-war only.

Set No. 5. Train and Hotel
**   Staff** £75 – –

Set of six figures. Price 2/-. Issued
1934. Deleted 1940. Reissued 1948.
Deleted 1960.

Set No. 6. Shepherd Set £125 – –

This set was issued pre-war and post-
war, with a set of six figures. Price
2/-. Issued 1934/35. Deleted 1940.
Reissued 1948. Deleted 1960.

FIRE ENGINES AND STATIONS

Fire engines have always played an important part in the
world of collectors. Having one of every model in this range,
I know how magnificent the models and stations look when
fully displayed. Many of the first models were never
individually boxed, and for these I quote mint and good
condition only.

No. 25h . Streamlined Fire
**   Engine** – £65 £20

Red. Price 9d. Issued April 1936.
Deleted 1940. 101mm. DC/RT/TP.

No. 25H. Streamlined Fire
**   Engine** – £45 £5

Red. Supplied in boxes of 6. Price
2/9d. Issued 1948. Renumbered 1954
as 250. Deleted 1960/62. 101mm.
DC/RT/TP.

No. 25k. Streamlined Fire Engine

| | | £175 | £50 |

Red, with six tin-plate firemen. Price 5/6d. Issued 1938. Deleted 1940. 101mm. DC/RT/TP.

No. 250. Streamlined Fire Engine

| £95 | £25 | £15 |

Red with silver ladder and grey bell. Price 3/2d. Issued 1954. Deleted 1962. This was the reissue of 25H. 99mm. DC/TP/RT.

No. 259. Fire Engine

| £65 | £20 | £10 |

Red with 'Fire Brigade' on each side. With bell and on-detachable ladder. Price 5/9d. Issued November 1961. Deleted 1970. 115mm. DC/TP/P/RT.

No. 263. Airport Fire Rescue Tender

| £95 | £20 | £10 |

Golden yellow livery with ladder and words 'Airport' and 'Rescue' on the sides in white letter with red base, plus '51' on doors at each side. With red hubs, silver bumpers and white interior. Price £2.75p. Issued 177mm. DC/P. This model was the same basic casting as 266, ERF.

No. 266. ERF Fire Tender

| £80 | £20 | £10 |

With removable extending ladder with wheels. Red livery. Price £2.99p. Issued 1976. Deleted 1980. 223mm. DC/P.

No. 271. Ford Transit Fire Appliance

| £80 | £20 | £10 |

Redesign of model 286. Red with automatic hose and rewind system. Price £2.25p. Issued 1975. Deleted 1977. 129mm. DC/P.

No. 276. Airport Fire Tender

| £60 | £30 | £15 |

Red with words 'Airport Fire Control' on sides. Model also appeared with the 'Fire Brigade' transfers of 259. Mint and boxed model is rare. With bell, flashing roof lights and rotating roof extinguisher with foam. Price 10/6d. Issued August 1962. Deleted 1970. 120mm. DC/P/RT/TP.

No. 282. Land Rover Fire Appliance

£65   £20   £10

Red with plastic Speediwheels and the words 'Fire Service' on sides. Price £1.25p. Issued 1973. Deleted 1978. 119mm.

No. 282. Land Rover Fire Appliance

£150   £50   £25

Dark red with the words 'Danske Redingskorps'. Issued in Denmark 1974. Deleted 1978. 119mm.

No. 285. Merryweather Marquis Fire Tender

£75   £40   £20

First issue is in metallic red and is worth double the normal red livery which was issued from 1974. With silver trim, wheels etc. With operating water pump and extending ladder with twin bells. Complete with hose. Price 14/11d. Issued 1964, then in 1974 (plain red). Deleted 1980. 177mm. DC/P.

No. 285. Merryweather Marquis Fire Engine

£175   £60   £30

Plain red for the Danish market. Issued 1974. Deleted 1978. 177mm. DC/P.

No. 286. Ford Transit Fire Appliance

£95   £30   £15

Red with yellow ladder and twin bells on roof. With automatic hose rewind with opening doors at side and rear. Words 'Fire Services' and badge on sides. With silver wheels and bumpers etc. The 1975 version has second grille and one piece rear door. Price 9/11d. Issued 1962. Reissued as 271 in 1975. Deleted 1980. 122m.

MODEL	M/B	M/U	G/C
No. 286. Ford Transit	£175	£60	£30

Red. Made for the Danish market in
1974. Deleted 1978. 122mm.
DC/Plastic.

No. 384. Convoy Fire Rescue Truck	£65	£30	£15

Red with removable ladder, etc. Price
£2.75p. Issued 1977. Deleted 1980.
126mm.

No. 555. Fire Engine with Extending Ladder	£95	£30	£15

Red and silver. Renumbered with bell
and brown ladder. Price 9/6d. Issued
November 1952. Finally deleted 1970.
145mm. RT/TP. Model with brown
ladder worth double.

No. 954. Fire Station	£75	£40	£20

Red, yellow and brick. Words 'Dinky
Toys Fire Station' on front and
station has clear plastic roof. Price
21/-. Issued November 1961. Deleted
1964. P. Base 252mm x 203mm.

No. 955. Fire Engine with Extending Ladder	£125	£50	£25

Red and silver. Metal and then later
with plastic hubs. With windows from
1960. Silver or grey hoses (non-
working). Price 7/6d. Issued January
1955 as renumbering of 555. Deleted
1970. 145mm. DC/TP/RT.

No. 956. Turntable Fire Escape with Windows	£175	£80	£20

Red; yellow. Also in blue, worth
double. Made in metal and later in
plastic with windows from 1960
(Bedford cab). All angle ladder action.
Price 13/-. Issued February 1958.
Deleted 1970. 200mm.

No. 956. Berliet Fire Escape	£250		

Red and silver. Made for Danish
market. Price £1.55p. Issued 1974.
Deleted 1978. 200mm. DC/P.

No. 956A. Turntable Fire Escape	£175	£80	£20

The first 956 model was replaced by
this turntable fire escape with a
French Dinky Berliet Cab. Turntable

and escape are the same as those used on the Bedford one. Price £2.75p. Issued 1970. Deleted 1972. 200mm. DC/P

	M/B	M/U	G/C
No. 3276. Mogul Fire Engine	£75	£25	£15

This model has a strong towing hook in front and a trailing hook behind. In red and black with a large extending ladder and fire hose. It has extra robust axles and tough working parts, originally made for the toddlers of the collecting world. This is definitely a Dinky product and advertised in their catalogues. Not a very successful product. Price £2.25p. Issued 1978. Deleted 1980. 390mm. P.

CRANES, EXCAVATORS AND BULLDOZERS WITH CONSTRUCTION SITE VEHICLES

MODEL	M/B	M/U	G/C
No. 380. Convoy Skip Truck	£50	£20	£10

Green and orange with thick black bumpers. Yellow chassis with orange rear from 1978. Model was the first of five large toys. Price 97p. Issued 1977. Deleted 1980. 112mm. D.

	M/B	M/U	G/C
No. 382. Convoy Dumper Truck	£50	£20	£10

Yellow chassis and cab with white interior and orange body. With black bumpers. Price 75p. Issued 1977. Deleted 1980. 118mm.

	M/B	M/U	G/C
No. 382. Convoy Dumper Truck	£40	£15	£5

Red cab and red chassis with fawn body. Price 95p. Issued 1978. Deleted 1980. 118mm.

	M/B	M/U	G/C
No. 430. Johnson 2-Ton Dumper	£55	£20	£10

Orange chassis, red skip, blue driver and silver hubs. Price £1.75p. Issued 1976. Deleted 1980. 106mm. DC/P.

	M/B	M/U	G/C
No. 432. Foden Tipping Lorry	£55	£20	£10

White cab, lemon body and lemon plastic wheels on black chassis and lemon bumpers. Price £1.25p. Issued 1976. Deleted 1980. 175mm. DC/P.

No. 437. Muir Hill 2 WL Loader

£50   £20   £10

Red with full working parts. Price
8/6d. Issued 1962. Deleted 1979.
121mm. DC/P.

No. 25c. Flat Truck

–   £350   £150

Dark brown or green with open
chassis and tin-plate radiator (Type 1)
with no lights. Price 9d. Issued 1934.
Deleted 1940. 105mm. DC/TP/RT.
Not in individual box.

No. 25c. Flat Truck

–   £250   £100

Green. With open chassis, diecast
radiator (Type 2) and lights. Price 9d.
Issued 1938. Deleted 1940. 105mm.
DC/RT/TP.

No. 25C. Flat Truck

–   £125   £50

Green. With plain chassis, diecast
radiator (Type 3) with lights. Price
1/6d. Issued 1946. Deleted 1947.
105mm. DC/RT.

No. 25C. Flat Truck

–   £95   £45

Orange, with moulded chassis, diecast
radiator (Type 4) with lights and
bumpers. Price 2/-. Issued 1947.
Deleted 1950. 110mm. DC/RT.

No. 25M. Bedford End Tipper

–   £95   £45

Orange, red and cream. With tail
board hinges. With tipping handle.
Price 5/9d. Issued March 1948.
Deleted 1954 when renumbered 410.
98mm. DC/TP/RT.

No. 25X. Breakdown Lorry with Working Crane

£250   £100   £50

Renumbered 430 in 1954. Orange and
green. With the words 'Dinky Service'

MODEL	M/B	M/U	G/C

on sides. Price 5/6d. Issued 1950.
Deleted 1954. 123mm. DC/TP/RT.

No. 30e. Bedford Breakdown Van

	–	£275	£100

Red, green or grey. With rear window
in cab and wire hook on crane. Price
9d. Issued August 1935. Deleted
1940. 92mm. DC/RT.

No. 30E. Bedford Breakdown Van

	£95	£40	£20

Red, green or grey. With no rear
window, although I have seen models
which have. Wire hook on crane.
Price 5/11d. Issued 1946. Deleted
1948. 92mm. DC/RT.

No. 30M. Rear Tipping Wagon

	£65	£20	£10

Orange. Handle tips and tailboard
hinges. Price 2/11d. Issued 1950.
Deleted 1954 when renumbered 414.
99mm. DC/TP/RT.

No. 410. Bedford End Tipper

	£95	£40	£20

Brown and yellow or blue and yellow.
Renumbering of 25M. The rear tips
by handle and the tailboard hinges.
Price 5/3d. Issued 1954/55. Deleted
1963. 97mm. DC/TP/RT.

No. 410. Bedford End Tipper

	£85	£20	£10

Red and cream. Exactly as 410 but
with new colours and windows. Price
6/11d. Issued 1963/4. Deleted 1970.
97mm. DC/TP/RT.

No. 430. Commer Breakdown Lorry

	£125	£50	£25

Renumbering of 25X Working Crane.
Green and orange. With the words
'Dinky Service' on sides. Price 4/11d.
Issued 1954. Deleted 1964. 123mm.
DC/TP/RT.

No. 430. Commer Breakdown Lorry

	£95	£30	£15

Red and grey. With the words 'Dinky
Service' on sides. With windows.
Price 7/6d. Issued 1964. Deleted
1969. 123mm. DC/TP/RT/P.

MODEL	M/B	M/U	G/C

No. 434. Bedford TK Crash Truck

$85 £40 £20

White with green flash. Words 'Top Rank Motorway Services' on sides. With operating winch and four wheels. Price 7/11d. Issued April 1964. Deleted 1970. 122mm. DC/RT/P.

No. 435. Bedford TK Tipper

£95 £40 £20

Light grey, blue and orange. Rear tips and three flaps let down. With six wheels. Price 7/11d. Issued May 1964. Deleted 1971. 120mm. DC/RT/P.

No. 437. Muir Hill 2 WL Loader

£50 £20 £10

Yellow with red wheels and driver. Silver grey or grey trim. Black plastic wheels also appear on this model. Price 12/11d. Issued 1970. Deleted 1978. 121mm. DC/P.

No. 438. Ford D800 Tipper Truck

£50 £20 £10

Red cab with opening doors and white interior with yellow body on tipper and grey chassis with yellow wheels. Hinged tailboard. Price 12/11d. Issued 1970. Replaced in 1977 by No. 440 which had sealed doors. Deleted 1978. 132mm.

No. 439. Ford D800 Snow Plough Tipper Truck

£95 £50 £20

Purple, red and yellow with white wheels and tipping body. Price 12/11d. Issued 1971. Deleted 1977. 194mm. DC/P.

MODEL	M/B	M/U	G/C

No. 440. Ford D800 Tipper Truck

| | £50 | £20 | £10 |

Orange and lemon with white cab interior and grey chassis. Price £1.25p. Issued 1977. Deleted 1978. 132mm. DC/P.

No. 442. Land Rover Breakdown Crane

| | £75 | £40 | £20 |

White and red with word 'Motorway Rescue' on sides. Price £1.25p. Issued 1973. Deleted 1980. 121mm. DC/P.

No. 442. Land Rover Breakdown Crane

| | £125 | £150 | £25 |

White and red. Made for Dutch market only. Issued 1974. Deleted 1978. 121mm. DC/P.

No. 561. Blaw-Knox Bulldozer

| | £60 | £30 | £15 |

Red with lifting blades and rubber treads. Price 11/6d. Issued January 1949. Deleted 1949. Renumbered 961 in 1954. Deleted 1975. 138mm. DC/TP.

No 562. Muir Hill Dumper Truck

| | £65 | £30 | £15 |

Yellow. Price 9/-. Issued September 1948. Deleted 1954 when renumbered 962. 105mm. DC/TP.

No. 563. Heavy Tractor

| | £65 | £30 | £15 |

Red. Also in blue with pale blue wheels and green tracks, worth double. Rubber tracks. Price 6/9d. Issued 1948. Deleted 1954 when renumbered 963.

No. 564. Elevator Loader

| | £45 | £20 | £10 |

Yellow and blue with all working parts and rubber treads. Price 22/6d. Issued 1962. Renumbered 964 in 1954. 230mm. DC.

No. 571. Coles Mobile Crane

| | £95 | £50 | £25 |

Yellow and black. Crane works by handle. Price 9/11d. Issued December 1949. Renumbered 971 in 1954. 160mm. DC/TP/RT.

MODEL	M/B	M/U	G/C

No. 752. Goods Yard Crane

	£85	£30	£15

Blue and yellow with working crane.
Price 13/9d. Issued February 1953.
Renumbered 973 in 1954. Base
100mm. Height 195mm. DC.

No. 924. Aveling Barford
'Centaur' Dump Truck

	£65	£30	£15

Red cab and white interior and yellow
tipper with hydraulic system. Red
hubs and thick black ribbed wheels.
Price £1.25p. Issued 1973. Deleted
1978. 180mm. DC/P.

No. 958. Snow Plough with
Guy Warrior Chassis

	£75	£30	£15

Yellow and black. Four wheels with
one spare and blue roof light. With
lifting plough blade and tailboard
hinged. Price 12/6d. Issued January
1961. Deleted 1966. 195mm.
DC/TP/RT.

No. 959. Foden Dump Truck
with Bulldozer Blade

	£95	£50	£25

Red and silver with six wheels and
lifting blade. The rear tips. Price
16/3d. Issued October 1961. Deleted
1969. 169mm. DC/RT.

No. 960. Albion Lorry
Concrete Mixer

	£75	£40	£20

Orange, yellow and blue. Or red,
yellow and blue. The latter livery
worth at least double. Cement hopper
rotates and tips. Six wheels and one
spare. Price 8/9d. Issued August 1960.
Deleted 1969. 128mm. DC/TP/RT/P.

No. 961. Blaw-Knox Bulldozer

	£75	£50	£20

Red and later in yellow. Also in green
and orange which livery is worth
double. With driver, elevating blade
and rubber tracks. Price 12/6d. Issued
January 1955. Deleted 1964.
Renumbering of 561. 138mm.
DC/TP.

MODEL	M/B	M/U	G/C

No. 962 Muir Hill Dumper Truck

$65 $30 $15

Yellow model had metal hubs and black rubber tyres from 1962. Price 6/9d. Issued 1955. Deleted 1964. 105mm.

No. 963. Blaw-Knox Heavy Tractor

$65 $40 $20

Red and later in yellow. Also later in orange. With rubber tracks and driver. Renumbering of 563. Price 7/9d. Issued January 1955. Deleted 1959. 116mm. DC/TP.

No. 963. Road Grader

$55 $20 $10

Red, yellow and black. With silver shovel and hubs. Price £1.55p. Issued 1970. Deleted 1978. 238mm. DC/P.

No. 964. Elevator Loader

$65 $30 $15

Yellow. Also in blue, worth double. With all working parts and rubber tracks on loader. Renumbering of 564. Price 18/-. Issued January 1955. Deleted 1969. 230mm. DC.

No. 965. Euclid Rear Dump Truck

$95 $50 $20

Yellow with grey background, or red background. Grey livery is worth double. With the words 'Euclid Stone Ore Earth' on the door and sides. Price 9/6d. Issued 1955. Deleted 1956. 142mm. DC/RT.

No. 966. Multi Bucket Unit

$65 $30 $15

Yellow with grey buckets. Six wheels and all working parts. Price 10/9d. Issued December 1960. Deleted 1964. 115mm. DC/RT.

No. 967. Muir Hill Loader and Trencher

$65 $30 $15

Orange and black, also in yellow and black. Price £1.45p. Issued 1973. Deleted 1978. 163mm. DC/P.

No. 970. Jones Fleetmaster Cant Crane

Red and white, or metallic red and white from 1971. With the words 'Jones' Fleetmaster' on the side and the word 'Jones' shown clearly on a red disc on the spare wheel. Price 21/-. Issued 1967. Deleted 1977.

	M/B	M/U	G/C
Red and white	£75	£40	£20
Metallic red	£60	£30	£15

No. 971. Coles Mobile Crane

£60 £30 £15

Yellow and black. Crane worked by handle. Renumbering of 571. Price 9/11d. Issued January 1955. Deleted 1966. 160mm. DC/TP/H.

No. 972. Coles 20 Ton Lorry Mounted Crane

£95 £50 £25

Red and orange with black and white stripes. With working crane, orange wheels and black tyres. With driver and the words 'Coles Giant Crane' on sides. Price 20/3d. Issued 1955. Deleted 1970. 245mm. DC/RT/TP.

No. 973. Goods Yard Crane

£75 £30 £15

Yellow and blue worth double. Price 11/6d. Issued January 1955. Deleted 1959. Base 100mm. Height 195mm. DC.

No. 973. Eaton Vale Artic Tractor Shovel

£55 £20 £10

Red and mustard yellow, with silver hubs and large black ribbed wheels. Price £1.35p. Issued 1973. Deleted 1978. 178mm. DC/P.

No. 975. Ruston Bucyrus Excavator

£175 £50 £30

Red, yellow and grey. With rubber tracks. Price 27/6d. Issued October 1963. Deleted 1968. 190mm. DC/TP/P.

MODEL	M/B	M/U	G/C

No. 976. Michigan 180-111 Tractor Dozer

£75 £30 £15

Yellow and orange with driver. With removable cab and engine hatch and the word 'Michigan' on each side. Price 18/11d. Issued 1968. Deleted 1977. 147mm. DC/P.

No. 977. Servicing Platform Vehicle

£125 £50 £25

Red and cream with side supports which fold down and elevating crane etc. With six wheels and one spare. The chassis is an international size. Price 13/6d. Issued September 1960. Deleted 1964. 197mm. DC.

No. 977. Shovel Dozer

£50 £20 £10

Yellow and black, with red roof and red and silver shovel. Silver or black plastic tracks. Price £1.99p. Issued 1973. Deleted 1978. 151mm. DC/P.

No. 980. Coles Hydra Truck 150T

£75 £30 £15

Dark grey and mustard. With silver hubs and working crane. Price £2.25p. Issued 1973. Deleted 1978. 210mm. DC/P.

No. 984. Atlas Digger

£75 £40 £20

Yellow. Price £2.25p. Issued 1974. Deleted 1978. 247mm. DC/P.

No. 986. Mighty Antar Low Loader and Propeller

£175 £80 £40

Red and grey. With driver and plastic propeller load. 6 x 6 wheels. Price 14/11d. Issued June 1959. Deleted 1964. 295mm. DC/RT/P.

No. 3209. Mogul Heavy Duty Dumper

£50 £20 £10

Orange and black with white plastic wheels. Price £1.75p. Issued 1974. Deleted 1980. 330mm. DC/P.

No. 3299. Mogul Mobile Crane

	£50	£20	£10

Bright lemon and black with silver
wheels. Price £2.25p. Issued 1974.
Deleted 1980. 337mm. DC/P.

ROAD ROLLERS

No. 25P. Aveling Barford Roller

	£250

First issue had no individual box and
is a very dark green. Cast in H/D/SW.
Price 5/9d. Issued 1948. Deleted and
renumbered 251 in 1954. 110mm.
DC/TP. Were delivered to shops in
boxes of 6.

No. 25P. Aveling Barford Roller

	£75	£40	£20

Model had a box but first models
were still very dark green and are
worth double the light green model.
Price 5/9d. Issued 1948. Renumbered
251 in 1954. 110mm. DC/TP.

No. 251. Aveling Barford Roller

	£65	£40	£10

Green and red, and grey with red
rollers. Front roller swivel. Price
4/10d. Issued May 1955. Deleted
1963. 110mm. DC/TP/D/S/W.

No. 279. Aveling Barford Roller

	£65	£40	£10

Orange and green, with two base-
metal rollers and grey plastic engine
cover. Price 9/11d. Issued 1965.
Deleted 1978. 116mm. DC/Plastic.

No. 279. Aveling Barford Roller

£65 £30 £15

Lower body in orange and cab in yellow with black roof but the cab does not lift off. With silver rollers and grey plastic engine cover. The first bubble packs were introduced in this year and some were in boxes. The boxed items are worth double. Price 9/11d. Issued 1971. Deleted 1980. 116mm. DC/P.

STREET SIGNS, LETTERBOXES AND FURNITURE

No. 12a. GPO Pillar Box

£75

Red. With the words 'Post Office', 'G.R.' and crown. Price 3d. Issued June 1935. Deleted 1940. Height 50mm. DC. Boxes of 6.

No. 12b. Air Mail Pillar Box

£75

Blue. With the words 'Air Mail', 'G.R.' and crown. Price 3d. Issued June 1935. Deleted 1940. Height 50mm. DC. Boxes of 6.

No. 12c. Telephone Box

£120

Cream and silver. Price 4d. Issued April 1936. Deleted 1940. Height 62mm. DC. Boxes of 6.

No. 12C. Telephone Box

£100

Red and silver. Price 1/-. Issued 1948. Renumbered 750 in 1954. Deleted 1968. Height 58mm. DC. Boxes of 6.

No. 46. Pavement Set

£55

Grey cardboard. Price 6d. Issued 1937. Deleted 1940.

No. 46. Pavement Set

£30

Cardboard, grey in colour. Price 1/9d. Issued 1948. Deleted 1950.

No. 47. Roadsigns

Twelve in all. Black white and red.
They were also bought in two for 3d.
Contains: 47E 30 Mile Limit; 47F
De-restriction; 47G School; 47H Steep
Hill; 47K Bend; 47M Left Hand
Corner; 47N Right Hand Corner; 47P
Road Junction; 47Q Right Hand
Corner; 47R Main Road Ahead; 47S
Crossing, No Gates; 47T
Roundabout. Price 1/6d. Issued
December 1935. Deleted 1940. DC.

Set   £75

No. 47. Post-War Road Signs

Set of 12. Contains: 47E; 47F; 47G;
47H; 47K; 47M; 47N; 47P; 47Q;
47R; 47S and 47T. Set was made
from pre-war castings in 1947. Price
for set 2/3d. For packet of two 5d.
Issued 1947. Deleted 1954.

Set   £50

No. 47a. Four-Face Traffic Lights

                   £50

Black and white. Price 3d. Issued
June 1935. Deleted 1940. DC. Boxes
of 6.

No. 47A. Four-Face Traffic Lights

                   £50

Black and white. Price 4d. Issued
1947. Deleted 1954. Height 62mm.
DC. Boxes of 6.

No. 47b. Three-Face Traffic Lights

                   £50

Price 3d. Issued 1935. Deleted 1940.
DC. Boxes of 6.

No. 48B. Three-Face Traffic Lights

                   £35

Post-war. Price 4d. Issued 1947.
Deleted 1954. Boxes of 6.

No. 47c. Two-Face Traffic Lights (right angle)

                   £55

Black and white. Price 3d. Issued
October 1935. Deleted 1940. DC.
Boxes of 6.

MODEL	M/B	M/U	G/C

No. 47c. Two-Face Traffic Lights (back to back) £50

Black and white. Price 3d. Issued August 1935. Deleted 1940. DC. Boxes of 6.

No. 47C. Two-Face Traffic Lights £45

Post-war. Black and white. Price 4d. Issued 1947. Deleted 1954. DC. Boxes of 6.

No. 47C. Two-Face Traffic Signs (back to back) £35

Post-war. Black and white. Price 4d. Issued 1947. Deleted 1954. DC. Boxes of 6.

No. 47d. Belisha Beacon (Safety) £50

Black, white and orange. Price 3d. Issued June 1935. Deleted 1940. Boxes of 6.

No. 47D. Belisha Beacon £35

Black, white and orange. Price 4d. Issued 1946. Deleted 1954. Height 51mm. DC. Boxes of 6.

No. 750. Telephone Call Box £75

Red. Price 1/-. Renumbering of 12C (post-war) in 1954. Issued 1960. Height 58mm. DC. Boxes of 6.

No. 753. Police Controlled Crossing £25 £10 £5

Grey base and black and white. A police controlled crossing with a revolving policeman. Price 3/6d. Issued November 1962. Deleted 1967. 151mm. P.

No. 754. Cardboard Pavement Set £15 £8 £4

Vastly different from the pre-war set. Price 2/5d. Issued November 1948. Deleted 1962.

No. 755. Lamp Standard Single Arm £25 £10 £4

Grey and fawn with diecast base and plastic standard. With orange lights. Price 1/11d. Issued March 1960. Deleted 1964. Height 145mm. DC/P.

MODEL	M/B	M/U	G/C

No. 756. Lamp Standard Double Arm

£30 £10 £5

Grey and fawn. Also in yellow and
fawn with orange lights. Price 2/6d.
Issued March 1960. Deleted 1964.
Height 145mm. DC/P.

No. 760. Pillar Box

£65

Red and black. This is a different
casting from 12b, being stouter and
has the 'Post Office' sign above,
'E.II.R'. Price 10d. Issued July 1954.
Deleted 1960. Height 42mm. DC.
Boxes of 6.

No. 763. Poster for Road Hoardings

£15 £8 £4

Various colours in paper (6). Price
2/6d. Issued September 1959. Deleted
1964.

No. 764. Posters for Road Hoardings

£15 £8 £4

Six more paper posters with self-
adhesive labels in various colours and
adverts. Price 9d. Issued September
1959. Deleted 1963.

No. 765. Road Hoardings

£15 £8 £4

Green plastic with the words 'David
Allen & Sons Ltd', complete with six
posters. Price 3/3d. Issued September
1959. Deleted 1964. 205mm.

No. 766. British Road Signs (Country Set)

Set of 6. Price 2/8d. Issued 1960.
Deleted 1964.

Set of 6

£50

No. 767. British Road Signs Country Set B

Set of 6. Price 2/8d. Issued 1960.
Deleted 1964.

Set of 6

£35

MODEL	M/B	M/U	G/C

No. 768. British Road Signs Town Set A

Set of 6. Black, white and red. Price 2/8d. Issued 1960. Deleted 1964. Average height 55mm. DC.

Set of 6	£35		

No. 769. British Road Signs Town Set B

Six signs in black, white and red. Price 2/8d. Issued 1960. Deleted 1964. Average height 55mm. DC.

Set of 6	£35		

No. 771. International Road Signs

Twelve signs in various colours. Price 3/9d. Issued August 1953. Deleted 1965. Average height 35-45mm. DC.

Set of 12	£95		

No. 772. Twenty-four British Road Signs

In various colours. Price 10/6d. Issued 1959. Deleted 1964. Average height 55mm. DC.

Set of 24	£125		

No. 773. Four-Faced Traffic Lights

	–	£5	£2

Black and white. This is the same casting as 47A but without orange beacon on top. Price 1/-. Issued 1959. Deleted 1963. Height 62mm. DC. Never individually boxed.

No. 777. Belisha Beacon

	£45		

Black, white and orange. With the same casting as 47D but without orange beacon on top. Price 8d. Issued 1962. Deleted 1963. DC. Boxes of 6.

No. 787. Building Lighting Kit

	£15	£5	£2

This kit was made for Dinky Toy Buildings. Price 2/11d. Issued 1960. Deleted 1964.

MODEL	M/B	M/U	G/C

No. 788. Spare Bucket for 966 — £10 £4 £2

Grey. Price 1/9d. Issued December
1960. Deleted 1969. 68mm. DC/TP.

No. 790. Imitation Granite Chippings

Made for Dinky Wagons and Hornby
Dublo Railways. Came in clear
packets. Price 9d. Issued 1961.
Deleted 1964.

Packet only — £5

No. 791. Imitation Coal

Made for Dinky Wagons. Came in
clear packets. Price 9d. Issued 1961.
Deleted 1964.

Packet only — £5

No. 792. Packing Cases — £5 £3 £1

Three packing cases and lids in fawn
with the words 'Hornby Dublo' on
sides. Price 1/6d. Issued 1960/61.
Deleted 1969. 30 x 28 x 19mm. P.

No. 793. Pallets

Orange. To be used with 930 Bedford
Pallet Jecta Van. Three in a packet.
Also used with model 404. Price
1/11d. Issued 1960. Deleted 1969.

Packet of 3 — £10

No. 794. Loading Ramp — £12

For the Pullmore Car Transporter.
Price 1/6d. Issued December 1954 or
January 1955. Renumbered 794 in
1960. Deleted 1964.

No. 846. Six Oil Drums

French Dinky import from 1960/61.
Made in France 1959. Equivalent
price 1/4d. Deleted 1970.

Six — £15

No. 847. Six Barrels

French Dinky import from 1960/61.
Equivalent price 1/4d. Made in
France 1959. Deleted 1970.

Six — £15

MODEL	M/B	M/U	G/C

No. 849. Six Packing Cases

French Dinky import from 1960/61.
Equivalent price 1/4d. Made in
France 1959. Deleted 1970.

Six £15

No. 850. Six Crates of Bottles

French Dinky import from 1960/61.
Equivalent price 1/4d. Made in
France 1959. Deleted 1970.

Six £15

No. 851. Pairs Sets (Nos. 846, 847, 849 and 850)

French Dinky imports from 1960/61.
Made in France in 1959. Price 1/6d.
Issued September 1961. Deleted 1970.

Set of 8 £15

No. 0036. 1½ Volt Battery — £5

Novelty collectors' item. To go with
models 276 and 277. Price 5d. Issued
August 1962. Deleted 1964. Not
individually boxed.

No. 0037. Red Lamp £10

Price 5d. Issued December 1962.
Deleted 1964. Not individually boxed.

No. 0038. Blue Lamp £10

Novelty collectors' item. To go with
model 276. Price 10d. Issued August
1962. Deleted 1964. Not individually
packed.

TAXIS

No. 36g. Taxi with Driver — £750 £300

Green. A promotional model for the
Old London Cab Co. Sold or given
away at several taxi stands to tourists.
Word 'Taxi' cast on roof. Price 11d.
Limited issue in 1938. Deleted 1938.
72mm. DC/RT. Not individually
boxed.

MODEL	M/B	M/U	G/C

No. 36g. Taxi with Driver
| | – | £95 | £40 |

Yellow and black or light green and
black. Also royal blue and black. With
open rear window. 'Taxi' cast in roof.
Price 11d. Issued 1938. Deleted 1940.
72mm. DC/RT. Not individually
boxed.

No. 36G. Taxi with Open Rear Window
| | – | £65 | £35 |

Maroon and black, light green and
black, dark green and black. 'Taxi'
cast on roof. Price 2/6d. Issued 1946.
Deleted 1947. 72mm. DC/RT. Not
individually boxed, but packed in
boxes of 6.

No. 36G. Taxi with No Rear Window
| | – | £55 | £25 |

Maroon and black, light green and
black, and dark green and black.
Model also in brown and black and
red and black, rare colours worth
treble. Price 2/9d. Issued 1947.
Deleted 1949. 72mm. DC/RT.

No. 40H. Austin Taxi

Blue or yellow. Early models never
had individual box but were sold in
boxes of 6. 'Taxi' sign on roof. Price
3/10d. Issued November 1951.
Renumbered 254 in 1955. 94mm.
DC/RT.

	M/B	M/U	G/C
Box of 6	£850		
Early model no box	–	£125	£45
Model with first boxes	£95	£50	£25
No. 115. 'U.B.' Taxi	£150	£80	£30

One of the last do or die efforts by
Dinky in 1978 to try and get some
sales. Chassis was adapted from
475/485; and 109 Model T Ford and
made for export only. Box of 120 but
packed in plain cardboard boxes. With
word 'Taxi' on door in medium blue
or dark blue. Body with gold trim on
all doors, bonnet and rear. Solid
yellows wheels and black tyres. A
good investment considering it was
the last Taxi, and one of the last
models ever made by Dinky. Price
£1.35p. Issued 1978. Deleted 1978.
86mm. DC/P.

No. 115. 'U.B.' Taxi

Dark blue and black with yellow mudguards and solid yellow wheels, gold headlights and radiator. A promotional taxi issued by the Taxi Biscuit Company. Another rather vain event to try and get the Dinky Company out of serious trouble near the end of 1979. One had to collect biscuit wrappers to acquire this model and therefore there is no original price but it has a high value in the collector's world being quite rare. Issued and Deleted 1979. 86mm. DC/P. If the box has a 25th Anniversary of the Coronation and franked by an official GPO stamp it is worth more, so I will give the prices for the model without a box, also the model with an ordinary box with a normal GPO stamp and then the price of the boxes with the Coronation stamp upon it.

	M/B	M/U	G/C
Normal stamped box	£150		
Coronation stamped box	£350		
No. 120. Happy Cab	£65	£20	£10

Made from same mould as the 'U.B.' Taxi. With solid wheels in yellow with yellow mudguard, gold radiator and bumper. Base of body is white with upper part in light blue with a white roof and the words 'Happy Cab' in blue, red and yellow. Decked with flowers on bonnet and sides. Price £1.35p. Issued 1978. Deleted 1980. 86mm. DC.

	M/B	M/U	G/C
No. 254. Austin Taxi	£65	£30	£15

Dark blue and also in yellow. 'Taxi' sign on roof. Price 3/5d. Issued 1954. Deleted 1956. 94mm. DC/RT. A very good investment.

	M/B	M/U	G/C
No. 254. Austin Taxi (two-tone)	£75	£45	£20

Green and yellow. 'Taxi' sign on roof. Price 3/5d. Issued January 1956. Deleted 1962/63. 94mm. DC/RT.

	M/B	M/U	G/C
No. 254. Taxi	£275	£100	£50

Black with silver hubs. This was the last livery and model issue of 254. Price 4/11d. Issued 1960. Deleted 1961. 94mm. DC/RT.

MODEL	M/B	M/U	G/C

No. 265. Plymouth U.S. Taxi with Windows

£75 £35 £15

Yellow and mustard with dark or medium red roof. 'Taxi' sign on roof and fare information on sides. Price 5/9d. Issued October 1960. Deleted 1964. Replaced by 266 in 1965. 108mm.
DC/TP/P/RT/LHD/SW/SS/S/W.

No. 266. Plymouth Metro Cab

£75 £35 £15

Yellow with red roof. Canadian version of 265. '450 Metro Cab' on doors. Price 5/11d. Issued 1965. Deleted 1967. 108mm. DC.

No. 268. Renault Dauphine Mini Cab

£65 £30 £15

Red. With windows and advertisements. This was a French Dinky casting No. 24E/524 but with English wheels and baseplate. Mini cab version only made in England. Price 3/3d. Issued June 1962. Deleted 1967. 12mm. DC/TP/P/RT.

No. 278. Plymouth Yellow Cab

£75 £30 £15

Bright yellow with red interior and 'Yellow Cab' transfers on doors and roof sign plus aerial. Price £1.49p. Issued 1978. Deleted 1980. 134.5mm. DC/RT/P.

No. 282. Austin 1800 Taxi

£65 £30 £15

Medium blue with red interior and 'Taxi' sign on roof. White bonnet and boot. Opening boot and bonnet. Price 6/11d. Issued 1966. Deleted 1969. 101mm.

No. 284. London Taxi

£65 £30 £15

Black with silver trim and opening doors. All plastic Speediwheels. Metal wheels and rubber tyre Speediwheels

from 1978. Price £1.25p. Issued 1972.
Deleted 1980. 112mm.

No. 284/SJ. Silver Jubilee Taxi Special

£150   £75   £35

Silver with royal crest on the doors.
Issued in 1977 for the commemoration
of the Silver Jubilee. Only a limited
number were made available and were
soon snapped up by tourists and eager
collectors. Price £1.55p. 112mm.
DC/P. Very scarce and a good
investment.

TRAINS

No. 16. LNER Train Set
£75   £40   £20

Price 4/11d. Issued 1946. Deleted
1950.

No. 16. Silver Jubilee Set
£75   £40   £20

Price 1/6d. Issued 1935. Deleted
1940.

No. 16. Train Set in British Rail Colours
£150   £75   £25

Price 12/6d. Issued 1954. Deleted
1959.

No. 16z. Streamlined Diesel Articulated Train
£95   £50   £25

An imported French Dinky in 1935.
Price 2/11d. Deleted 1940.

No. 17. Diecast Passenger Train Set
£65   £30   £15

This had a miniature diecast model
17A Locomotive and Tender with a
coach and guards van. Price 2/3d.
Issued 1935. Deleted 1940.

No. 18. Goods Train Set
£65   £30   £15

With tank locomotive and three
wagons. Price 1/9d. Issued 1935.
Deleted 1940.

MODEL	M/B	M/U	G/C

No. 19. Mixed Goods Train Set

	M/B	M/U	G/C
	£75	£40	£20

With tank locomotive, one wagon, a petrol tanker and a lumber wagon. Price 1/11d. Issued 1935. Deleted 1940.

No. 20. Passenger Train Set

£150 £75 £35

Containing tank locomotive, two coaches and a guard's van. Price 2/6d. Issued 1935. Deleted 1940.

No. 21. Modelled Miniatures Set

£145 £75 £25

Price 1/11d. Issued 1935. Deleted 1940.

No. 26. GWR Rail Car

– £125 £45

Red with cream roof. This model runs on small plastic bobbins. Price 6d. Issued April 1934. Deleted 1948. 106mm. DCP. Not individually boxed.

No. 26z. Diesel Rail Car

– £125 £45

Cream and orange or white and yellow. Runs on small bobbin stand. Price 5d. Imported from France 1937. Issued in France 1934. Deleted 1940.

No. 784. Dinky Goods Train Set

£55 £30 £15

Non-motorised and no track required, but may be used on OO or HO track. The engine was in blue with 'G.E.R.' on side. Length 115mm. With yellow truck and red trucks, both 92mm each. Price £1.55p. Issued 1972. Deleted 1975.

No. 798. Express Passenger Set

£75 £50 £20

Price 10/6d. Issued 1954. Deleted 1959.

VANS

Note: Many of these models were never individually boxed. Hence M/U and G prices only.

MODEL	M/B	M/U	G/C

No. 14z. Three-Wheel Delivery Van

Green with opening and driver cast in. White tyres in rubber stamped 'Dunlop'. Made in France from 1935 to 1939 with black or white Dunlop tyres on metal hubs. From 1940 to 1949 model had all metal wheels and from 1950 to 1952 with black 'M' tyres. First version only imported. Price 10d. Imported 1937 to 1940. 70mm. DC/RT.

Dunlop	–	£125	£50
All metal	–	£95	£35
'M'	–	£65	£25

No. 22d. Delivery Van

Various colour schemes to this model. Best known are grey or blue and blue and yellow two-tone, with no headlights on tin-plate radiator. Two distinct types of model. Hornby series came first between December 1933 and April 1934, Dinky came after, from 1935 to 1936. Price 8d. 83mm with metal wheels. DC/TP.

Hornby series	–	£650	£250
Dinky toys	–	£550	£150

No. 22d. Delivery Van with Morris Cab

Meccano type in blue and yellow with metal wheels. No headlights on tin-plate radiator. With the words 'Meccano. Engineering for Boys' on each side in red. This colour is very rare. More common is green with gold and red lettering. I will give prices for each colour. Strictly speaking, this model is of the 28 series Type 1 Class as it appeared in the 28/2 Dinky delivery vans set. Although Gibson actually mentions the 28 Type 1 Vans as having rubber

tyres on metal hubs, as distinct from
the 22 series van, which had solid
metal wheels, I dispute this. All the
26 Type 1 Vans I have come across
and valued have had the same solid
metal wheels as the 22 series and are
definitely cast in lead. Consequently,
no fatigue is possible. With regard to
the Meccano van, I would be
surprised if any collectors have the
model in blue and yellow. These were
snapped up by the very fortunate few.
I have only seen one. This is one of
the most precious items in the whole
Dinky range. Sold in sets of six as
well as being sold in the 28/2 set of
six. Price 9d. Issued May 1934.
Deleted 1936. 83mm. DC/TP.

Blue and yellow	–	£2500	£1000
Green with red and gold lettering	–	£550	£350

No. 25b. Covered Wagon 'Meccano'

Gold with red on sides. With
advertising 'Meccano Engineering for
Boys' in black. Model has an open
chassis, diecast radiator, with lights as
Type 2. Price 6d. Issued 1938/39.
Deleted 1940. 105mm. DC/TP/RT.

Pre-war	–	£250	£100
Post-war	–	£195	£75

No. 25f. Market Gardener's Van

	–	£350	£150

Although I use the term 'van', this
model is an open lorry with slatted
sides and its successor is called a farm
produce wagon. Light green, dark
green, dark blue with black chassis
and there are other colours connected
with this model. Very dark green is
quite rare and worth double. With
black open chassis, tin-plate radiator
and no lights as Type 1. Price 9d.
Issued April 1934. Deleted October
1938. 107mm. DC/QT/TP.

No. 25f. Market Gardener's Van

Green or black chassis and yellow
body. Model has an open chassis with
diecast radiator and lights as Type 2.

MODEL	M/B	M/U	G/C

Type 2 trucks also appeared briefly after the war in 1946 until they were replaced by Type 3, where only the axle thicknesses were different. Price 9d. Issued 1938. Deleted 1940. 105mm. DC/RT.

Pre-war	–	£200	£100
Post-war	–	£150	£75

No. 25F. Market Gardener's Van

	–	£75	£25

Green with black plain chassis, diecast radiator with lights as Type 3 model. Price 9d. Issued 1946. Deleted 1947. 110mm. DC/RT.

No. 25F. Market Gardener's Van

	–	£65	£15

Yellow with black moulded chassis, diecast radiator with lights and bumper Type 4 model. Price 9d. Issued 1947. Deleted 1950. 110mm. DC/RT.

No. 28a. Delivery Van

See 22D Meccano Van for general details on Type 1/28 series. With words 'Hornby Trains British and Guaranteed' in gold lettering on sides and Hornby train in yellow. Type 1: has tin-plate radiator. Price 9d. Issued April 1934. Deleted 1936. 84mm. Type 2: a Ford 7 model. Has rubber tyres and cast in Zamac so suffers badly from fatigue. Divide price by five for fatigued mint or good examples. Price 6d. Issued August 1935. Deleted 1938. 81mm. Both models DC/RT/TP.

Type 1	–	£550	£350
Type 2	–	£350	£200

No. 28a. Delivery Van

	–	£750	£250

Yellow. The words 'Golden Shred Marmalade' with the design in red and blue. Price 6d. Issued April 1936. Deleted 1940. 84mm. DC/RT/TP.

No. 28b. Delivery Van. 'Pickfords' Type 1

	–	£750	£250

Blue. With the words 'Pickfords Removals and Storages. Over 100

Branches' in gold lettering. Price 9d.
Issued 1934. Deleted 1936. 84mm.
DC/RT.

No. 28b. Delivery Van.
'Pickfords' Type 2

– £550 £250

Removal van in blue. Words as Type
1. Price 6d. Issued 1935. Deleted
1938. 81mm. DC/RT.

No. 28b. Delivery Van.
'Seccotine' Type 2

– £550 £250

Blue. With the words 'Seccotine
Sticks Everything' in gold letters.
Price 6d. Issued 1936. Deleted 1940.
81mm. DC/RT.

No. 28b. Delivery Van.
Bedford 'Seccotine' Type 3

– £450 £200

This model is liable to fatigue. With
the words as on Type 2. Price 6d.
Issued early 1939. Deleted late 1939.
83mm. DC/RT.

No. 28c. Delivery Van.
**'Manchester Guardian'
Type 1**

– £800 £350

Red and brown. With the words
'Manchester Guardian' in gold
lettering. Price 9d. Issued April 1934.
Deleted August 1935. 84mm. DC/RT.

No. 28c. Delivery Van.
**'Manchester Guardian'
Type 2**

– £450 £200

Brown, or reddish brown, which is
worth double. The wording is as on
Type 1. Price 9d. Issued August
1935. Deleted 1940. 84mm. DC/RT.

No. 28d. Delivery Van.
'Oxo' Type 1

– £1000 £350

Blue. With the words 'Oxo, Beef in
Brief' on the left side and 'Oxo, Beef
at its Best' on the right side in gold.
These models were made in very
small production numbers and being
more expensive were found in the
middle class homes only. Very hard to
find in perfect condition. Price 9d.
Issued April 1934. Deleted August
1935. 81mm. DC/RT.

MODEL	M/B	M/U	G/C

**No. 28d. Delivery Van.
'Oxo' Type 2** — £450 £200

Blue. Lettering on sides as on Type 1.
Price 6d. Issued August 1935. Deleted
1939. 81mm. DC/RT.

**No. 28d. Delivery Van.
'Oxo' Type 3** — £350 £200

Blue with the words as on Types 1
and 2 Price 6d. Issued 1939. Deleted
1940. 83mm. DC/RT.

**No. 28e. Delivery Van.
'Ensign' Type 1** — £900 £350

Grey and dark green with words
'Ensign Cameras' on each side, with a
photograph of a camera on the doors.
Other colours do exist. Price 9d.
Issued and deleted 1934. Few models
issued in Type 2 range but most
destroyed in warehouse fire. 84mm.
DC/RT/TP.

**No. 28e. Delivery Van.
'Firestone' Type 1** — £700 £300

Dark blue. The words 'Firestone
Tyres' in red. Price 9d. Issued
September 1934. Deleted August
1935. 84mm. DC/RT.

**No. 28e. Delivery Van.
'Firestone' Type 2** — £450 £200

Dark blue. With lettering as Type 1.
Price 6d. Issued August 1935. Deleted
1939. 81mm. DC/RT.

**No. 28e. Delivery Van.
'Firestone' Type 3** — £450 £200

Dark blue. Price 6d. Issued 1939.
Deleted 1940. 83mm. DC/RT.

**No. 28f. Delivery Van.
'Palethorpes' Type 1** — £650 £350

Light green. Words on sides
'Palethorpes Royal Cambridge' and
design 'Palethorpes Model Factory
Tipton' on rear. Price 9d. Issued
April 1934. Deleted August 1935.
84mm. DC/RT.

**No. 28f. Delivery Van.
'Palethorpes' Type 2** — £450 £250

Light green with the word as Type 1.
Price 6d. Issued August 1935. Deleted
1937. 81mm. DC/RT.

No. 28f. Delivery Van. 'Virol' Type 2

| | – | £450 | £200 |

Yellow. The words 'Give Your Child a Virol Constitution' and the design of Virol on the sides. Price 6d. Issued 1937. Deleted 1940. 81mm. DC/RT.

No. 28g. Delivery Van. 'Kodak' Type 1

| | – | £950 | £350 |

Red and blue. With the words 'Use Kodak Film' and also 'To be Sure' on sides etc. Price 9d. Issued May 1934. Deleted August 1935. 84mm. DC/RT.

No. 28g. Delivery Van. 'Kodak' Type 2

| | – | £350 | £200 |

Yellow. With wording as on Type 1. Price 6d. Issued August 1935. Deleted 1939. 84mm. DC/RT.

No. 28g. Delivery Van. 'Kodak' Type 3

| | – | £450 | £250 |

Yellow. With the wording as on Types 1 and 2. Price 6d. Issued May 1939. Deleted 1940. 83mm. DC/RT.

No. 28h. Delivery Van. 'Sharps' Type 1

| | – | £850 | £350 |

Black and white, also in blue with gold lettering. Other colours do exist but I have only seen the two listed above. With the words 'Sharps Toffees'. Price 9d. Issued 1934. Deleted 1935. 84mm. DC/RT.

No. 28h. Delivery Van. 'Dunlop' Type 2

| | – | £450 | £250 |

Red. With the words 'Dunlop Tyres' in gold letters on sides. Price 6d. Issued August 1935. Deleted 1939. 81mm. DC/RT.

No. 28h. Delivery Van. 'Dunlop' Type 3

| | – | £350 | £200 |

Red with the wording in gold letters as on Type 2. Price 6d. Issued 1939. Deleted 1940. 83mm. DC/RT.

No. 28k. Delivery Van. 'Marsh's' Type 2

| | – | £800 | £350 |

Dark green. Gold design and the words 'Marsh's Sausages'. Price 6d. Issued August 1935. Deleted 1939. 81mm. DC/RT.

MODEL	M/B	M/U	G/C

No. 28k. Delivery Van.
'Marsh's' Type 3   –   £450   £250

Dark green. Wording and design as
on Type 2. Price 6d. Issued 1939.
Deleted 1940. 83mm. DC/RT.

No. 28l. Delivery Van.
'Ensign Cameras' Type 1   –   £900   £350

Black. Design and wording on sides
'Ensign Cameras' in red and gold.
Price 9d. Issued April 1934. Deleted
1934/35. 84mm. DC/RT.

No. 28l. Delivery Van.
'Crawfords' Type 1   –   £900   £350

Red. With the words 'Crawfords
Biscuits' in gold lettering. Price 9d.
Issued May 1934. Deleted 1935.
84mm. DC/RT.

No. 28l. Delivery Van.
'Crawfords' Type 2   –   £450   £250

Red and very dark red. Latter is rare
and worth double. With the wording
in gold as Type 1. Price 6d. Issued
1935. Deleted 1939. 81mm. DC/RT.

No. 28l. Delivery Van.
'Crawfords' Type 3   –   £350   £200

Dark red. With wording as Type 2.
Price 6d. Issued 1939. Deleted 1940.
83mm. DC/RT.

No. 28m. Delivery Van.
'Wakefield's' Type 1   –   £1300   £500

Green. With the wording 'Wakefield's
Castrol Motor Oil' in red. Price 9d.
Issued May 1934. Deleted 1935.
84mm. DC/RT.

No. 28m. Delivery Van.
'Wakefield's' Type 2   –   £450   £250

Green. With wording as Type 1.
Price 6d. Issued August 1935. Deleted
1939. 81mm. DC/RT.

No. 28m. Delivery Van.
'Wakefield's' Type 3   –   £350   £200

Green and dark green, with the latter
being more valuable. Price 6d. Issued
1939. Deleted 1940. 83mm. DC/RT.

MODEL	M/B	M/U	G/C

**No. 28n. Delivery Van.
'Marsh & Baxters' Type 1**   –   £800   £350

Green. With the words 'Marsh &
Baxters Sausages Make a Fine Meal'.
Price 9d. Issued May 1934. Deleted
1935. 84mm. DC/RT.

**No. 28n. Delivery Van.
'Atco' Type 2**   –   £500   £200

Green and dark green. With the
words 'Atco Sales and Service' in
gold, and 'Motor Mowers' in red.
Price 6d. Issued August 1935. Deleted
1938. 81mm. DC/RT.

**No. 28o Delivery Van.
'Raleigh' Type 2**   –   £650   £350

Green. Also green with black roof,
worth more than the ordinary green.
With the words 'Raleigh – the All
Steel Bicycle'. Price 6d. Issued 1936.
Deleted 1937. 81mm. DC/RT.

**No. 28p. Delivery Van.
'Crawfords' Type 2**   –   £500   £200

Maroon. With the words 'Crawfords
Biscuits' in gold. Price 6d. Issued
August 1935. Deleted 1936. 81mm.
DC/RT.

**No. 28r. Delivery Van.
'Swans' Type 2**   –   £500   £200

Black. The words 'Swan Pens' with
design in gold. Price 6d. Issued May
1936. Deleted 1939. 81mm. DC/RT.

**No. 28r. Delivery Van.
'Swans' Type 3**   –   £450   £200

Black. Wording and design as on
Type 2. Price 6d. Issued April 1939.
Deleted 1940. 83mm. DC/RT.

**No. 28s. Delivery Van.
'Fry's' Type 2**   –   £650   £350

Dark brown or chocolate. With
wording and design in gold 'Fry's
Chocolate'. Price 6d. Issued May
1936. Deleted 1940. 81mm. DC/RT.

**No. 28t. Delivery Van.
'Ovaltine' Type 2**   –   £650   £350

Red with the words 'Drink Ovaltine
for Health' in green and black. Price
6d. Issued May 1936. Deleted 1939.
81mm. DC/RT.

MODEL	M/B	M/U	G/C

**No. 28t. Delivery Van.
'Ovaltine' Type 3**   – £450 £200

Red. Wording as Type 2. Price 6d.
Issued 1939. Deleted 1940. 83mm.
DC/RT.

**No. 28u. Delivery Van.
'Carter's' Type 2**   – £650 £350

Red or black. Very rare model. With
words and design 'Carter's Little
Liver Pills'. Price 6d. Issued May
1936. Deleted 1937. 81mm. DC/RT.

**No. 28v. Delivery Van.
'Rington's' Type 2**   – £650 £350

Black with the words 'Rington's Tea'
in green and gold lettering. Model
was specially produced for the
Rington's Tea Company at
Newcastle on Tyne,
Northumberland and is extremely
rare. Price 6d. Issued 1936. 81mm.
DC/RT.

**No. 28w. Delivery Van.
'Osram' Type 2**   – £650 £350

Yellow with the words 'Osram
Lamps, a G.E.C. Product'. Price 6d.
Issued May 1936. Deleted 1939.
81mm. DC/RT.

**No. 28w. Delivery Van.
'Osram' Type 3**   – £450 £200

Yellow. Wording as Type 2. Price 6d.
Issued 1939. Deleted 1940. 83mm.
DC/RT.

**No. 28x. Delivery Van.
'Hovis' Type 2**   – £650 £350

White with the words 'Hovis' in gold.
Price 6d. Issued May 1936. Deleted
1939. 81mm. DC/RT.

**No. 28y. Delivery Van.
'Exide' Type 2**   – £650 £350

Red. The words 'Drydex Batteries' on
left side and 'Exide Batteries' on right
side in gold lettering. Price 6d. Issued
May 1936. Deleted 1940. 81mm.
DC/RT.

**No. 28y. Delivery Van.
'Bentalls' Type 3**   – £650 £350

Green and yellow sides and cream
roof. Extremely rare model with the

words 'Bentalls Kingston on Thames
Phone Kin 1001'. Price 6d. Issued
July 1936. Deleted 1940. 81mm.
DC/RT.

No. 30e. Bedford Breakdown Van

Red, green or grey. Also in blue with
dark blue wings. Other colours have
black wings. Open window in cab
(briefly) post-war, only the axle
thicknesses differ. Wire hook on
crane. Price 9d. Issued August 1935.
Deleted 1940. Reissued 1946. Deleted
1948.

	M/B	M/U	G/C
Pre-war	–	£300	£150
Post-war	£350	£200	£75

No. 30V. Electric Dairy Van 'N.C.B.'

£350	£200	£75

Cream and red. This is the rarer of
the two Dairy vans. Price 3/6d. Issued
1949. Renumbered 491 in 1954.
Deleted 1960. 85mm. DC/RT. Had
an individual box.

No. 30V. 'Express' Electric Dairy Van

£150	£50	£25

Grey and blue. Also red and cream,
worth double. With the words
'Express Dairy' on nose. Price 3/-.
Issued April 1951. Renumbered 490
in 1954. Deleted 1956. 85mm.
DC/RT.

No. 31. 'Holland Coachcraft' Van

–	£950	£350

One of the rarest models ever
produced by Dinky. Blue or green.
With the words 'Holland Coachcraft
Registered Design' in gold. Price 6d.
Issued January 1935. Deleted 1940.
88mm. DC/RT. Never had individual
box.

No. 31A. 'Esso' Trojan Van 15 cwt

£175	£60	£30

Red with the word 'Esso' on sides.
Price 2/6d. Issued February 1951.
Renumbered 450 in 1954. Deleted
1957. 85mm. DC/RT/TP. This model
was the reason for many more people

turning to collecting diecast toys. My advice to all collectors is to keep these models as the price will increase enormously within a very short time. The Trojan models are the investments to have for the future.

No. 31B. 'Dunlop' Trojan 15 cwt Van

	M/B	M/U	G/C
	£150	£50	£25

Red, with the words 'Dunlop the World's Master Tyre' on the sides. Price 2/6d. Issued June 1952. Deleted 1957. 85mm. DC/RT/TP.

No. 31C. 'Chivers' 15 cwt Trojan Van

	£175	£60	£30

Green with the words 'Chivers Jellies' and design on each side. Price 2/6d. Issued October 1953. Renumbered 452 in 1954. Deleted 1957. 85mm. DC/RT/TP.

No. 31D. 'Oxo' Trojan 15 cwt Van

	–	£350	£100

Blue with the words 'Beefy Oxo' on the sides. Model never had an individual box but delivered to shops in boxes of 6 as initially were the other Trojan series, only going into boxes from 1954, most of which are dual numbered. Price 2/2d. Issued October 1953. Deleted 1954. 85mm. DC/RT/TP.

No. 33d. Box Van Trailer 'Hornby'

Green with the words 'Hornby Trains. British and Guaranteed' in gold on sides. Price 8d. Issued 1936. Deleted 1938. 70mm. DC/RT/TP.

	M/B	M/U	G/C
Trailer only	–	£250	£75
With matching tug	–	£250	£75

No. 33d. Box Van Trailer 'Meccano'

Green, with the words 'Meccano Engineering for Boys' in black, green and gold on sides. Price 8d. Issued 1938. Deleted 1939. 70mm. DC/RT/TP. With green tug.

	M/B	M/U	G/C
Trailer only	–	£250	£75
With matching tug	–	**£250**	**£75**

MODEL	M/B	M/U	G/C

No. 33r. Mechanical Horse 'G.W.R.'

| | – | £250 | £75 |

Brown with a grey or cream roof. With G.W.R. Motif and the number '2742' on sides. Price 1/6d. Issued October 1935. Deleted 1940. 65mm. DC/RT.

No. 33r. Trailer Van 'G.W.R.'

Brown with cream roof. Rare model. 'G.W.R.' motif and 'Express Cartage Services' on the sides. Price 1/6d. Issued October 1935. Deleted 1940. 70mm. DC/RT/TP.

| Trailer only | – | £250 | £75 |
| With G.W.R. Mechanical Trailer | – | £450 | £150 |

No. 33r. Mechanical Horse 'S.R.'

| | – | £750 | £250 |

Green with black or white roof. With '3016 M' on sides. Price 1/6d. Issued October 1935. Deleted 1940. 65mm. DC/RT.

No. 33r. Trailer Van 'S.R.'

| | – | £350 | £150 |

Green and black. With the words 'Southern Railway' and 'Express Parcels Service' on sides. Price 1/6d. Issued October 1935. Deleted 1940. 70mm. DC/RT/TP.

No. 33r. Mechanical Horse 'L.M.S.'

| | – | £500 | £150 |

Brown with a black roof. With the letters 'L.M.S.' on sides along with the number '2246'. Price 1/6d. Issued October 1935. Deleted 1940. 65mm. DC/RT.

No. 33r. Trailer Van 'L.M.S.'

Brown and black. With letters 'L.M.S.' on sides. Price 1/-. Issued October 1935. Deleted 1940. 70mm. DC/RT/TP.

| Trailer only | – | £250 | £100 |
| With L.M.S. Mechanical Horse | – | £450 | £150 |

No. 33r. Mechanical Horse 'L.N.E.R.'

| | – | £250 | £100 |

Blue with black roof. With the letters 'L.N.E.R.' on sides. Price 1/6d. Issued 1935. Deleted 1940. 65mm. DC/RT.

No. 33r. Trailer Van 'L.N.E.R.'

Blue and black with the letters 'L.N.E.R.' on sides. Price 1/6d. Issued October 1935. Deleted 1940. 70mm. DC/RT/TP.

Trailer only	–	£150	£50
L.N.E.R. Mechanical Horse	–	£400	£100

No. 34a. Royal Air Mail Service Car

	–	£350	£100

Blue. With the words 'Royal Air Mail Services' on sides. Price 6d. Issued October 1935. Deleted 1938. 83mm. DC/RT.

No. 34b Royal Mail Van

Red and black. With the words 'Royal Mail G.R.' and the Crown cast on sides. Pre-war and early post-war 34Bs have open windows. Set of 12. Price 10d. Issued 1938. Deleted 1940. 83mm. DC/RT/TP.

Pre-war	–	£300	£100
Early post-war	–	£200	£75

No. 34B. Royal Mail Van

	–	£30	£12

Office livery and designs. With 'Royal Mail G.R.' and Crown on sides. No rear windows. Price 2/2d. Issued 1948. Deleted 1952. 83mm. DC/RT/TP.

No. 34C. Loudspeaker Van

Brown with black speakers; grey with black speakers; blue with silver speakers. Wheel colour is normally as speaker colour. There is also a rare green livery with black speakers and black wheels. Price 2/2d. Issued February 1948. Renumbered 492 in 1945. Deleted 1957. 81mm. DC/RT. Not individually boxed until number change. I will give separate prices for colours as this is very important.

Brown with black speakers	–	£150	£50
Grey with black speakers	–	£120	£40
Blue with silver speakers	–	£125	£30
Green with black speakers	–	£500	£150

MODEL	M/B	M/U	G/C

No. 255. Mersey Tunnel Police Van

£150 £50 £25

Red. With the words 'Mersey Tunnel' on sides in yellow and orange, and 'Police' on roof. Price 2/10d. Issued September 1955. Deleted 1961. 77mm. DC/TP/RT.

No. 260. Royal Mail Van

£125 £50 £25

Red with black roof. With 'Royal Mail' on sides and Crown and post office designs on sides. Price 2/10d. Issued 1955. Deleted 1961. 78mm. DC/TP/RT.

No. 261. Telephone Service Van

£125 £50 £25

Green with black roof and grey ladder. With the words 'Post Office Telephones' on door and Crown on the sides. A good investment. Price 2/10d. Issued March 1956. Deleted 1961. 73mm. DC/RT/TP.

No. 262. Volkswagen Swiss Postal Van

£350 £100 £50

Yellow and black with 'P.T.T.' crest on sides. Made for sale only in Switzerland although many models were bought by holidaymakers and brought back to other countries. A very rare model. Casting as 181 which was a Volkswagen saloon but this is the best section for this somewhat confusing model. Equivalent price 5/11d. Issued 1956/59. 90mm. DC/TP/RT.

No. 273. RAC Patrol Van

Blue RAC authentic livery with red seats. With the words 'Road Service'

and 'RAC' badge on sides. Opening
rear doors with RAC sign and motif
on roof. Price 5/-. Issued 1965.
Deleted 1970. 78mm. DC/RT. There
were two paint schemes attached to
this number, and I price each one
separately.

	M/B	M/U	G/C
Early in blue emblem	£150	£50	£25
Later white and blue emblem	£100	£40	£20

No. 274. AA Patrol Mini-Van

Yellow and black with authentic AA
patrol wording and livery. As with
273, there were two colour schemes.
Earlier model all-over yellow with
crested emblem. Later version is
yellow van with white roof which
came into production in 1968/69 and
has square emblem. Price 4/11d.
Issued July 1964. Deleted 1973.
78mm. DC/P/RT.

	M/B	M/U	G/C
Early model	£250	£100	£25
Later model	£65	£30	£20

No. 275. Brinks Armoured Car

	M/B	M/U	G/C
	£500	£150	£50

Grey and blue. Model was tinted
green with two drivers, opening side
and rear doors with the words 'Brinks
Security Service 1859'. Complete with
crates and imitation gold bars. Price
12/11d. Issued November 1964.
Deleted 1969. 120mm.
DC/RT/SW/LHD/SS/S/W.

No. 275. Re-issue Brinks Armoured Car

	M/B	M/U	G/C
	£175	£50	£25

Darker shade of grey than previous
with a yellow tint. Made especially for
the U.S. market. May still be available
in some toy stores but these will soon

MODEL	M/B	M/U	G/C

disappear. Equivalent price £2.25p.
Issued 1979. Deleted 1980. Other
details as former model.

No. 280. Delivery Van Type 3

	–	£175	£75

This was the post war issue of the
28/280 Van. Type 3, which was a
Bedford. The model never had any
advertising connected with it after the
war. This model had no rear
window., Price 1/-. Issued 1937
Deleted 1940. 83mm. DC/RT.

No. 280a. Delivery Van.
'Viyella' Type 2

	–	£1500	£250

Light blue with the words 'Viyella for
the Nursery', in black and white.
Price 6d. Issued 1937. Deleted 1940.
81mm. DC/RT.

No. 280a. Delivery Van.
'Viyella' Type 3

	–	£1750	£300

Light blue. Wording as Type 2. Price
6d. Issued 1937. Deleted 1940. 81mm.
DC/RT.

No. 280b. Delivery Van.
'Lyons' Type 2

	–	£1500	£250

Dark blue with the words 'Lyons Tea'
in orange and 'Always the Best' in
white. Price 6d. Issued 1937. Deleted
1940. 81mm. DC/RT.

No. 280b. Delivery Van.
'Hartley's' Type 3

	–	£1750	£300

Cream with the words 'Hartley's is
Real Jam'. Price 6d. Issued 1939.
Deleted 1940. 83mm. DC/RT.

No. 280c. Delivery Van.
'Shredded Wheat' Type 2

	–	£2500	£350

Cream. With the words 'Shredded
Wheat' on a red band. 'Welwyn
Garden City, Herts' on side. Price 6d.
Issued 1937. Deleted 1940.

No. 280d. Delivery Van.
'Bisto' Type 2

	–	£2500	£350

Yellow. Of the two Bisto type vans,
this is the rarer model. With the
words 'Ah! Bisto' with original design.
Price 6d. Issued 1937. Deleted 1938.
81mm. DC/RT.

No. 280d. Delivery Van. 'Bisto' Type 2

	M/B	M/U	G/C
	–	£1500	£250

Yellow. With the word 'Bisto' and design. Price 6d. Issued 1938. Deleted 1940. 81mm. DC/RT.

No. 280e. Delivery Van. 'Ekco' Type 2

	–	£1000	£200

Green, with the words 'Ekco Radio' in gold. Price 6d. Issued 1937. Deleted 1940. 81mm. DC/RT.

No. 280e. Delivery Van. 'Yorkshire Evening News' Type 2

	–	£2000	£250

Cream with the words 'Yorkshire Evening News, the Original Buff' in black and gold. Price 6d. Issued 1938. Deleted 1939. 81mm. DC/RT.

No. 280e. Delivery Van. 'Yorkshire Evening Post' Type 3

	–	£1500	£250

Dark cream and cream with wording 'Yorkshire Evening Post'. Price 6d. Issued 1939. Deleted 1940. 83mm. DC/RT.

No. 280f. Delivery Van. 'Mackintosh's' Type 2

	–	£2000	£350

Red with the words 'Mackintosh's Toffee'. Price 6d. Issued 1937. Deleted 1940. 81mm. DC/RT.

No. 390. Customized Transit Van

	£85	£35	£15

Metallic blue with black, red, and yellow stick-on transfers (Vampire plus flashes etc.). Black grille, chromed wide wheels, 'Side-Winder' exhaust pipes and casting as 269, 274 and 417. Price £1.55p. Issued 1978. Deleted 1980. 133mm. DC/P.

PROMOTIONAL VANS

Many vans were used as promotional items by companies and show organisers, also by several toy shops etc. and two of the favourite Dinky products for this purpose were the 407 and the 410 series. Regardless of what name the van may have connected with it and whatever colour schemes are introduced, whether it be private or by the Dinky company itself, the models are worthwhile investments. No one can say definitely what is worth paying in this field. Therefore, I have set out my own prices to these models combined with the experience and research I have done in great detail. Any model is only worth whatever a collector will pay for it but any collector should get the prices for the promotional items as I have set out. Please feel free to write to me about any model you may have. I will be pleased to give private valuations to any person who may wish to have them.

MODEL	M/B	M/U	G/C
No. 407. Ford Transit 'Kenwood' Van	£200	£50	£25

Blue with white roof and the word 'Kenwood' on sides etc. Price 9/11d. Issued 1966. Replaced in 1970 by the 407 'Telefusion' then deleted in 1978. 122mm. DC/P.

No. 407. Ford Transit Van	£250	£75	£25

White with coloured letters 'Colour TV' on black strip. 'Telefusion' in black or with 'T' white on red. Price 9/11d. Issued 1970. Deleted and replaced in 1971 by 407 'Hertz'. This model is scarce. Finally deleted 1978. 122mm. DC/P.

No. 407. Ford Transit Van	£125	£50	£25

Model only available in prototype or kit form '1025' Action Kit but still collectable in the promotional series. Red body with the words 'Hertz Truck Rental' in black letters. Some are in gold letters. Also in yellow livery. Price £1.55p. Issued 1972. Deleted 1978. 122mm. DC/P.

No. 407. Ford Transit Van	£150	£50	£25

Two-tone red with red interior. Another model made from the Action Kit 1025. With words 'Avis Van Rental'. Price £1.55p. Issued 1972. Deleted 1981. 122mm. DC/P.

No. 410. Bedford Royal Mail Van	£400	£100	£50

Red with silver bumpers and black hubs and white cab interior. This van is the first of the Bedfords made by

MODEL	M/B	M/U	G/C

Dinky themselves as a promotional
model. Price £1.25p. Issued 1972.
Deleted 1980. 90mm. DC/P.

No. 410. Promotional Bedford Van

	M/B	M/U	G/C
	£250	£50	£25

Blue with the words 'John Menzies'.
Genuine promotional model sold only
by John Menzies. Price £1.25p. Issued
1974. Deleted 1974. 90mm. DC/P.

No. 410. Promotional Bedford Van

	£250	£50	£25

White with red or white interior.
With letters 'O.C.L.' on the sides.
Price £1.25p. Issued 1975. Deleted
1975. 90mm. DC/P.

No. 410. Promotional Bedford Van

	£500	£150	£75

Grey with white or grey interior. This
is one of the rare models to find as
there were only 150 models made
especially for a French collector with
the word 'Opel'. Issued 1975 and
deleted the same year. 90mm. DC/P.

No. 410. Promotional Bedford Van

	£1000	£250	£100

Made especially for the French market
and also for the U.S.A. market, with
the word 'Carter' on the sides. This
was a promotional model in an
election campaign for Jimmy Carter
and although some early models were
out in 1975 the majority were on sale
in 1976. A very rare model as only
100 were made. Price £2. Issued
1975/76 and deleted almost at once.
90mm. DC/P.

No. 410. Promotional Bedford Van

	£500	£150	£75

Green, with white or green interior.
Only 100 models were made by a
French collector in 1976 with the
word 'Parlophone'. Price £2. 90mm.
DC/P.

No. 410. Promotional Bedford Van

	£500	£150	£75

White with white or red interior with
the words 'M.J. Hire and Service'.

MODEL	M/B	M/U	G/C

Price £2.50p. Issued 1975/76 and
deleted almost at once. 90mm. DC/P.

No. 410. Promotional Bedford Van

£350 £75 £35

White. Made especially for the
Mikansue Company with the words
'Modeller's World' on sides. Only 200
models were made in 1976. Price
£2.50p. The models were almost
certainly deleted the same year they
were made and like many promotional
models can sometimes be found at
Swapmeets and collectors' shops etc.
90mm. DC/P.

No. 410. Promotional Bedford Van

£750 £150 £50

This model was made especially for a
large department store in Toronto,
Canada, to celebrate 100 years of
trading. Dark, medium or bright red,
with promotional stickers with the
word 'Simpson's'. Equivalent price
£1. Issued 1972. Still available 1975.
Almost obsolete now. There are still
some American dealers importing
them into various other countries.
90mm. DC/P.

No. 410. Promotional Bedford Van

£300 £100 £50

Red with the word 'Marley Tiles' on
sides. Promotional gimmick for the
Marley Tiles Company. Price £1.
Issued 1975. Deleted 1976. 90mm.
DC/P.

No. 410. Promotional Bedford Van

£350 £75 £35

Brown and black with the words
'Relaco' on sides. Price £2. Issued
1974. Deleted 1975. 90mm. DC/P.

No. 410. Bedford Van

£550 £150 £75

This was a standard Dinky toy made
for Denmark and it is their equivalent
of our Royal Mail in this country.
With words 'Danish Post'. Equivalent
price £1.50p. Issued 1974. Deleted
1976. 90mm.

No. 410. Promotional Bedford Van

£500   £150   £75

Red with the words 'Caledonian Autominologists'. Price £2.50p. Only 100 were made in 1977 for members of this association and it was deleted that same year. 90mm. DC/P.

No. 410. Promotional Bedford Van

£500   £150   £75

White with the words 'Collector's Gazette' on the side. There were only 200 made. Available from the paper itself at the head office or at Swapmeets, but most of these have been snapped up. Price £2.50p. Issued 1979. 90mm. DC/P.

No. 412. Bedford Van AA

£150   £40   £15

Authentic yellow and black AA colours. With the words 'AA Service' on sides. Price £1.45p. Issued 1974. Deleted 1980. 90mm. DC/P.

No. 416. Ford Transit Van

£150   £50   £25

Yellow with the word 'Motorways' on sides. The driver's door does not open. There are warning signs and red beacon on roof and bollard inside van. This model replaced the 407 Ford Transit and then the model was replaced in 1978 by 417. Price £1.45p. Issued 1975. Deleted 1978. 129mm. DC/P.

No. 417. Ford Transit Service Van

£55   £35   £15

Model replaced 416. With a third grille, otherwise it had the same features as 416. Opening side and rear doors and roof light, with red interior, silver bumpers, wheels etc. With medium or dark yellow body. Price £1.75p. Issued 1978. Deleted 1980. 133mm. DC/P.

No. 450. 'Esso' Trojan Van

£150   £50   £25

Red with the word 'Esso' on sides. This is one of the most sought-after ranges of models from the mid and late fifties. The price of these models will rise very quickly like the 31A and series which were renumbered 450. It is important to note that the empty boxes of these models are worth money as all collectors like to hear the words 'mint and boxed'. The practice of late has been the purchase of models in one place and the box in another. All early boxes are worth saving as people are keen to buy them. Price 2/5d. Issued 1955. Deleted 1957. 85mm. DC/TP/RT.

No. 450. Bedford 'T.K.' Van   £250   £75   £35

Metallic green and white with words 'Castrol, the Masterpiece in Oils' on the sides and front. Red interior and silver trim; opening door with the word 'Bedford' on the front radiator. Price 10/9d. Issued 1965. Deleted 1970. 143mm. DC/P.

No. 451. 'Dunlop' Trojan Van   £100   £30   £15

Red with the words 'Dunlop, the World's Master Tyre' on the sides. This was the renumbering of 31B. Price 2/5d. Issued November 1955. Deleted 1957. 85mm. DC/RT/TP.

No. 452. 'Chivers' Trojan Van   £240   £70   £30

Green. This was renumbered 31C. The words 'Chivers Jellies' on sides. Price 2/5d. Issued October 1954. Deleted 1957. 85mm. DC/RT/TP.

No. 454. 'Cydrax' Trojan Van   £100   £50   £25

Green. With the words 'Drink Cydrax' on the sides. Price 2/9d. Issued February 1957. Deleted March 1959. 85mm. DC/RT/TP.

No. 455. 'Brooke Bond' Trojan Van   £260   £100   £50

Red. With the words 'Brooke Bond Tea' on the sides. Price 2/5d. Issued May 1957. Deleted 1961. 85mm. DC/TP/RT.

No. 465. 'Capstan' Morris Van   £150   £75   £30

Blue and dark blue. With the words 'Have a Capstan' and other designs on sides. Price 2/11d. Issued March 1957. Deleted 1959. 78mm. DC/TP/RT.

No. 470. 'Shell-BP' Austin Van   £75   £25   £15

Red and green. With the words and letters 'Shell', 'B.P.' on sides. Price 2/5d. Issued May 1954. Deleted 1956.

MODEL	M/B	M/U	G/C

No. 471. 'Nestlés' Austin Van

£120 £50 £20

Red with the word 'Nestlés' on the sides. Price 2/5d. Issued October 1955. Deleted 1960. These Austin Vans are good investments. 89mm. DC/RT/TP.

No. 472. 'Raleigh' Austin Van

£100 £50 £25

Green with the word 'Raleigh Cycles' on each side. Price 2/5d. Issued April 1957. Deleted 1960. 89mm. DC/TP/RT.

No. 480. 'Kodak' Bedford Van

£175 £50 £25

Yellow. With the words 'Kodak Cameras and Films'. Price 2/5d. Issued June 1954. Deleted 1956. 83mm. DC/TP/RT.

No. 481. 'Ovaltine' Bedford Van

£150 £30 £15

Blue. With the word 'Ovaltine' in black or cream on sides; and 'Ovaltine biscuits' in gold or yellow or blue. Price 2/9d. Issued September 1955. Deleted 1960. 83mm. DC/TP/RT.

No. 482. 'Dinky Toys' Bedford Van

£120 £30 £15

Yellow with orange on lower body panels and red lettering. With the words 'Dinky Toys' on sides. Price 2/9d. Issued October 1956. Deleted 1960. 83mm. DC/TP/RT.

No. 490. Electric 'Express Dairy' Van

£65 £20 £15

Grey and blue, or cream and red. The words 'Express Dairy' on front. Price 3/4d. Issued 1954. Deleted 1956. 85mm. DC/TP/RT.

No. 491. 'N.C.B.' Electric Dairy Van

£175 £75 £35

Cream and red with letters 'N.C.B.' on front. This was seen at Swapmeets on the Continent, especially Amsterdam. Very scarce in England. Price 2/11d. Issued 1956 mainly for export. Deleted 1960. 85mm. DC/RT.

No. 492. Loudspeaker Van

£70 £30 £15

This was the renumbering of 34C. Price 2/3d. Issued 1954. Deleted

MODEL	M/B	M/U	G/C

1957. Boxes for this model are very rare. 81mm. DC/RT.

No. 492. Election Mini Van

	£250	£100	£50

White with orange loudspeaker. Words on van were 'Vote for Somebody'. With loudspeaker on roof and rear doors which opened, plus a candidate figure with microphone. Model never actually appeared in any Dinky catalogue and had a very short production run. Price 7/11d. Issued 1964. Deleted 1965. 78mm. DC/RT/P.

No. 514. 'Slumberland' Guy Van

	£750	£200	£50

Red. With the words 'Slumberland Spring Interior Mattresses' and crest on sides. With opening rear doors and four wheels. Price 5/8d. Issued December 1949. Deleted 1952. 134mm. DC/TP/RT. Another excellent investment.

No. 514. 'Lyons' Guy Van

	£1700	£250	£100

With the words 'Lyons Swiss Rolls' on sides. First type front with opening rear doors, four wheels and one spare. Price 7/9d. Issued November 1951. Deleted 1952. 134mm. DC/TP/RT. Condition matters a great deal, especially where the transfer is concerned. A chip off a transfer can make a £10 difference in the selling price, although from what I have seen, collectors will be willing to pay high prices for models in this range.

No. 514. 'Weetabix' Guy Van

	£2250	£500	£250

Yellow. Opening rear doors with four wheels and one spare. Price 7/9d. Issued June 1952. Deleted 1954. 134mm. DC/TP/RT.

No. 514. 'Spratts' Guy Van

	£1500	£250	£100

Red and cream. With the word 'Spratts' on each side. Opening rear doors, first type front, four wheels and one spare. Price 7/-. Issued July 1953. Deleted 1954.

MODEL	M/B	M/U	G/C

No. 561. Citroën Delivery Van

£300 £75 £25

Metallic blue. With sliding door and
the word 'Cibie' on sides. Price 5/5d.
Issued July 1962. Deleted 1964.
90mm. DC/TP/RT. This was a
French Dinky toy imported into
England and genuinely made in
France, but it had different
advertisements as well as Cibie on the
side. Some models were still available
in 1968.

No. 561. Citroën Delivery Van

£750 £250 £100

Blue and white. Available only in
France. With the word 'Gervais' on
sides. Other details as previous 561.

No. 917. 'Spratts' Guy Van

£850 £200 £50

Red and Cream. With the word
'Spratts' on side. With first or second
type front, four wheels, one spare and
opening rear doors. Price 7/3d. Issued
January 1955. Deleted 1956. 132mm.
DC/TP/RT.

No. 918. 'Ever Ready' Guy Van

£500 £100 £50

Blue livery. With second type front.
Four wheels, one spare, and opening
rear doors. With the words 'Ever
Ready Batteries for Life' on sides.
Price 8/-. Issued December 1955.
Deleted 1958. 132mm. DC/TP/RT.
This is the commonest Guy van of
them all, but prices have doubled
within the last two years.

No. 919. 'Golden Shred' Guy Van

£1250 £250 £75

Red. With second type front, four
wheels, one spare and opening rear
doors. The words 'Robertson's

241

Golden Shred' and the golliwog
shown on sides. Price 8/9d. Issued
June 1957. Deleted 1958. 132mm.
DC/TP/RT.

No. 920. 'Heinz' Guy Warrior Van

                                     £1750   £500   £150

The words 'Heinz 57 Varieties' and
tomato ketchup bottle on sides. With
rear opening doors, red cab and
chassis, transfers as 923/B Bedford.
Because of the short production run,
this is the rarest post- war Dinky van
of them all, even though it is less than
the Weetabix van in price at the
moment. 8/9d. Issued 1960. Deleted
1961. 137mm. DC/TP/RT/P.

No. 920. 'Heinz' Guy Warrior Van

                                     £550   £150   £50

With words 'Heinz 57 Varieties' and a
picture of a bean can displayed on
sides. Details otherwise as previous
920. This is a very rare model.

No. 923. 'Heinz' Big Bedford Van

                                   £400   £200   £100

With the words 'Heinz 57 Varieties'
with baked beans tin on sides. With
no hook, four wheels, one spare and
opening rear doors. Price 8/3d. Issued
December 1955. Deleted 1958.
146mm. DC/TP/RT.

No. 923. 'Heinz' Big Bedford Van

                                 £1500   £500   £150

Red and yellow, with the words
'Heinz 57 Varieties' and showing
tomato ketchup bottle. This is much
rarer than the version with tin. Price
9/6d. Issued 1958. Deleted 1960.
146mm. DC/TP/RT.

No. 930. Bedford Pallet-Jecta Van

                                 £200   £75   £25

Orange and yellow, with windows.
With the words 'Dinky Toys' on sides
and the word 'Meccano' on front. A
handle works the interior system and
rear doors open. This model is scarce.

With three plastic pallets. Marked No.
793 it is worth double the ordinary
model 930. Price 14/3d. Issued
January 1960. Deleted 1964. 177mm.
DC/TP/RT/P.

No. 988. ABC TV Transmitter Van

	M/B	M/U	G/C
	£195	£100	£50

Cream and grey with red flash. With
windows and rotating aerial on roof.
With the letters 'A.B.C.' on front.
Price 7/9d. Issued May 1962. Deleted
1969. 111mm. DC/TP/RT/P.

LORRIES, TRUCKS AND COMMERCIAL VEHICLES

I now come to another of the real Dinky investment gems.
All commercials are much sought after, especially 'The Big
Wheelers' as they are nicknamed. Anyone having the rare
early pre-war models is indeed fortunate. Most of the early
models had no individual boxes, and therefore I will only
quote mint unboxed and good condition for these.

No. 14A. Electric Truck

Blue or grey. Price 3/3d. Issued July
1948. Deleted 1954. 85mm.
DC/TP/RT. This model was
renumbered 400 in 1954, when a box
was provided.

	M/B	M/U	G/C
Pale blue	–	£25	£5
Grey	–	£35	£10
Dark blue	–	£20	£7.50

No. 14C. Coventry Climax Truck 'Fork-Lift'

	M/B	M/U	G/C
	£40	£15	£7.50

Green and orange. Brown and green.
Box in brown or blue cardboard. Fork
raised by handle. Renumbered 401 in
1954. Price 5/9d. Issued November
1949. Deleted 1954. 108mm.
DC/RT/SW/D.

No. 22c. Motor Truck

	M/B	M/U	G/C
	–	£200	£150

Blue and fawn. Blue and red. With
metal wheels. It has no headlights on
tin-plate radiator. Price 8d. Issued
December 1933. Deleted 1935. 84mm.
DC/TP.

MODEL	M/B	M/U	G/C
No. 22c. Motor Truck	–	£10	£7

Red or green or blue. With rear
window in cab. Price 6d. Issued May
1935. Deleted 1940. 84mm. DC/RT.

No. 22s. Small Searchlight Lorry	–	£295	£75

Green or dark blue. Also in dark grey.
Price 1/-. Issued between 1935 and
1939. Deleted 1940. 84mm. DC/RT.

No. 25a. Wagon	–	£125	£30

Red with black chassis. With open
chassis, tin-plate radiator and as Type
1 with no lights. Price 9d. Issued
April 1934. Deleted 1938. 108mm.
DC/RT/TP.

No. 25a Wagon

Blue, red or grey body and black
chassis. Some Type 2s had coloured
chassis (pre-war only). This model had
open chassis, diecast radiator and
classed as Type 2 with lights. Price
9d. Issued 1938. Deleted 1940.
105mm. DC/RT/TP. Type 2 came
out briefly post-war with thicker axles.

Pre-war model	–	£95	£30
Post-war	–	£40	£10
Pre-war with coloured chassis	–	£65	£30

No. 25a/2. Wagon

Orange with pale green chassis. Blue
body with orange chassis. Otherwise
details as previous 25A.

Orange and pale green	–	£95	£45
Blue and orange	–	£125	£45

No. 25A. Wagon	–	£55	£15

Grey, blue or green, with black
chassis, diecast radiator and lights as
Type 3. Price 9d. Issued 1946.
Deleted 1947. 105mm. DC/RT.

No. 25A. Wagon	–	£55	£15

Grey, red or in red and cream. Body
with black moulded chassis, diecast
radiator, and lights and bumpers as
Type 4. Price 9d. Issued 1947.
Deleted 1950. 110mm. DC/RT.

MODEL	M/B	M/U	G/C

No. 25b. Covered Wagon

	M/B	M/U	G/C
	–	£75	£40

Blue or cream, or blue and cream with canvas top and black chassis. It makes little difference what advertising matter is attached to this model as none are common. The only advertisements I have seen are for 'Meccano' and 'Carter Paterson'. Both are for Type 2 and are listed later on. I have not seen adverts on Type 1, which is the model with open chassis, tin-plate radiator and no lights. Price 9d. Issued April 1934. Deleted 1938. 108mm. DC/TP/RT. Prices for 25B/1.

No. 25b. Covered Wagon

Grey body with grey canvas and black chassis. With no publicity. Open chassis, diecast radiator with lights as Type 2. Price 9d. Issued 1938. Deleted 1940. 105mm. DC/RT/TP. Type 2 was a post-war model for a brief spell.

	M/B	M/U	G/C
Pre-war	–	£95	£30
Post-war	–	£50	£20

No. 25b. 'Carter Paterson' Covered Wagon

There are two Carter Paterson transfers. The first is in green or grey made in 1939 and deleted in 1940. It also had a red band with 'Carter Paterson' in white, but also showed 'Express Carrier London'. It came with open chassis and diecast radiator with no lights as Type 2. Price 9d. 105mm. DC/TP/RT. For a while the model came out post-war with thicker axles.

	M/B	M/U	G/C
Pre-war	–	£250	£75
Post-war	–	£150	£5

The second Carter Paterson transfer had a green body and a cream canopy, with the words 'Carter Paterson, Express Carriers, London, Brighton and Seaside'. Otherwise details as above.

	M/B	M/U	G/C
Pre-war model	–	£450	£95
Post-war	–	£250	£75

MODEL	M/B	M/U	G/C

No. 25B. Covered Wagon

| | – | £65 | £25 |

Green with black plain chassis. Also
pale grey with dark grey canvas.
Diecast radiator with lights as Type 3.
This model has no publicity. Price 9d.
Issued 1946. Deleted 1947. 105mm.
DC/TP/RT.

No. 25B. Covered Wagon

| | – | £55 | £25 |

Yellow body, blue hubs, blue canvas.
Cream body, red hubs and red canvas.
With black moulded chassis, diecast
radiator and lights and bumpers as
Type 4. No publicity. Price 9d.
Issued 1947. Deleted 1950. 110mm.
DC/TP/RT.

No. 25c. Flat Truck

| | – | £150 | £50 |

Grey, blue, black, or red, with black
chassis. With open chassis, tin-plate
radiator and no lights as Type 1.
Price 9d. Issued April 1934. Deleted
1938. 105mm. DC/TP/RT.

No. 25c. Flat Truck

With open chassis, diecast radiator
and lights as Type 2. Price 9d. Issued
1938. Deleted 1940. Reissued 1946.
Deleted 1950. Post-war model had
thicker axles and different wheels.

| Pre-war | – | £75 | £35 |
| Post-war | – | £45 | £15 |

No. 25C. Flat Truck

| | – | £35 | £10 |

Green with black plain chassis with
diecast radiator and lights as Type 3.
Price 9d. Issued 1946. Deleted 1947.
105mm. DC/RT.

No. 25C. Flat Truck

| | – | £35 | £10 |

Orange body with black moulded
chassis. Also green with black chassis.
Diecast radiator with lights and
bumpers as Type 4. Price 9d. Issued
1947. Deleted 1950. 110mm. DC/RT.

No. 25d. Petrol Tank Wagon

| | – | £75 | £35 |

Red or pale green with black chassis.
With open chassis and tin-plate
radiator and no lights as Type 1.
Price 9d. Issued April 1934. Deleted
1938. 108mm. DC/RT/TP.

MODEL	M/B	M/U	G/C

No. 25d. 'Shell B.P.' Tank Wagon

| | – | £350 | £150 |

Red with black chassis. The letters 'B.P.' on sides in yellow. With open chassis, tin-plate radiator, and no lights as Type 1. Price 9d. Issued 1936. Deleted 1938. 108mm. DC/RT/TP.

No. 25d. Tank Wagon

Red or dark green body with black chassis and the word 'Petrol' in black or white on sides. Open chassis, diecast radiator and lights as Type 2. This model also had a short run post-war but with thicker axles. Price 6d. Issued 1938. Deleted 1940. 104mm. DC/RT.

| Pre-war | – | £75 | £35 |
| Post-war | – | £55 | £25 |

No. 25d. 'Texaco' Petrol Wagon

| | – | £550 | £100 |

Red with black open chassis, diecast radiator and lights as Type 2. The model shows a white star and the words 'Texaco Petroleum Products' on each side in white. Price 9d. Issued 1936. Deleted 1940. 107mm. DC/RT.

No. 25d. 'Shell B.P.' Tank Wagon

| | – | £350 | £150 |

Red with black chassis of the open type with diecast radiator and lifts Type 2. The words 'Shell B.P.' in yellow on sides. Price 9d. Issued 1939. Deleted 1940. 107mm. DC/RT.

No. 25d. 'Power' Tank Wagon

| | – | £350 | £150 |

Green with black open chassis, diecast radiator with lights as Type 2. Word 'Power' in gold on sides. Price 9d. Issued 1939. Deleted 1940. 107mm DC/RT.

No. 25d. Tanker Wagon

| | – | £750 | £250 |

Mid-green with 'Pratts' in gold lettering. Type 1 with no headlights and tinplate radiator. Price 9d. Issued April 1934. Deleted 1936. Never had individual box. 108mm. DC/RT/TP. Very rare model.

No. 25d. 'Esso' Tank Wagon

Green body with black open chassis,
diecast radiator with lights as Type 2.
The word 'Esso' in gold on sides.
Price 9d. Issued 1939. Deleted 1940.
107mm. DC/RT. Also available post-
war.

	M/B	M/U	G/C
Pre-war	–	£350	£150
Post-war	–	£250	£100

No. 25d. 'Mobil Oil' Tank Wagon

Red with black open chassis, diecast
radiator and lights as Type 2. Words
'Mobil Oil' in blue with a white band
along the sides. Price 9d. Issued 1939.
Deleted 1940. 107mm. DC/RT.
Model was also brought out for a
short time post-war.

	M/B	M/U	G/C
Pre-war	–	£350	£150
Post-war	–	£250	£100

No. 25d. 'Castrol' Tank Wagon

Green with black open chassis, diecast
radiator and lights as Type 2. With
the words 'Wakefield Castrol Motor
Oil' in red and black on the sides.
This model was also brought out post-
war. Price 9d. Issued 1939. Deleted
1940. 107mm. DC/RT.

	M/B	M/U	G/C
Pre-war	–	£350	£150
Post-war	–	£250	£100

No. 25d. 'Redline Glico' Petrol Wagon

	M/B	M/U	G/C
	–	£500	£100

Dark blue with black open chassis,
diecast radiator and lights as Type 2.
Model has a red band along each side
with the words 'Redline Glico' in
gold. Price 9d. Issued 1939. Deleted
1940. 107mm. DC/RT.

No. 25d. 'Pool' Petrol Wagon

	M/B	M/U	G/C
	–	£500	£100

Grey with front wings which are
sometimes white. With black open
chassis, diecast radiator and lights as
Type 2. With the words 'Pool' in
white on each side. Price 9d. Issued
January 1940. Deleted October 1940.
DC/RT.

MODEL	M/B	M/U	G/C

No. 25D. Petrol Tank Wagon   –   £100   £30

Green or red body with black plain
chassis. With diecast radiator and
lights as Type 3. The word 'Petrol'
shows in black or white along each
side. Price 9d. Issued 1946. Deleted
1947. 110mm. DC/RT.

No. 25D. Petrol Tank Wagon

Dark green or orange and light green.
With the word 'Petrol' on each side.
This model was Type 4. Price 9d.
Issued 1948. Deleted 1950. 110mm.
DC/RT. The orange and light green
colour are scarcer than the dark green,
so I give prices as follows.

Dark green	–	£100	£30
Orange, or light green	–	£150	£35

No. 25e. Tipping Wagon   –   £550   £250

Maroon and yellow with black
opening chassis, tin-plate radiator and
no lights as Type 1. Price 9d. Issued
April 1934. Deleted 1938. 108mm.
DC/RT/TP.

No. 25e. Tipping Wagon

Fawn or brown body with opening
chassis, diecast radiator and lights as
Type 2. Also briefly available in post-
war days in the colours of grey or
fawn. Price 9d. Issued 1938. Deleted
1940. 105mm. DC/RT.

Pre-war	–	£550	£250
Post-war	–	£60	£25

No. 25E. Tipping Wagon   –   £50   £20

Grey, yellow, green or beige body
with black plain chassis, diecast
radiator, and lights as Type 3. Price
9d. Issued 1946. Deleted 1947.
105mm. DC/RT.

No. 25E. Tipping Wagon   –   £50   £20

Brown body, or blue and pink body
with black moulded chassis, diecast
radiator, and lights and bumper as
Type 4. Price 2/3d. Issued 1947.
Deleted 1950. 110mm. DC/RT.

No. 25f. Market Gardener's Van

Green or military green or black chassis and yellow body. This model has an open chassis with diecast radiator and lights as Type 2. Type 2 trucks also appeared briefly after the war in 1946 until they were replaced by Type 3, where only the axle thickness was different. Price 9d. Issued 1938. Deleted 1940. 105mm. DC/RT.

	M/B	M/U	G/C
Pre-war	–	£450	£140
Post-war thicker axles	–	£250	£100

No. 25F. Market Gardener's Van

	–	£70	£30

Green with black plain chassis, diecast radiator with lights Type 3 model. Price 9d. Issued 1946. Deleted 1947. 110mm. DC/RT.

No. 25F. Market Gardener's Van

	–	£60	£20

Yellow with black moulded chassis, diecast radiator with lights and bumper Type 4 model. Price 9d. Issued 1947. Deleted 1950. 110mm. DC/RT.

No. 25T. Flat Truck and Trailer

Brown, grey or blue. A matching truck (25C) and trailer (25G). Type 2 post-war was in fawn and Type 3 was in grey or green; the only difference between Types 3 and 4 is that the latter came in a box. Price 3/6d. Issued 1946. Deleted 1951. Overall length 179mm. DC/RT.

	M/B	M/U	G/C
Type 2	–	£150	£75
Type 3	–	£150	£75
Type 4	£350	£150	£75

No. 25g. Trailer

	–	£50	£7

Blue, green or dark green. Front axle swivels and has tin-plate tow bar. Price 7d. Issued June 1935. Deleted 1940. 69mm. DC/TP/RT.

No. 25G. Trailer

Grey, blue or green trailer made to match 25C Flat Truck series 2 or 3. Green or orange to match 25C Type 4. Green or red to match 30R Ford Thames. The rear hook was cast integrally at first with tin-plate draw-bar, then came the wire draw-bar from 1948 and then the tin-plate hook at rear from 1950. Only 429 has an individual box as all the others came in boxes of 6. Price 7d. Issued 1947. Renumbered 429 in 1954. Deleted 1960. 69mm. DC/RT.

Tin-plate draw-bar	–	£35	£15
Wire draw-bar	–	£25	£10

No. 25M. Bedford End Tipper

Orange; dark green or cream with red chassis and cream rear. The handle tips at rear and tailboard hinges. Price 5/9d. Issued March 1948. Renumbered 410 in 1954. Deleted 1960. 98mm. DC/TP/RT. This model has boxes.

Orange and cream	£275	£100	£45
Cream	£375	£150	£100
Red and cream	£250	£75	£35

No. 25R. Forward Control Lorry

	–	£55	£25

Red, green or grey, also in cream and orange or brown with green wheels. Price 2/6d. Issued May 1948. Renumbered 420 in 1954. Deleted 1961. 107mm. DC/TP/RT.

No. 25s. Six-Wheeled Wagon

	–	£250	£50

Brown with grey tin-plate canopy. Holes in seats for driver and passenger. Price 1/-. Issued 1937. Deleted 1940. 101mm. DC/RT/TP.

No. 25S. Six-Wheeled Wagon

	–	£150	£35

Green or blue, also in brown with grey tin-plate canopy. Later models have no holes for driver or passenger. Price 1/-. Issued 1946. Deleted 1948. 101mm. DC/TP/RT.

No. 25V. Bedford Refuse Wagon

| | £75 | £45 | £25 |

Fawn and green. Body tips and side and rear doors open. Price 5/6d. Issued October 1948. Renumbered 252 in 1954. Deleted 1960. 107mm. DC/TP/RT. Model came with a box.

No. 25W. Bedford Truck

| | £95 | £45 | £25 |

Green or brown. Latter colour is rare and worth double. Price 5/6d. Issued February 1949. Renumbered 411 in 1954. Deleted 1960. 104mm. DC/TP/RT. Model came with a box.

No. 25X. Breakdown Lorry

Colours for this model are important as far as price and value is concerned. Orange and green, dark grey cab, dark blue rear; light fawn cab and dark blue rear; dark brown cab and light green rear; and light brown cab and light green rear. With the words 'Dinky Service'. Price 5/6d. Issued September 1950. Renumbered 430 in 1954. Deleted 1960. 123mm. DC/TP/RT.

Orange and green, dark grey, dark blue, dark brown, and light green	£150	£50	£25
Light fawn and dark blue	£195	£75	£45
Light brown and light green	£150	£50	£25

No. 30J. Austin Wagon

| | – | £75 | £35 |

Blue or brown. Price 2/4d. Issued June 1950. Renumbered 412 in 1954. Deleted 1960. 104mm. DC/RT/TP. Only had box as 412.

No. 30M. Rear Tipping Wagon

| | – | £75 | £35 |

Orange with green rear; maroon with green rear and dark blue with grey rear. The handle works tipping action and tailboard hinges. Price 2/11d. Issued August 1950. Renumbered 414 in 1954. Deleted 1960. 99mm. DC/RT/TP.

No. 30P. Petrol Tanker

| | – | £150 | £45 |

Red or green. Word 'Petrol' shown on each side. Tanker had Studebaker cab. Price 2/6d. Issued 1950. Deleted 1952. 112mm. DC/TP/RT. Never had individual box.

MODEL	M/B	M/U	G/C
No. 30P. Petrol Tanker	–	£150	£45

Red. With the word 'Mobilgas' in white letters. Price 3/4d. Issued 1952. Renumbered 440 in 1954. 112mm. DC/TP/RT.

No. 30PA. Petrol Tanker	–	£150	£45

Green. The word 'Castrol' in red on white on sides. Price 2/6d. Issued 1952. Renumbered 441 in 1954. 112mm. DC/TP/RT.

No. 30PB. Petrol Tanker	–	£150	£45

Red. With the words 'Esso Motor Oil Petrol'. Price 3/4d. Issued August 1952. Renumbered 442 in 1954. 112mm. DC/RT/TP.

No. 30R. Fordson Thames Flat Truck

Red or light or dark green. Price 2/5d. Issued February 1951. Renumbered 422 in 1954. 112mm. DC/TP/RT.

Red or dark green	–	£150	£45
Light green	–	£100	£35

No. 30S. Austin Covered Wagon	–	£150	£45

Maroon and fawn, or blue and light blue. Also in maroon with red rear, very scarce and worth double. Price 2/10d. Issued September 1950. Renumbered 413 in 1954. 104mm. DC/RT/TP.

No. 30W. Electric Articulated Lorry	£195	£75	£35

Maroon with 'British Railways' on front and the trailer states '30W Hindle Smart Helics'. Price 4/6d. Issued February 1953. Renumbered 421 in 1954. 135mm. DC/RT/TP.

No. 33a. Mechanical Horse	–	£180	£75

Various colours, most common being grey. Only boxed when in a 33 series set with five trailers, commonly in red. With three wheels. Price 6d. Issued June 1935. Deleted 1940. 65mm. DC/RT.

MODEL	M/B	M/U	G/C

No. 33b. Flat Truck Trailer

	–	£100	£25

Grey or green and only boxed when
in 33 series set. Price 6d. Issued June
1935. Deleted 1940. 64mm. DC/RT.

No. 33b. Open Truck Trailer

	–	£100	£25

Grey or green. Also in yellow or red
and only boxed when in 33 series set.
Price 6d. Issued June 1935. Deleted
1940. 64mm. DC/RT.

No. 33d. Box Van Trailer

	–	£150	£75

Grey or green and only boxed when
in 33 series set. Price 8d. Issued June
1935. Deleted 1940. 70mm.
DC/RT/TP.

No. 33e. Refuse Wagon Trailer

	–	£150	£75

Most common colours are dark blue
or yellow. Also grey and green. Part
diecast on lower and pale blue upper
part tin-plate. Only boxed when in 22
series set. Price 8d. Issued June 1935.
Deleted 1940. 64mm. DC/RT/TP.

No. 33E. Refuse Wagon Trailer

	–	£75	£25

Grey or red and blue. Latter colour is
worth at least treble. This model is
much scarcer than the pre-war model.
Price 9d. Issued 1946. Deleted early
1947. 61mm. DC/RT/TP.

No. 33f. Petrol Tank Trailer

	–	£150	£50

Green with red tank. Also in green
with green tank, which is worth
double. Also a red with green tank
and a red with red tank. Only boxed
when with set 33. Price 8d. Issued
June 1935. Deleted 1940. 61mm.
DC/TP/RT.

No. 33f. 'Esso' Petrol Tank Trailer

Green with red tank. With green tug
and the word 'Esso' in gold on sides.
Price 1/6d. Issued 1937. Deleted
1940. 61mm. DC/RT/TP.

Trailer only	–	£250	£100
With matching tug	–	£350	£150

No. 33f. 'Castrol' Petrol Tank Trailer

Red with green tank and red tug. The words 'Wakefield Castrol Motor Oil' in red and black on sides. Price 1/6d. Issued 1937. Deleted 1940. 61mm. DC/RT/TP.

Trailer only	–	£250	£100
With matching tug	–	£350	£150

No. 33W. Mechanical Horse and Open Wagon

Colours are very important with regard to this model. With grey cab and grey rear; dark green cab and dark green rear; dark green cab and maroon rear; red cab and fawn rear; blue cab and cream rear; brown cab and brown rear; and yellow cab and yellow rear. Price 2/6d. Issued October 1947. Renumbered to 415 in 1954. Deleted 1959. 102mm. DC/RT/TP.

Dark green and darker green	–	£150	£45
Dark green and maroon	–	£175	£55
Red and fawn or yellow and yellow	–	£150	£45
Grey and grey or brown and brown	–	£125	£35
Blue and cream	–	£250	£75

No. 60y. Thompson Aircraft Tender

The box for this model is very, very rare and any collector will pay £150 for the empty box and possibly more. Red with the word 'Shell Aviation Services' on sides in gold. With three wheels and driver cast in. Price 8d. Issued 1938. Deleted 1940. 84mm. DC/TP/RW.

Box	£150		
Model	£1750	£500	£100

No. 107A. Sack Truck

£450

Blue. Only boxed in sets of six, for which I give a mint and boxed price. Price 9d. Issued June 1949. Renumbered 385 in 1954. 65mm. DC.

MODEL	M/B	M/U	G/C

No. 151b. Six-Wheeled Transport Wagon
| | – | £450 | £100 |

Green. With six wheels and one spare. Holes in seats for passenger at rear. Price 1/1d. Issued February 1938. Deleted 1940. 100mm. DC/TP/RT.

No. 151B. Six-Wheeled Transport Wagon
| | – | £350 | £75 |

Green. Model has six wheels and one spare. Holes in seat for driver and passenger, also holes in rear, plus a tin-plate cover over rear. Price 3/6d. Issued 1946. Deleted 1948. 99mm. DC/TP/RT. Military model.

No. 151c. Cooker Trailer with Stand
| | – | £95 | £25 |

Green. Price 7d. Issued February 1938. Deleted 1940. 60mm. DC/RT. Military model.

No. 151C. Cooker Trailer with Stand
| | – | £65 | £15 |

Green. Price 1/-. Issued 1946. Deleted 1948. 60mm. DC/RT. Military model.

No. 151d. Water Tank Trailer
| | – | £95 | £25 |

Green. Price 4d. Issued February 1938. Deleted 1940. 52mm. DC/RT. Military model.

No. 151D. Water Tank Trailer
| | – | £65 | £15 |

Green. Post-war models in this series are scarce. They all have much thicker axles. Price 1/-. Issued 1946. Deleted 1948. 52mm. DC/RT. Military model.

No. 252. Refuse Wagon with Bedford Chassis
| £150 | £80 | £45 |

Fawn and green. Also in cream and green which is worth double. Tipping body with side and rear opening doors. Price 6/4d. Issued March 1954. Deleted 1964. 107mm. DC/TP/RT. This model had a box.

MODEL	M/B	M/U	G/C

No. 252. Refuse Wagon with Bedford Chassis

Fawn and green. Also in pale grey with orange cab; black with green shutters; green with black shutters. The orange, grey and green model also made with silver rather than black radiator grille. With windows. Price 5/6d. Issued 1960. Deleted 1965. 107mm. DC/RT/TP.

	M/B	M/U	G/C
Fawn and green	£100	£50	£25
Orange, grey and green	£120	£60	£35
Green and black	£150	£75	£35

No. 267. Emergency Paramedic Truck

	M/B	M/U	G/C
	£95	£55	£25

Red with silver trim, bumpers and wheels etc. Based on the television series 'Emergency' this model could also be in 'Fire Engines' or 'Ambulances'. Price £2.25p. Issued 1978. Deleted 1980. 119mm. DC/P.

No. 321. Guy 2-Ton Lorry

	M/B	M/U	G/C
	£95	£45	£15

Renumbering of 511 or 911. Second type front. Two-tone blue. Price 5/9d. Issued 1956. Deleted 1958. 132mm. DC/TP/RT.

No. 340. Land Rover

From its first issue in 1955 to 1964, the colours were green with cream seats, orange with dark green seats with all parts metal except tyres. From 1964 to 1968, the model was orange with dark green seats and red plastic wheels. Then the third version came out in 1968 and was deleted in 1971, in red with red or yellow seats, red plastic wheels, black plastic steering wheel in a completely new casting with body and seats much shallower. The body was minutely narrower with front bumper reinforced. Renumbering of 27D with tin-plate screen, spare wheel and driver. Price 4/5d. 90mm. DC/TP/RT/P.

MODEL	M/B	M/U	G/C
1955/64 version in green and cream	£80	£35	£20
1955/64 version in orange and green	£50	£25	£15
1964/68 version	£35	£20	£10
1968/71 version	£30	£15	£10

No. 341. Land Rover Trailer

Renumbering of 27M in 1955. There were three matching trailers: 1. Orange with red wheels or green with cream wheels and grey tyres; 2. Red plastic wheels with orange body with grey or black tyres; 3. Red with red or yellow plastic wheels. Price 2/-. Issued 1955. Deleted 1971. 79mm. DC/RT/TP.

	M/B	M/U	G/C
Green with cream wheels	£50	£25	£15
Orange with red wheels	£45	£20	£15
Orange with plastic wheels	£45	£20	£10
Red with red or yellow P/Ws	£35	£20	£10

No. 380. Convoy Skip Truck   £50   £30   £15

Lemon cab and chassis, and orange skip, black bumper and silver wheels. White cab interior. Price £1.45p. Issued 1978. Deleted 1980. 112mm. D/P.

No. 383. Convoy N.C.L. Truck   £50   £30   £15

All lemon cab, chassis and body with orange flash along each side. With the words 'National Carriers' and 'Medallion Guaranteed Deliveries' on sides. Black bumper, silver hubs. Price £1.45p. Issued 1978. Deleted 1980. 110mm. DC/P.

No. 384. Convoy Fire Rescue Truck   £65   £35   £15

Red and orange with the word 'Rescue' on yellow plastic board on sides. Price £1.25p. Issued 1977. Deleted 1980. 126mm. DC/P.

No. 385. Convoy Mail Truck   £65   £35   £15

Red with white cab interior complete with Royal Mail transfers and motifs. Price £1.25p. Issued 1978. Deleted 1980. 110mm. DC/P.

MODEL	M/B	M/U	G/C

No. 385. Sack Truck

Renumbering of 107A. Blue. Few
models in red, worth double. Price
9d. Issued 1954. Deleted 1958. 65mm.
DC. Never boxed except in sixes.

Price for box of 6	£50		

No. 386. Convoy 'Avis' Truck

	£50	£30	£15

Red with black chassis and the word
'Avis' on side. Price £1.25p. Issued
1977/78. Deleted 1980. 110mm.
DC/P.

No. 387. Convoy 'Pickfords' Truck

	£50	£30	£10

Dark blue with red cab, red chassis
and wide red flash on each side. With
the word 'Pickfords' in white lettering
on sides. Price £1.35p. Issued 1978.
Deleted 1980. 110mm. DC/P.

No. 400. BEV Electric Truck

	£45	£25	£10

Renumbering of 14A. Blue. Price
2/9d. Issued 1954. Deleted 1960.
85mm. DC/TP/RT.

No. 401. Coventry Climax Fork Lift Truck

	£45	£25	£5

Renumbering of 14C. Orange, black
and green with grey tyres. Driver cast
in. Price 6/7d. Issued 1954. Deleted
1964. 108mm. DC/TP/RT.

No. 402. Bedford 'Coca-Cola' Lorry

	£150	£75	£25

Red with white roof and crate load.
With the words 'Coca-Cola' and
designs on sides and front etc. Price
15/6d. Issued 1966. Deleted 1969.
121mm. DC/RT/P.

No. 404. Conveyancer Fork Lift Truck

Red and yellow with red pallet in plastic (stamped 973) and black forks with blue plastic driver and yellow plastic safety frame. Then from 1977 the body colour was yellow and orange with other details identical. Word 'Conveyancer' on front and sides. Price 12/11d. Issued 1969. Deleted 1980. 97mm. DC/P.

	M/B	M/U	G/C
Red and yellow 1969/1977	£45	£25	£10
Yellow and orange	£35	£25	£5

No. 405. Universal Jeep

Green or red and post 1966 models have red plastic wheels and body is all red. Tin-plate screen with spare wheel on right side of body at rear (LHD). Price 3/2d. Issued 1955. Deleted 1969. 83mm. DC/SW/TP/RT.

	M/B	M/U	G/C
1955/66 model	£55	£35	£15
1966/69 model	£45	£25	£10

No. 406. Commer Articulated Lorry

	M/B	M/U	G/C
	£175	£95	£35

This model was mentioned by Gibson, but no details ever given. Export only item, being 424 minus the plastic accessories. There are two colours, the first is a yellow cab with grey rear and blue plastic wheels, windows and interior. The second colour, dark green with black rear, green plastic wheels etc. is much rarer and worth treble. Price 9/11d. Issued 1963. Deleted 1966. DC/TP/RT. The boxes are very rare.

MODEL	M/B	M/U	G/C

No. 408. Big Bedford Lorry   £225   £100   £50

Blue cab and yellow trailer. Yellow
wheels with grey tyres. Price 9/11d.
Issued 1963. Deleted 1966. 165mm.
DC/RT.

**No. 409. Bedford Articulated
    Lorry**   £110   £60   £35

Yellow or orange cab with matching
trailer. Red wheels and black tyres.
Silver or black grille, bumper,
radiator and lights. Price 6/9d.
Issued 1954. Deleted 1960. 165mm.
DC/RT.

No. 410. Bedford End Tipper   £100   £50   £30

Red cab and chassis. Black wheels
and mudguards and cream or fawn
end tipper with hinged tail board.
Red wheels. Price 5/4d. Issued 1954.
Deleted 1960. 98mm. DC/RT/TP.

No. 411. Bedford Truck   £80   £40   £25

Renumbering of 25W. Green. Price
3/8d. Issued 1954. Deleted 1960.
104mm. DC/TP/RT.

No. 412. Austin Wagon   £80   £40   £25

Renumbering of 30J. Blue and
maroon. Also in yellow with blue
wheels. Price 2/9d. Issued 1954.
Deleted 1960. 104mm. DC/TP/RT.

No. 413. Austin Covered Wagon   £120   £50   £30

Blue with blue canvas. Maroon with
cream canvas. Blue with cream
canvas, worth double. Price 3/5d.
Issued 1954. Deleted 1960. 104mm.
DCTP/RT.

No 413. Austin Covered Wagon   £100   £40   £25

Red body and chassis. Off-white
cover on rear and matching lorry
wheels. Silver or black grille,
radiator and bumpers. Also red
bumpers. Price 3/5d. Issued 1954.
Deleted 1960. 104mm, DC/RT/TP.

**No. 414. Dodge Rear Tipping
    Wagon**

Renumbering of 30M. Green and
orange, grey and blue or maroon and
green. With tipping body and hinged
tailboard. Price 3/5d. Issued 1954.
Deleted 1964. 99mm. DC/RT/TP.

	M/B	M/U	G/C
Orange and green	£100	£50	£25
Maroon and green	£70	£40	£20

MODEL	M/B	M/U	G/C
Red and green	£65	£35	£15
Blue and grey	£50	£20	£15

No. 415. Mechanical Horse and Open Wagon

	£60	£30	£20

Renumbering of 33W. Blue horse with cream trailer. Also with red cab and beige rear. The box for this model is very rare and worth £10. Some models have rounded, rather than crimped axle ends, as does the blue and cream model. It is a 1954 or later issue. The 415 models have coloured hubs rather than black ones. A three-wheel tractor and two-wheel trailer. Price 2/10d. Issued 1954. Deleted 1959. 102mm. DC/RT.

No. 417. Leyland Comet Lorry

Renumbering of 531 and 931. Blue and yellow, red and yellow or green and yellow. With four wheels and one spare. Price 3/3d. Issued 1956. Deleted 1959. 144mm. DC/TP/RT.

Blue and yellow	£150	£65	£35
Red and yellow	£110	£65	£35
Green and yellow	£100	£45	£23

No. 418. Leyland Comet with Hinged Tailboard

	£100	£65	£35

Renumbering of 532 and 932. Green and orange. Price 5/6d. Issued 1956. Deleted 1959. 142mm. DC/TP/RT.

No. 418. Leyland Comet With Hinged Tailboard

	£150	£75	£45

Dark blue cab and chassis and sky blue body. Yellow wheels and grey tyres. Silver bumpers. Issued 1956. Deleted 1960. Price 6/3d. 142mm. DC/TP/RT.

No. 419. Leyland Comet Lorry

	£150	£75	£45

Renumbering of 533 and 933. Yellow with the words 'Portland Cement' and 'Ferrocrete' on sides. With four wheels and one spare. Price 5/6d. Issued 1956. Deleted 1959. 142mm. DC/TP/RT.

No. 420. Leyland Forward Control Lorry

Green with red wheels and grey interior. Also red, cream or grey.

MODEL	M/B	M/U	G/C
Price 2/5d. Issued October 1954. Deleted 1961. 107mm. DC/TP/RT.			
Green, red and grey	£150	£75	£35
Red, cream and grey	£110	£65	£25

No. 421. Hindle Smart Electric Lorry

	£150	£100	£35

Renumbering of 30W. Maroon with the words 'British Railways' on front trailer. Price 3/11d. Issued 1955. Deleted 1959. 135mm. DC/TP/RT.

No. 422. Thames Flat Truck

Renumbering of 30R. Green, dark green or red. Price 2/3d. Issued March 1954. Deleted 1960. 112mm. DC/TP/RT.

Green or dark green	£125	£75	£35
Red	£85	£50	£25

No. 424. Commer Convertible Truck

	£100	£50	£25

With yellow cab, grey rear, blue wheels and grey plastic stake sides or blue plastic canvas top as 406. Casting is the same as 430 at rear, but cab has seats and windows added. Four wheels and one spare, plus two wheels. Price 9/11d. Issued May 1963. Deleted 1966. 171mm. DC/TP/RT/P.

No. 425. Bedford TK Coal Wagon

	£95	£45	£15

Red and grey, with six bags of coal and set of scales. Silver petrol tank, bumpers etc. On door is a blue and yellow sign with 'Approved Coal Merchants' in white letters. The cab is red with the rear in red or grey, and also a grey or silver chassis. Price 9/3d. Issued 1964. Deleted 1969. 118mm. DC/RT/TP.

No. 428. Large Trailer

Grey, red or blue. Red model has silver wheels. The trailer was made to be used with Dinky toys 251, 300, 301, 340, 408, 409, 431 and 432. The trailer was also made to be used with Dinky Supertoys 905, 934, 961 and 962. All models were fitted with towing hooks. Price 3/10d. Issued 1955. Deleted 1964. 105mm. DC/TP/RT.

MODEL	M/B	M/U	G/C
Grey	£40	£10	£5
Red	£35	£7	£4
Blue	£55	£25	£15

No. 429. Trailer — £40 £10 £5

Green or red. With front wheel swivel and tow bar. Price 1/10d. Issued 1955. Deleted 1963. 69mm. DC/T.

No. 430. Breakdown Lorry — £75 £45 £15

Model replaced 25X. Green and orange, with grey tow hook. With working crane in silver finish and the words 'Dinky Service' on sides. Price 5/9d. Issued 1962. Deleted 1964. 123mm. DC/TP/RT.

No. 430. Commer Breakdown Lorry — £75 £45 £15

Red and grey with windows. Model was part plastic. Price 5/9d. Issued 1962. Deleted 1964. 123mm. DC/TP/RT.

No. 431. Guy Warrior 4-Ton Lorry — £90 £60 £15

Green and fawn Completely new casting, with four wheels and one spare. Price 4/9d. Issued 1958. Deleted 1964. 136mm. DC/TP/RT.

No. 432. Guy Flat Truck — £95 £55 £25

Renumbering of 512 and 912. Blue and red. Type 2 front with four wheels and one spare. Price 5/3d. Issued 1956. Deleted 1958. 132mm. DC/RT/TP.

No. 432. Guy Warrior Flat Truck — £550 £100 £65

Red and green. Price 5/3d. Issued 1958. Deleted 1964. 136mm. DC/TP/RT.

No. 433. Guy Flat Truck with Tailboard

Red and black. Also in two shades of green, blue cab, and orange rear. Type 2 front. Price 5/6d. Issued 1955. Deleted 1958. 132mm. DC/RT/TP.

Model	M/B	M/U	G/C
Red and black	£150	£75	£35
Two shades of green	£195	£100	£45

No. 434. Bedford TK Crash Truck

White with green flash. Also 'Top Rank' version with red cab, pale grey rear. Also rare red and cream. Also with red cab and white body with the words 'Auto Services'. With the words 'Top Rank Motorway Services' with operating winch and four wheels. Price 7/11d. 'Top Rank' made between 1964/65, and the red cab/pale grey rear made 1966/73. 122mm. DC/TP/RT/P.

Model	M/B	M/U	G/C
Red and cream	£115	£75	£25
Top Rank model	£95	£65	£15
Red and grey	£75	£35	£10

No. 435. Bedford TK Tipper

Light grey, blue and orange and a yellow version with black cab roof which was made between 1966 and 1971. With tipping rear and three let down flaps. This is a six wheeler. Price 7/11d. Issued 1964. Deleted 1971. 120mm. DC/RT/TP.

Model	M/B	M/U	G/C
Grey, blue and orange	£90	£50	£25
Yellow, black and silver	£75	£25	£10

No. 436. Atlas Copco Compressor Lorry

Yellow or mustard. With the words 'Atlas Copco' on sides. Sides open to show compressor. Price 6/9d. Issued February 1963. Deleted 1969.

Model	M/B	M/U	G/C
Yellow	£90	£50	£25
Mustard	£150	£75	£35

No. 437. Muir Hill 2WL Loader

Until 1969 in red. Then made in yellow from 1970 until 1978. With the words 'Taylor Woodrow' on rear. With working shovel. Price 9/11d. Issued February 1962. Deleted 1978. 117mm. DC/RT/P.

Model	M/B	M/U	G/C
Red	£65	£25	£10
Yellow	£50	£20	£10

No. 438. Bedford D800 Tipper Truck

Red cab, green tipper and white interior, with silver chassis, bumpers etc. Replaced by 440 in 1977, with a casting as per 438, but doors do not open. Price 9/11d. Issued 1970. Deleted 1978. 132mm. DC/P.

	M/B	M/U	G/C
No. 438 with red cab and yellow rear	£90	£45	£15
No. 440 with red cab and orange rear	£45	£20	£10

No. 439. 800 Ford Snow Plough Tipper

	£115	£65	£25

Blue, red and yellow with red stripe. Also with blue cab, pale grey rear and yellow plough. Main casting is the same as 438 and the plough as 958, nearly ten years later. Price 10/6d. Issued 1971. Deleted 1977. 194mm. DC/P.

No. 440. 'Mobilgas' Petrol Tanker

Renumbering of 30P, with two different transfers. First type is the same as 30P with white letters directly into red body and the second type is 440 only, and has blue letters on white background with the word 'Mobilgas'. Price 2/10d. Issued January 1956. Deleted 1961. 112mm. DC/TP/RT.

	M/B	M/U	G/C
First type	£150	£75	£35
Second type	£100	£40	£25

No. 441. 'Castrol' Petrol Tanker

	£175	£100	£50

Renumbering of 30PA. Green. Price 2/10d. Issued August 1954. Deleted 1960. 112mm. DC/TP/RT.

No. 442. 'Esso' Petrol Tanker

	£175	£100	£50

Renumbering of 30PB. Red with the words 'Esso Motor Oil Petrol'. Price 2/8d. Issued August 1954. Deleted 1960. 112mm. DC/TP/RT.

No. 442. Land Rover Breakdown Truck

	£95	£45	£25

White with red bonnet and red doors. With black crane and the words 'Motorway Rescue' on doors. Opening bonnet and opening doors. Price £1.75p. Issued 1973. Deleted 1980. 121mm. DC/P.

No. 442. Land Rover Breakdown Crane

	M/B	M/U	G/C
	£55	£25	£10

White, orange and black with orange panels on doors and bonnet. With silver trim and full working crane at rear. All plastic Speediwheels from 1976. Price £1.35p. Issued 1973. Deleted 1978, although some models may still be found in normal toyshops. Model mainly found in the fleamarkets etc. 121mm. DC/P.

No. 443. 'National Benzole' Petrol Tanker

	£350	£100	£45

Yellow with the words 'National Benzole Mixture' on sides. Price 2/-. Issued January 1957. Deleted 1958. 112mm. DC/TP/RT.

No. 448. Chevrolet El Camino Pick-Up and Trailers

	£150	£75	£35

Green and white with red trailers, open type. One trailer open and one closed. Both have two wheels plus door trailer. With the words 'Acme Trailer Hire'. Price 10/6d. Issued June 1963. Deleted 1968. 224mm. DC/TP/RT/P.

No. 448. Chevrolet Pick-Up Truck and Trailers

	£90	£45	£20

Turquoise, white and orange, with matching silver blue wheels. With bumper bar, headlights and red interior for cab, silver mudguards. The Acme badge is on the square box trailer at rear. Price 8/11d. Issued 1963. Deleted 1968. Overall length approx. 224mm. DC/TP/RT/P.

No. 449. Chevrolet El Camino Pick-Up

Green, turquoise and white. Also in red and gold. Price 4/11d. Issued August 1961. Deleted 1969. 111mm. DC/TP/RT/LHD/SS/FTS/S/W.

	M/B	M/U	G/C
Green, turquoise and white	£75	£45	£15
Red and gold	£150	£75	£35

No. 449. Johnston Road Sweeper

First introduced in 1971 in orange and metallic green, as No. 451.

With opening cab doors. Then
replaced in 1977 by No. 449, with
revised casting, when doors did not
open, but produced in the same colour
scheme. From 1978 the model was in
lemon or yellow with black fittings
and silver bumpers etc. Finally deleted
in 1980. Price 15/11d. 142mm. DC/P.

	M/B	M/U	G/C
No. 451 green and orange	£150	£75	£35
No. 449 green and orange	£75	£45	£15
No. 449 yellow	£60	£25	£10

No. 501. Foden Diesel Eight-Wheel Wagon

One of the most sought after series in
the Dinky range. Very popular but
also very expensive at time of issue.
For a while as far as collecting is
concerned, the Fodens were greatly
ignored until about 1976 and they are
now much prized and fairly expensive.
First version above could be called
501/2. Remarks about first and second
cabs for Guy Trucks apply here.
Model was renumbered 901 in 1954.
Colours are red and fawn and two-
tone blue. Price 7/6d. Issued October
1952. Renumbered in 1954. Deleted
1957. 188mm. DC/TP/RT.

	M/B	M/U	G/C
Red and fawn	£750	£150	£75
Two-tone blue	£550	£100	£50

No. 501. Foden Diesel Eight-Wheel Wagon

Early version had a one colour body
and cab. Colours known are: brown,
dark blue and grey (this model is also
known as 501/1A). Later on model
came in two colours. Red and fawn or
red and brown or brown and red or
fawn and brown, also in dark blue and
light blue. All colours are high priced.
Type 1 cab with eight wheels. the
later two-tone colour model known as
501/1B. With hook. With eight wheels
and one spare. Price 10/-. Issued
October 1947. Deleted 1952. 188mm.
DC/TP/RT.

	M/B	M/U	G/C
No. 501/1A	£395	£175	£75
No. 501/1B	£295	£125	£65

No. 502. Foden Flat Truck

Model was renumbered 902 in 1955.
Orange and green. Also with dark
blue cab and chassis with orange rear.
Price 7/-. Issued 1956. Deleted 1955.
Type 2 cab with eight wheels and one
spare. 188mm. DC/RT/TP.

	M/B	M/U	G/C
Orange and green	£350	£100	£50
Dark blue and orange	£275	£100	£50

No. 502. Foden Flat Truck

Red and blue. Also in dark green.
Other colours exist and I call this first
version 502/1A. Next version is
502/1B with blue cab and chassis, red
rear; or with orange cab and chassis
and green rear, and I price them
separately. With eight wheels and one
spare. Price 10/-. Issued October
1947. Deleted 1952. 188mm.
DC/TP/RT.

	M/B	M/U	G/C
No. 502/1A	£350	£125	£75
No. 502/1B	£250	£100	£50

No. 503. Foden Flat Truck with Tailboard

Early version as 503/1A in grey or
brown, and later as 503/1B in dark
blue and orange rear. Also red and
black or red and green with Type 1
cab. Price 10/-. Issued October 1947.
Deleted 1952. 188mm. DC/TP/RT.

	M/B	M/U	G/C
No. 503/1A	£395	£125	£75
No. 503/1B	£300	£125	£75

No. 503. Foden Flat Truck with Tailboard

	M/B	M/U	G/C
	£250	£100	£50

Model was renumbered 903 in 1955.
Blue and orange. Type 2 cab. Price
7/-. Issued 1952. Deleted 1955.
188mm. DC/TP/RT.

No. 504. Foden 14-Ton Tanker

Red and fawn, or in two-tone blue.
With first type cab with eight wheels
and one spare. This model I will price
as 504/1A. The second type cab
without advertising is in red and fawn
and this I call 504/1B. Price 9/6d.
Issued December 1948. Deleted 1952.
Both types were 188mm. DC/RT/TP.

	M/B	M/U	G/C
No. 504/1A	£450	£200	£100
No. 504/1B	£300	£100	£50

MODEL	M/B	M/U	G/C

No. 504. Foden 14-Ton Tanker 'Mobilgas'

	£400	£100	£50

Red. With the word 'Mobilgas' and motif in white on sides. Price 8/3d. Issued 1953. Renumbered 941 in 1954. 188mm. DC/TP/RT.

No. 505. Foden Flat Truck with Chains

Green, or the rare colour of red and grey. This Type 1 cab Foden with chains is very scarce because of its short run when made. Price 11/6d. Issued January 1952. Deleted September 1952. 188mm. DC/TP/RT.

Green	£250	£150	£75
Red and grey	£350	£170	£75

No. 505. Foden Flat Truck with Chains

	£300	£150	£75

Green or maroon. Type 2 cab with eight wheels and one spare. Price 11/6d. Issued September 1952. Renumbered 905 in 1955. 188mm. DC/RT/TP.

No. 511. Guy 4-Ton Lorry

Early Guy models have body and cab in one colour, brown or grey, while the later models were in two-tone blue and red and fawn. Type 1 front with four wheels and one spare. Price 7/-. Issued October 1947. Renumbered 911 in 1954. 132mm. DC/RT/TP.

Brown or grey	£350	£150	£175
Two-tone blue or red and fawn	£250	£100	£50

No. 512. Guy Flat Truck

Yellow or maroon when first made. Later colours were dark blue and red; or dark blue and orange. Type 1 in yellow or maroon with four wheels and one spare. Price 7/-. Issued October 1947. Renumbered 912 in 1954. 132mm. DC/RT/TP.

Yellow or maroon	£250	£100	£50
Dark blue and red	£150	£75	£35
Dark blue and orange	£100	£50	£25

No. 513. Guy Flat Truck with Tailboard

This model came out in two-colour variations which I call A and B. The

MODEL	M/B	M/U	G/C

first in yellow or brown and also in the rare dark blue. Then two-tone green; blue and orange; and also two-tone red and black. Type 1 front with four wheels and one spare. Price 7/-. Issued October 1947. Deleted 1954. 132mm. DC/TP/RT.

MODEL	M/B	M/U	G/C
A. Yellow or brown	£150	£75	£35
A. Dark blue	£350	£150	£75
B. Two-tone green or dark blue and orange	£160	£100	£50
B. Two-tone red and black	£95	£50	£25

No. 521. Bedford Articulated Lorry

	M/B	M/U	G/C
	£75	£35	£15

Red or yellow with black wings and wheels. Four wheels, one spare and two wheels. Price 7/6d. Issued April 1948. Renumbered 921 in 1954. 166mm. DC/RT/TP.

No. 522. Big Bedford Lorry

	M/B	M/U	G/C
	£95	£35	£15

Blue and yellow, red and yellow or red and brown. Price 5/-. Issued June 1949. Renumbered 931 in 1954. 144mm. DC/TP/RT.

	M/B	M/U	G/C
Blue and yellow.	£220	£100	£50
Others	£95	£35	£15

No. 531. Leyland Comet Lorry

	M/B	M/U	G/C
	£95	£35	£15

Blue and yellow, red and yellow or red and brown. Price 5/-. Issued June 1949. Renumbered 931 in 1954. 144mm. DC/TP/RT.

No. 532. Leyland Comet with Hinged Tailboard

	M/B	M/U	G/C
	£115	£75	£45

Green and orange. Also two-tone blue and the rare two-tone green, worth double. Price 7/9d. Issued January 1952. Renumbered 932 in 1954. 142mm. DC/TP/RT.

No. 533. Leyland Cement Wagon

	M/B	M/U	G/C
	£75	£35	£15

Yellow. With the words 'Ferrocrete' and 'Portland Cement' on the sides. With four wheels and one spare. Price 6/-. Issued February 1953. Renumbered 973 in 1954. 142mm. DC/TP/RT.

No. 551. Trailer

Red, green or grey. Four wheels with front axle swivel. Price 3/5d. Issued May 1948. Renumbered 951 in July 1954. 105mm. DC/TP/RT.

	M/B	M/U	G/C
Red and green	£35	£15	£5
Grey	£25	£15	£4

No. 563. Renault Pick-Up Truck

	£55	£30	£15

Orange with green removable canvas hood. French Dinky imported into England. With four wheels and one spare. Price 6/5d. Issued in France 1960. Introduced in UK 1962. Deleted 1967. 96mm. DC/TP/RT/P.

No. 579. Simca Glaziers Lorry

	£135	£75	£35

Another French Dinky. Yellow and green. Also in grey and green and the model often has 33C on the box which was the original French number from 1956 to 1959. Model had mirror and pane of glass. With the words 'Saint-Gobain' and 'Miroitier' on sides. Price 8/8d. Issued in France 1956. Deleted 1965. Issued in UK 1962. Deleted 1965. 128mm. DC/RT/TP/P.

No. 581. Horsebox

	£125	£75	£35

Maroon. With side and rear opening doors and words 'British Railways' and 'Express Horsebox Hire Service' on each side. Price 15/11d. Issued April 1953. Renumbered 981 in 1954. 175mm. DC/RT.

No. 581. Berliet Truck with Container

	£125	£75	£35

Another French Dinky. Red and grey with six wheels and one spare with removable container. Often has 34B on box. Price 9/-. Issued in France 1956. Deleted 1971. Issued in UK 1962. Deleted 1966. 130mm. DC/RT.

No. 582. Pullmore Car Transporter

	£150	£100	£45

Blue and grey. This is on a Bedford Tractor with the words 'Dinky Toys Delivery Service' on sides. Rear folds down. Price 14/6d. Issued May 1953.

MODEL	M/B	M/U	G/C

Renumbered 982 in 1954. 250mm.
DC/TP/RT.

No. 591. A.E.C. Tanker

	M/B	M/U	G/C
No. 591. A.E.C. Tanker	£500	£200	£75

Red and yellow. This is an A.E.C.
Monarch Thompson Tanker with the
words 'Shell Chemicals Ltd' on sides.
Price 8/8d. Issued September 1952.
Renumbered 991 in 1954. 151mm.
DC/TP/RT.

No. 618. A.E.C. Articulated Transporter with Helicopter

	M/B	M/U	G/C
No. 618. A.E.C. Articulated Transporter with Helicopter	£250	£150	£75

Military colours. Price £2.25p. Issued
1976. Deleted 1980. 318mm. DC/P.

No. 642. R.A.F. Pressure Refueller

	M/B	M/U	G/C
No. 642. R.A.F. Pressure Refueller	£100	£50	£25

R.A.F. blue. Price 7/9d. Issued May
1957. Deleted 1962. 142mm including
hook. DC/TP/RT. Also a Military
model.

No. 893. Unic Pipe Line Transporter

	M/B	M/U	G/C
No. 893. Unic Pipe Line Transporter	£150	£100	£50

Sandy or grey. With ten wheels, two
spares and six removable pipe lengths.
Price 13/-. Imported from France
1962. Deleted 1966. Issued in France
1959. Deleted 1970.

No. 894. Unic/Boillot Car Transporter

	M/B	M/U	G/C
No. 894. Unic/Boillot Car Transporter	£250	£100	£50

French Dinky imported into England.
Grey or dark blue, worth double.
With lowering ramp, 6 x 2 wheels and
one spare. With the words 'Dinky
Toys Service Liaison' on sides. Price
35/-. 325mm. DC/TP/RT/P.

No. 901. Foden Diesel Eight-Wheeled Wagon

Red and grey. Also in two shades of
blue. Type 2 cab with six wheels and
one spare. Price 7/9d. Issued January
1955 as renumbering of 501. Deleted
1957. 188mm. DC/TP/RT.

	M/B	M/U	G/C
Red and grey	£150	£100	£50
Blue	£100	£75	£35

No. 902. Foden Flat Truck

Orange and green. Also blue and
orange. Type 2 cab with eight wheels

and one spare. Price 7/3d. A
renumbering of 502/2 in 1955.
Deleted 1960. 188mm. DC/RT/TP.

	M/B	M/U	G/C
Orange and green	£500	£100	£75
Blue and orange	£400	£100	£50

No. 903. Foden Flat Truck with Tailboard

	£150	£75	£35

Blue and orange. Type 2 cab with
eight wheels and one spare. Price
7/3d. Issued January 1955 as
renumbering of 503. Deleted 1960.
188mm. DC/TP/RT.

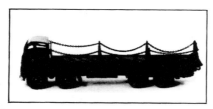

No. 905. Foden Flat Truck with Chains

Maroon or green. Also in maroon or
red and grey. Type 2 cab with eight
wheels and one spare. Price 9/6d.
Issued January 1955 as renumbering
of 505. Deleted 1964. 188mm.
DC/TP/RT.

	M/B	M/U	G/C
Maroon or green	£150	£75	£35
Red and grey	£180	£100	£50

No. 908. Mighty Antar with Transformer

	£650	£200	£100

Yellow and grey. The transformer is a
French Dinky from the 898 Berliet
Transformer Carrier. With 5 x 2
wheels and one spare. Price 21/-.
Issued October 1962. Deleted 1964.
295mm. DC/RT/P.

No. 911. Guy 4-Ton Lorry

	£150	£75	£45

Two-tone blue. With Type 2 front.
Price 5/6d. Issued January 1954 as
renumbering of 911. Renumbered 431
in 1956. 132mm. DC/TP/RT.

No. 912. Guy Flat Truck

	£195	£100	£50

Blue and orange. With Type 2 front.
Price 5/6d. Issued 1954 as

renumbering of 512. Renumbered 432
in 1956. 132mm. DC/RT/TP.

No. 913. Guy Flat Truck with Tailboard

Blue and orange. Also two-tone green.
With Type 2 front. Price 5/11d.
Issued 1954 as renumbering of 513.
Renumbered 433 in 1956. 132mm.
DC/TP/RT.

	M/B	M/U	G/C
Blue and orange	£175	£100	£50
Two-tone green	£180	£75	£35

No. 914. AEC Articulated Lorry

£150 £100 £50

Red and green, or red and green with
green or grey canopy. With the words
'British Road Services' on sides. Price
7/11d. Issued 1965. Deleted 1971.
210mm. DC/RT/P.

No. 915. AEC Vehicle with Flat Trailer

£125 £100 £50

Red cab and white rear, and the
words 'Truck Hire Company' in
white letters on cab doors. Price
£1.25p. Issued 1973. Deleted 1975.
210mm. DC/P.

No. 917. Mercedes Truck and Trailer

£95 £40 £25

Blue, yellow, and white. With silver
bumpers, grille, etc. Opening cab
doors and red interior of cab. With
detachable canopies on special box
bodies. Price 42/6d. Issued 1967.
Then replaced by No. 940 in 1977.
397mm. DC/P.

No. 917. Mercedes Truck and Trailer

£175 £125 £75

Black cab with red interior, with
orange box trailers and lift off white
covers. White wheels and white top
on cab roof. Price 42/6d. Issued 1967.
Replaced by No. 940 in 1977.
397mm. DC/P.

No. 921. Bedford Articulated Lorry

£150 £100 £50

Yellow. With four and two wheels.
Price 5/11d. Issued 1954 as
renumbering of 521. Renumbered 409
in 1956. 166mm. DC/TP/RT.

MODEL	M/B	M/U	G/C

No. 922. Big Bedford Lorry

Maroon and fawn. Blue and yellow.
With four wheels and one spare. Price
8/9d. Issued 1954 as renumbering of
522. Renumbered 408 in 1956.
156mm. DC/TP/RT.

Maroon and fawn	£195	£100	£50
Blue and yellow	£150	£75	£35

No. 924. Aveling Barford Centaur Dump Truck

	£75	£50	£25

Yellow, black and red. This model
should also appear in the Construction
Site Vehicles section. Price £1.45p.
Issued 1972. Deleted 1977. 180mm.
DC/P.

No. 925. Leyland Dump Truck

	£185	£100	£50

Chassis in silver, cab is white with
blue roof and the dumper body is red
or orange, with tilting cab. Price
6/11d. Issued 1965. Deleted 1970.
192mm. DC/RT.

No. 931. Leyland Comet Lorry

Blue and yellow. Also in red and
yellow. Price 5/3d. Issued January
1955 as renumbering of 531.
Renumbered 417 in 1956. 144mm.
DC/TP/RT.

Blue and yellow	£90	£50	£25
Red and yellow	£75	£40	£15

No. 932. Leyland Comet with Hinged Tailboard

Two-tone blue or green and orange.
Price 6/-. Issued January 1955 as
renumbering of 532. Renumbered 418
in 1956. 142mm. DC/TP/RT.

Two-tone blue	£95	£60	£25
Green and orange	£65	£45	£15

No. 932. Leyland Comet Truck with Hinged Tailboard

	£95	£55	£25

Green and orange. Colours are darker
than previous 932. Price 6/-. Issued
1954. Deleted 1956. 142mm.
DC/TP/RT.

MODEL	M/B	M/U	G/C

No. 933. Leyland Cement Wagon

	M/B	M/U	G/C
	£200	£75	£35

Yellow. Price 5/6d. Issued 1954 as renumbering of 533. Renumbered 419 in 1956. 142mm. DC/RT/TP.

No. 934. Leyland Octopus Wagon

	£420	£100	£75

Yellow, green and red. With eight wheels and one spare. Price 8/9d. Issued April 1956. Deleted 1964. 194mm. DC/RT/TP.

No. 935. Leyland Octopus Flat Truck with Chains

	£700	£250	£100

Blue and grey. Eight wheels and one spare. Price 10/9d. Issued 1963. Deleted 1963. 192mm. DC/TP/ Chains/RT.

No. 936. Leyland Eight-Wheeled Chassis

	£100	£50	£35

Red and silver. Also in red, white and grey. With the words 'Another Leyland on Test' plus yellow five-ton weights. Price 14/11d. Issued September 1964. Deleted 1970. SW/D/12 wheels and three movable weights. 197mm. DC/RT/P.

No. 940. Mercedes Benz Truck

	£95	£50	£20

White with grey canopy, red plastic wheels and red chassis. This is 917 minus the Trailer and re-cast. The cab doors do not open. Price £2.76p. Issued 1977. Deleted 1980. 200mm. DC/P.

No. 941. 'Mobilgas' Foden Tanker

	£500	£250	£100

Red with Type 2 casting. Price 10/6d. Issued January 1955 as the renumbering of 504. Deleted 1957. 188mm DC/TP/RT.

No. 942. 'Regent' Foden Tanker

£650   £250   £100

Red, blue and white, with Type 2 casting. Eight wheels and one spare. Price 10/6d. Issued June 1955. Deleted 1957. 188mm. DC/RT/TP.

No. 943. 'Esso' Leyland Octopus Tanker

£550   £150   £75

Red with eight wheels and one spare. With the words 'Esso', 'Petroleum Company' on sides. 192mm. DC/TP/RT.

No. 944. 'Shell B.P.' 4000 Gallon Tanker

£295   £150   £100

Yellow and white with eight wheels and one spare. Plastic tank. With the words 'Shell B.P.' and badges on sides etc. Price 10/6d. Issued July 1963. Deleted 1964. 192mm. DC/TP/RT/P.

No. 945. Oil Tanker, Promotional 'Lucas' Special

£900   £400   £250

Manufactured by Dinky products for the Lucas Oil Company as a promotional sales gimmick in 1978, using the old casting of 945, and deleted the same year. Green body with black trailer cab chassis and black cab interior. With white lettering showing the words 'Lucas Oil Company'. With grey opening tops. Price £4.95p. 266mm. DC/P.

No. 945. 'Esso' Fuel Tanker

£100   £50   £25

White with red and blue markings and the word 'Esso' on sides. With opening tops. Price 19/11d. Issued 1966. Deleted 1977. 266mm. DC/RT/TP.

MODEL	M/B	M/U	G/C
No. 948. 'McLean' Tractor Trailer	£250	£100	£75

Red and grey with opening rear doors. Tractor with six wheels, and trailer with eight wheels. With two bogies. The words 'McLean Winston Salem', and badge on sides of Tractor. With the words 'McLean Trucking Company', on trailer. Price 16/6d. Issued 1961. Deleted 1965/66. Overall length 290mm. DC/RT/P. Well known as a rare and expensive 1960s Dinky toy.

No. 950. Foden S20 Fuel Tanker

First colour scheme was red cab, black cab chassis, white plastic tank with black fillers on red chassis, with red wheels and black cab interior. The second colour scheme was the same as first type from the wheels which are cream, the fillers which are silver and the cab chassis is red. With detachable cab and opening door. Price £5.52p. Issued 1977. Deleted 1980. 266mm. DC/P.

	M/B	M/U	G/C
First colour type (1977)	£125	£75	£35
Second colour type (1978)	£95	£55	£25
No. 950. Car Transporter Set	£750	–	–

The cars in this set are standard, apart from the Mini-Moke (342) which has no roof. First made in 1969, with 974 Hoynor Car Transporter; 136 Vauxhall Viva; 138 Hillman Imp; 162 Triumph 1300; 168 Ford Escort; and the 342 Austin Mini Moke. Price 67/6d. Issued 1969. Deleted 1970. Mint and boxed set only.

	M/B	M/U	G/C
No. 951. Trailer	£35	£15	£10

Renumbering of 551. Grey. With four wheels. Price 3/2d. Issued 1954. Renumbered 428 in 1955. 105mm. DC/TP/RT.

	M/B	M/U	G/C
No. 974. Hoynor Car Transporter	£125	£75	£35

Orange and yellow with blue cab. With silver hubs etc, eight wheels, plus two. Price 29/11d. Issued 1968. Deleted 1976. 322mm. DC/P.

No. 978. Refuse Wagon

First version was in light grey and green, made in October 1964. The second was issued in 1973 when the green became metallic with silver wheels and black chassis. The grey became much darker. In 1978 the third version came with the yellow cab, otherwise as the second model. Model was deleted in 1980. The words 'Refuse Collector' and crest on sides. The body tips forward and back with opening rear doors, tip-down foot stands and two buckets. Price 14/11d. SW/S/W. 152mm. DC/RT/TP.

	M/B	M/U	G/C
First version	£80	£30	£15
Second version	£65	£25	£15
Third version	£60	£20	£10

No. 979. Racehorse Transporter Wagon

	M/B	M/U	G/C
	£350	£175	£75

Light grey and yellow with two plastic horses. With the words 'Newmarket Racehorse Transport Service Ltd' on sides. Price 15/3d. Issued October 1961. Deleted 1964. 173mm. DC/RT/P.

No. 980. Coles Hydra Truck 150T

Yellow, silver and black with swing-down outriggers, a rotating telescopic boom and a winding mechanism. Issued in 1972 in bright yellow. In 1978 a much darker yellow model came out. Finally deleted in 1980. Price £3.35p. 210mm. DC/P.

	M/B	M/U	G/C
1973 model	£120	£80	£45
1978 model	£75	£65	£25

No. 981. Horsebox

	M/B	M/U	G/C
	£125	£75	£35

Maroon. The words 'British Railways' on sides. Price 14/11d. Issued January 1955 as renumbering of 581. Replaced by 979 in 1961. Deleted 1964. 175mm. DC/RT.

MODEL	M/B	M/U	G/C

No. 982. Pullmore Car Transporter

Renumbering of 582. Early model was all pale-blue with fawn tracks for the cars. From 1958 the model had a mid-blue cab with pale-blue rear and tracks painted differently. From 1960 the model had windows. Price 14/6d. Issued 1955. Deleted 1964. 250mm. DC/TP/RT.

	M/B	M/U	G/C
First version 1955	£150	£100	£50
Second version 1958	£120	£75	£35
Third version 1960	£95	£55	£25

No. 983. Dinky Car Carrier and Trailer
£260 £100 £50

This set contains models 984 and 985. Red and grey. With the words 'Dinky Toys Delivery Service' on sides. This is a first class investment and much sought after. Price 38/6d. Issued July 1958. Deleted 1963. Overall length 450mm. DC/TP/RT.

No. 984. Car Carrier
£100 £40 £30

Red and grey with the words 'Dinky Auto Service' in yellow or orange on sides. The rear ramp lowers and the upper storey hinges. Worked by a handle. Price 22/-. Issued July 1958. Deleted 1963. 240mm. DC/RT/TP.

No. 985. Dinky Trailer
£50 £30 £15

Red and grey with the words 'Dinky Auto Service' on sides in yellow and orange. The rear ramp lowers and hinges and front wheels swivel. Price 16/-. Issued July 1958. Deleted 1963. 196mm. DC/RT.

No. 989. Car Transporter
£225 £100 £50

Yellow, blue and grey. Made for the U.S.A. market and is scarce. Words 'Auto Transporters' on sides. Equivalent price 28/11d. Issued 1963. Deleted 1969. 240mm. DC/TP/RT.

No. 991. A.E.C. 'Shell Chemicals' Tanker
£200 £100 £75

Renumbering of 591. Red and yellow. With words 'Shell Chemicals Ltd' on the sides. Price 6/3d. Issued January 1955. Deleted 1958. 151mm. DC/RT.

MODEL	M/B	M/U	G/C

No. 994. Loading Ramp for Pullmore Carrier

£7   £5   £2

Blue. Price 1/6d. Issued December 1954. Deleted 1964. 233mm TP.

No. 3201. Mogul Dump Truck

£50   £30   £10

Orange and black with white wheels. The making of such items as these brought about the end of Dinky toys, but at the same time, the end of Dinky as a firm, meant the start and rise of investment toys for collectors. Price £2.45p. Issued 1977. Deleted 1980. 286mm.

No. 3222. Articulated Tipper

£50   £30   £10

Mustard and black, with the word 'Mogul' in thick black letters on white background. With large thick black plastic tyres and silver hubs on wheels. Price £2.45p. Issued 1976. Deleted 1978. 525mm. P/Steel Toy.

No. 3243. Tractor Digger

£50   £30   £10

Lime, black and white plastic. With thick black tyres and plastic hubs. Price £2.45p. Issued 1977. Deleted 1980. 303mm. P/Steel.

No. 3265. Tractor and Trailer

£50   £30   £10

Orange, grey and black with thick tyres and plastic hubs. Price £2.45p. Issued 1976. Deleted 1980. 463mm. P/Steel toy.

No. 3294. Breakdown Truck

£50   £30   £10

Medium rich blue, orange and black, with silver hook and blue wheels. Thick tyres and the word 'Mogul'. Price £2.45p. Issued 1976. Deleted 1980. 268mm. P/Steel toy.

No. 3294. Mogul Breakdown Truck

£65   £45   £25

White and blue, with blue plastic wheels and red crane. Price £2.45p. Issued 1977. Deleted 1980. 268mm. P/Steel toy.

SHIPS, BOATS AND PLANES
AND OTHER CRAFT

Information on Dinky ships is very hard to find but I trust this section will please the collectors of these fine diecast items, who have waited a very long time for such information regardless of how little it may be.

MODEL	M/B	M/U	G/C
No. 50. Complete Gift Set			
Special presentation box (15 pieces). Contains: 50a, 50b (two of same); 50c, 50d, 50f (three of same), 50g, 50h (three of same) and 50k. Price 3/7d. Issued July 1935. Deleted 1940.			
Price of set only	£450		
No. 50a. Battle Cruiser 'Hood'	–	£40	£10
Royal Navy livery. Only boxed in set 50. Price 9d. Issued June 1934. Deleted 1940. Scale 1 inch to 150 ft.			
No. 50b. Battleship 'Nelson'	–	£40	£10
Royal Navy livery. Only boxed in set 50. Price 6d. Issued June 1934. Deleted 1940. Scale as 50a.			
No. 50c. Cruiser 'Effingham'	–	£50	£15
Royal Navy livery. Only boxed in set 50. Price 4d. Issued June 1934. Deleted 1940. Scale as 50a.			
No. 50d. Cruiser 'York'	–	£50	£15
Royal Navy livery. Only boxed in set 50. Price 4d. Issued June 1934. Deleted 1940. Scale as 50a.			
No. 50e. Cruiser 'Delhi'	–	£50	£15
Royal Navy livery. Only boxed in set 50. Price 4d. Issued June 1934. Deleted 1940. Scale as 50a.			
No. 50f. Destroyer 'Broke' Class	–	£40	£10
Royal Navy livery. Only boxed in set 50. Price 1d. Issued June 1934. Deleted 1940. Scale as 50a.			

MODEL	M/B	M/U	G/C

No. 50g. Submarine 'K' Class

	–	£40	£10

Royal Navy livery. Only boxed in set 50. Price 1d. Issued July 1935. Deleted 1940. Scale as 50a.

No. 50h. Destroyer 'Amazon' Class

	–	£40	£10

Royal Navy livery. Only boxed in set 50. Price 1d. Issued 1935. Deleted 1940. Scale as 50a.

No. 50k. Submarine 'X' Class

	–	£50	£15

Royal Navy livery. Only boxed in set 50. Price 1d. Issued July 1935. Deleted 1940. Scale as 50a.

No. 51. Gift Set

Complete set of six ships in a special presentation box, all in their authentic liner liveries. Includes: 51b Europa; 51c Rex; 51d Empress; 51e Strathaird; 51f Queen of Bermuda; and 51g the Britannic. Price 3/6d. Issued June 1934. Deleted 1940.

Mint and boxed set only £450

No. 51a. Liner 'United States of America'

	£95	£50	£15

Made to the same scale as the 'Queen Mary', and in a nice presentation box and on rollers. Price 1/-. Issued 1936. Deleted 1938. Very scarce as only a few were released.

No. 51b. Liner 'Europa Star'

	–	£95	£35

Authentic livery and on the same scale as the 'Queen Mary'. Only boxed in set 51. Price 1/-. Issued June 1934. Deleted 1940.

No. 51c. The 'Rex'

	–	£95	£35

Authentic livery and on the same scale as the 'Queen Mary'. Only boxed in set 51. Price 9d. Issued June 1934. Deleted 1940.

No. 51d. The 'Empress of Britain'

	£95	£50	£15

Authentic livery. In nice presentation box on the same scale as the 'Queen Mary'. Price 8d. Issued June 1934. Deleted 1940.

MODEL	M/B	M/U	G/C
No. 51e. The 'Strathaird'	–	£55	£25

Authentic livery and on the same scale as the 'Queen Mary'. Only boxed in set 51. Price 6d. Issued June 1934. Deleted 1940.

No. 51f. The 'Queen of Bermuda'	–	£40	£10

Authentic livery and on the same scale as the 'Queen Mary'. Only boxed in set 51. Price 6d. Issued June 1934. Deleted 1940.

No. 51g. The 'Britannic'	–	£50	£15

Authentic livery and on the same scale as the 'Queen Mary'. Only boxed in set 51. Price 6d. Issued June 1934. Deleted 1940.

No. 52a. Cunard White Star Liner

The Cunard White Star was introduced as above title in June 1934, and by December that year it had gained the name of 'Queen Mary'. Deleted 1940. Reissued post-war from 1946. Deleted 1952. Pre-war model has plastic rollers and the post-war item has brass rollers. There was also a 52m pre-war without rollers in a plain box. Price 1/- in fancy presentation box, 9d in a plain box. Scale was 1 inch to 150 ft.

	M/B	M/U	G/C
52a or 52b pre-war	£50	£30	£15
52m pre-war	£40	£20	£10
52A post-war	£25	£15	£5

No. 52c. French Liner 'Normandie'	£75	£55	£25

Made to the same scale as the 'Queen Mary' by French Dinky Meccano (France) Ltd. Price 1/6d. Issued in France 1935. Imported to UK during same period. Deleted 1940. In presentation box.

No. 53az. The Battleship 'Dunkerque'	£75	£55	£25

Made in France. Imported into England. Casting 'steam' from funnel. Price 6d. Issued 1937. Deleted 1940. Scale as 50a. In special presentation box.

MODEL	M/B	M/U	G/C
No. H1. Speed Boat 'Hawk'	£250	£100	£50

Red and cream. With clockwork
motor the boat travels over 100 ft on
one winding. Price 2/11d. Issued
1937. Deleted 1940. Length 270mm,
beam 85mm. In presentation box.

No. H1/a.	£95	£55	£25

Blue and white. Otherwise as H1.

No. H1/b.	£95	£55	£25

Green and ivory. Otherwise as H1.

No. H2. Speed Boat 'Swift'	£95	£55	£25

Red and cream. Long running
clockwork motor which runs for over
300 ft on one winding. Price 7/6d.
Issued 1937. Deleted 1940. Length
360mm. Beam 85mm.

No. H2/a	£150	£75	£45

Blue and white. Otherwise as H2.

No. H2/b	£250	£100	£75

Yellow and white. Otherwise as H2.

No. H3. Speed Boat 'The Condor Special'	£225	£100	£65

One of the best boats ever made. This
model could travel over 500 ft on one
winding of the strong clockwork
motor. Price 12/6d. Issued 1937.
Deleted 1940. Length 416mm. Beam
85mm.

No. H3/a. Speed Boat 'Gannet'	£275	£150	£100

Blue and white. Otherwise as H3.

No. H3/b. Speed Boat 'Curlew'	£275	£150	£100

Green and ivory. Otherwise as H3.

No. H4. Limousine Boat 'The Venture'	£275	£175	£75

Red and cream. Another clockwork
model. Travels over 500 ft on one
winding. Price 15/6d. Issued 1938.
Deleted 1940. Length 416mm. Beam
85mm.

No. H4/a	£300	£150	£100

Blue and white. Otherwise as H4.

MODEL	M/B	M/U	G/C

No. H4/b
£350 £150 £100

Jade and ivory. Otherwise as H4.

No. H5. 'The Viking' Cabin Cruiser
£350 £150 £100

Red and cream. With strong clockwork motor that makes the boat travel 600 ft on one winding. Price 16/6d. Issued 1938. Deleted 1940. Length 416mm. Beam 85mm.

No. H5/a
£350 £150 £100

Blue and white. Otherwise as H5.

No. H5/b
£450 £250 £150

Jade and ivory. Otherwise as H5.

No. H6. Toy Water Duck Boat

Tin-plate model with strong clockwork motor, in the shape of a duck. The model travels over 150 ft on one winding. Price 2/6d. Issued 1939. Deleted 1940. Length approximately 250mm. Beam 85mm. The first few models brought out were in a special presentation box.

	M/B	M/U	G/C
Special presentation box	£350	£150	£50
Ordinary box	£175	£100	£50

No. SB1. Racing Boat Racer I Special
£250 £150 £50

Cream and green. With strong clockwork motor which travels over 150 ft on one winding. Price 4/6d. Issued 1938. Deleted 1940. Length 216mm. Beam 54mm.

No. SB2. Racing Boat Racer II Special
£350 £150 £100

Cream and blue. Travels fast over 200 ft on one winding. Price 8/6d. Issued 1938. Deleted 1940. Length 324mm. Beam 85mm.

No. SB3. Racing Boat Racer III Special
£1250 £500 £250

Red and cream. This boat won many awards at the time of its release. It travels fast over 300 ft on one winding. Price 14/6d. Issued 1939. Deleted 1940. Length 432mm. Beam 98mm. Special gift box.

MODEL	M/B	M/U	G/C
No. SB3/a	£1450	£750	£350

Green and ivory. Otherwise as SB3. A
rare colour.

	M/B	M/U	G/C
No. SB3/b	£1450	£750	£350

Cream and blue. Otherwise as SB3.
Another rare colour.

	M/B	M/U	G/C
No. 281. Military Hovercraft	£25	£10	£5

There is a gunner on top of cabin
with aerial on one side. Otherwise
casting is identical to 290. Green and
black with white plastic parts and
black gunner, with the word 'Army'
and Union Jack on sides. Price
£1.76p. Issued 1973. Deleted 1976.

No. 290. SRN-6 Hovercraft	£25	£10	£5

Red, white and yellow with black
base. All blue base from 1971. This
model has opening door, propeller and
radar scanner which turn as the model
is pushed along. Price 17/11d. Issued
1970. Deleted 1976. 139mm. DC/P.

No. DH1. Jumping Frog	£150	£50	£25

Green with brown dots. Model
released at the same time as the pre-
war boats and proved a great
favourite. Price 3/6d. Issued 1939.
Deleted 1940. 85mm. With strong
clockwork motor.

No. 671. Mk 1 Corvette	£25	£10	£5

Grey, brown and black, with rocket
firer. Price £1.58p. Issued 1976.
Deleted 1978. 260mm.

No. 672. OSA Missile Boat	£25	£10	£5

Grey, blue and black. Also fires
rockets. Price £1.58p. Issued 1975.
Deleted 1978. 206mm.

No. 673. Submarine Chaser	£25	£10	£5

Grey, dark blue and black. Price
£1.58p. Issued 1977. Deleted 1978.
197mm.

No. 673. Coastguard Amphibious Missile Launch	£25	£10	£5

Blue, grey, white and black. Also
blue, white and red with the word
'Coastguard' on sides. Price £2.25p.
Issued 1977. Deleted 1978. 155mm.

MODEL	M/B	M/U	G/C

No. 675. Motor Patrol Boat

£25 £10 £5

Grey, cream, black and red. Price
£1.55p. Issued 1973. Deleted 1978.
170mm.

No. 678. Air Sea Rescue Launch with Dinghy

£25 £10 £5

Mustard, black and blue, with orange
dinghy and black figure. With
transfers and markings on sides. Price
£2.25p. Issued 1974. Deleted 1977.
170mm.

No. 796. Healey Sports Boat on Trailer

£75 £45 £25

Cream with light green or dark green
top and boat interior. The figures are
the drivers from 113 M.G.B. and 125
Triumph Spitfire, only found in the
125 Fun Ahoy Set. Price 2/11d.
Issued 1960. Deleted 1962. 155mm.

AIRCRAFT

We now come to a very interesting section covering many aircraft
which have proved popular with collectors since they were first
introduced. And although the information has been very difficult to
acquire, I am pleased to be able to include it in the guide.

No. 60a. Imperial Airways Liner

– £125 £55

Red fuselage and wing tips, white
wing, nose and tail, blue and gold
with 'sunburst' effect on wings. Other
colours exist. This model and all the
60 series, with the exception of the
Autogiro, have cast fuselages and tin
wings. Price 9d. Issued 1934. Deleted
1940. Wing span 127mm. The model
was never boxed except when in set.

No. 60ab. Imperial Airways Liner

	M/B	M/U	G/C
	–	£175	£50

Gold or silver with the registration G-AB7. Otherwise all details the same as 60A.

No. 60b. D.H. Leopard Moth

Light green with yellow wing tips and tail. Also in blue with orange wing tips and tail. Or bright green, gold or silver with the registration G-ACP7. With open cockpit windows. From 1938 the side windows were filled in and from 1938 there was 66b which was a Dive Bomber Fighter in dark green and brown camouflage. Model was introduced in July 1940 with RAF markings and was deleted soon afterwards. Price 6d. Issued 1934. Deleted 1940. Wing span 76mm.

With open windows	–	£65	£35
With closed windows	–	£55	£25
Dive bomber	–	£75	£45

No. 60c. Percival Gull Plane

Up to 1938 the model had pierced windows. Then from 1938 to 1940 and from 1946 to 1948 it had solid windows. Pre-war model was marked 'Percival Gull' or it was not marked at all. The post-war markings were 'Percival Tower'. The model was also brought out in 1940 and called 66c as a two-seater fighter in camouflage with roundels. Colours for 60c with open windows are white with blue wing tips and tail or buff with orange wing tips and tail. The colours for the solid window version were silver or red or white with registration G-ADZO, either pre-war or post-war. Price 6d for all models. Issued 1934. Deleted 1940. Wing span 76mm.

With open windows	–	£65	£25
With closed windows	–	£55	£15
With post-war windows	–	£45	£5

No. 60c. Commemorative Special. Percival Gull

A model which was known as 60k which was a version of 60c and it was a commemorative model made for Amy Johnson's 1936 record breaking flight. Light blue fuselage, silver wings and the registration as C-ADZO in blue. It is also to be found with G-ADZO in black to commemorate the flight of H. L. Brooke for his 1937 record flight to South Africa. Either of these two models are very rare and come in special boxes. Price of these was 1/6d. Wing span 76mm.

	M/B	M/U	G/C
Either model	£275	£100	£50

No. 60d. Low Wing Monoplane

Red with cream wing tips and tail. No pilot. Then in yellow, orange and red with pilot from 1936. Also 66D which was a torpedo dive bomber from July 1940 until the end of that year in camouflage colours with roundels. Price of each model 6d. Issued June 1934. Deleted 1940. With a wing span of 76mm.

	M/B	M/U	G/C
With no pilot	–	£75	£35
With pilot	–	£65	£25
Box of 6	£350		

No. 60e. General Monospar Plane

First type was in gold with red wing tips and tail, or silver with royal blue wing tips and tail. Second type from 1936 was in gold or silver with the registration No. G-ABVP. In July 1940, the model came out as 66E Medium Bomber in camouflage and roundels priced 9d, compared with the others which were originally priced 6d. Issued June 1934. Deleted 1940. Wing span 80mm.

	M/B	M/U	G/C
First type	–	£175	£75
Second type from 1936	–	£150	£50

No. 60f. Cierva Autogiro

Gold with royal blue stabilisers tips and no pilot. Then model was in gold or silver with pilot. There was also a model 66f, which came out as the

MODEL	M/B	M/U	G/C

'Army Operational Autogiro' from July 1940 until September 1940, in camouflage and with roundels. Price 6d. Issued 1934. Deleted 1940. Pilot after 1937. Rotor diameter 72mm and length of fuselage 49mm.

Without pilot	–	£75	£35
With pilot	–	£65	£25

No. 60g. D.H. 'Comet' Aeroplane

First type had red and gold ailerons and rudder; or gold/red ailerons and rudder; silver with blue ailerons and rudder with no name stamped on the wing. Second type was in gold or silver with the registration G-ACSR and was gold, silver, or red, with registration G-ACSR and 'D.H. Comet' under with. It was reissued post-war from 1946 to 1949, in red, yellow, or silver with registration G-RACE and 'Light Racer' under wings. Price 6d. Issued 1936. Deleted 1940. Wing span 86mm. This is the model of the plane used by C. W. A. Scott and T. C. Black in their Australian flight.

First type	–	£75	£25
Second type	–	£55	£15
Post-war model	–	£45	£10

No. 60h. Short 'Singapore III' Flying Boat

Silver with RAF roundels; also as 60 m 'Four-Engined Flying Boat' in silver, blue or green with non-existent registrations. Price 1/-. Issued 1936. Deleted 1940. Wing span 126mm.

No. 60h in special box	£150	£100	£50

No. 60n. Fairey Battle Bomber

Silver with RAF roundels, with the words 'Fairey Battle Bomber' under wing from 1938. Also issued as 60s as a medium bomber in camouflage

between 1938 and 1940. Price 4½d.
Issued 1936. Deleted 1940. Wing span
75mm.

	M/B	M/U	G/C
No. 60n with no name	–	£50	£15
No. 60n with name	–	£35	£10
No. 60s	–	£35	£10

No. 60p. Gloster Gladiator

This is a light biplane in silver with
RAF roundels. It had the name under
the wing from 1937. Price 2/-. Issued
1936. Deleted 1940. Wing span
44mm.

	M/B	M/U	G/C
No name	–	£75	£25
With name	–	£55	£15

	M/B	M/U	G/C
No. 60r. Empire Flying Boat	–	£70	£15

Silver. Price 9d. Issued 1935. Deleted
1940. Wing span 126mm.

	M/B	M/U	G/C
No. 60t. Douglas DC3	£320	£100	£35

Red and cream or silver with black
wing tips. It had a registration mark
PM-ALI and was also marked
'Douglas Airliner' under wing. Price
2/11d. Issued 1938. Deleted 1940.
Wing span 132mm. Not reissued after
war.

	M/B	M/U	G/C
No. 60x. Atlantic Flying Boat	–	£55	£25

Silver and black. Price 9d. Issued
1935. Deleted 1940. Wing span
126mm.

	M/B	M/U	G/C
No. 60v. Armstrong Whitworth Whitley	–	£55	£25

Civilian aircraft in red and silver or
blue and silver. Price 6d. Issued 1935.
Deleted 1940. Wing span 86mm.

	M/B	M/U	G/C
No. 60w. Sikorsky Clipper III	–	£375	£75

Red and silver or all gold. Price 6d.
Issued 1935. Deleted 1940. Wing span
126mm.

	M/B	M/U	G/C
No. 62a. Spitfire	–	£75	£25

In camouflage. Price 9d. Issued 1939.
Deleted 1940. Wing span 80mm.

No. 62a. Spitfire

This model was issued in a variety of
colours and made as a pendant. The
price of any of these models is in

between £60 and £75 Neatly boxed with references and information on the lid of the box.

	M/B	M/U	G/C
No. 62b. Blenheim	–	£50	£20

Silver. Price 9d. Issued 1938. Deleted 1940. Wing span 75mm

		M/U	G/C
No. 62d. Blenheim	–	£50	£20

In camouflage. Details otherwise as 62b.

		M/U	G/C
No. 62e. Spitfire	–	£50	£20

Silver with RAF roundels. Details otherwise as 62a.

		M/U	G/C
No. 62g. Hawker Hurricane	–	£50	£20

Silver. Also 62s in camouflage. Price 9d. Issued 1938. Deleted 1940. Wing span 188mm.

	M/B	M/U	G/C
No. 62q. Flying Fortress	£160	£50	£20

Silver and black. Price 1/-. Issued 1935. Deleted 1940. Wing span 126mm.

	M/B	M/U	G/C
No. 62k. King's Flight	£450	£100	£75

Colours vary. Price 9d. Issued 1938. Deleted 1940. Wing span 126mm.

		M/U	G/C
No. 62m. Airspeed Envoy	–	£50	£20

Colours vary. Price 6d. Issued 1938. Deleted 1940. Wing span 126mm.

	M/B	M/U	G/C
No. 62n. Junkers Ju90	£320	£50	£20

German Air Force colours. Price 9d. Issued 1938. Deleted 1940. Wing span 126mm.

		M/U	G/C
No. 62p. The Ensign	–	£50	£20

Colours vary. Price 1/-. Issued 1938. Deleted 1940. Wing span 126mm.

	M/B	M/U	G/C
No. 62r. D.H. Albatross	£130	£50	£20

Authentic company liner colours. Price 1/-. Issued 1938. Deleted 1940. Wing span 140mm.

	M/B	M/U	G/C
No. 62t. Armstrong Whitworth Whitley Bomber	£140	£50	£20

In camouflage. Price 9d. Issued 1938. Deleted 1940. Wing span 86mm.

		M/U	G/C
No. 62x. 40-Seater Airliner	–	£75	£25

Silver. Price 1/-. Issued 1938. Deleted 1940. 140mm.

MODEL	M/B	M/U	G/C
No. 62y. Frobisher	–	£50	£20

Grey. Price 1/-. Issued 1938. Deleted
1940. Wing span 88mm.

	M/B	M/U	G/C
No. 62y. High Speed Monoplane	–	£50	£20

Colours vary. Price 9d. Issued 1938.
Deleted 1940. Wing span 126mm.

	M/B	M/U	G/C
No. 63. Mayo Composite	£220	£50	£20

Colours vary. Price 1/-. Issued 1938.
Deleted 1940. Wing span 88mm.

	M/B	M/U	G/C
No. 66a. Imperial Airways Liner	–	£175	£75

Issued as a heavy bomber in dark
green and brown camouflage colours.
Although issued in 1934 it was not
made into a bomber until 1940 when
it had a very short run. Model is quite
rare. Details otherwise as 60a.

	M/B	M/U	G/C
No. 67a. Junkers Ju89 Bomber	–	£50	£20

German Air Force colours. Price 9d.
Issued 1938. Deleted 1940. Wing span
188mm.

	M/B	M/U	G/C
No. 68a. 40-Seater Airliner	–	£50	£20

Camouflage. Details otherwise as 62x.

	M/B	M/U	G/C
No. 68b. Frobisher	–	£50	£20

Camouflage. Details otherwise as 62y.

No. 700. Sea Plane

Originally issued as 63b known as the
Mercury Sea Plane. With the top half
of the Mayo Composite and
registration G-ADMJ. Issued 1939.
Deleted 1940. Marked 'Mercury Sea
Plane' under wings. Registration
G-AVKX from 1946 to 1949 and also
when re-issued from 1952 to 1954
when it was renumbered to 700.
Finally deleted in 1957. There were
no casting changes on the post-war
model but the Mercury pre-war item
was never individually boxed. Post-
war 700 was. Price 1/5d. Wing span
102mm.

	M/B	M/U	G/C
Mercury pre-war model	–	£50	£20
Post-war 700 model	£75	£35	£15

No. 700. Commemorative Special Issue. 'Spitfire Mark II'

£500   £250   £150

In silver with RAF roundels on a special green onyx stand. Only 5000 models made for Diamond Jubilee of the Royal Air Force. The model is

stamped with a medallion and the words 'Gilby Jubilee Collection'. With the words 'Per. Ardva. Ad. Astra. 1918-1978'. The words on the base of the stand read, 'Diamond Jubilee of the Royal Air Force'. Price £8.50p. Issued and deleted 1978. Wing span 135mm. In special blue presentation box.

No. 701. Short Shetland Aircraft

£100   £75   £25

Silver and blue design. Price 6/6d. Issued 1956. Deleted 1965. Wing span 126mm.

No. 704. Avro York Air Liner

£100   £50   £20

White, red or blue trim, with silver body and black letters. Originally 704 from 1952 until 1954. Deleted 1960. Only 704 has the number stamped under the wing. The registration is always G-AGJC. Price 2/11d. Wing span 102mm.

No. 705. Vickers Viking Airliner

Vickers Viking was originally issued as 70C in 1947 in grey with silver windows or in silver with blue windows. Registration is always G-AGOL. Renumbered 705 in 1954 and made in silver thereafter. Finally deleted in 1963. Never individually boxed and delivered to shops in boxes of six. Price 2/-. Wing span 140mm.

	M/B	M/U	G/C
Grey	–	£55	£25
Silver	–	£45	£15

No. 706. Air France Viscount

	£100	£55	£25

Blue and silver. Registration was always F-BGNL. Price 5/6d. Issued 1956. Deleted 1957. Wing span 408mm.

No. 708. Vickers Viscount 800 Airliner

	£95	£55	£25

A BEA aircraft in silver with red trim lines along the centre and a red bull tip design on nose with red props and decals in red. The registration was always G-AOJA. Price 4/11d. Issued 1957. Deleted 1965. Wing span 408mm.

No. 710. Beechcraft S35 Bonanza Aircraft

Red and white with black plastic wheels. From 1970 colours changed to bronze and yellow with black engine cover. From 1975 it was red, white and blue. Price 7/11d. Issued 1965. Deleted 1977. Wing span 133mm.

	M/B	M/U	G/C
1965 model	£45	£25	£15
1970 model	£35	£15	£10
1975 model	£25	£10	£5

No. 712. U.S. Army T/42A

	£45	£25	£10

Dark green with black interior and U.S.A. stars and stripes decals. Same basic casting as No. 715 but with wing tip tanks. Price 49p. Issued 1973. Deleted 1977. Wing span 153mm.

MODEL	M/B	M/U	G/C

No. 715. Bristol 173 Helicopter   £50   £25   £10

Turquoise. Registration G-AUXR.
With rotors. Price 2/8d. Issued 1956.
Deleted 1963. Wing span 127mm.

No. 715. Beechcraft C55 Baron

White, yellow and black with green
trim lines, with yellow engine covers
and prop. Model No. 715 was
originally the number used for the
Helicopter issue. There was a colour
change in 1972 when it became dark
orange with yellow centre line flash
with the same markings on the rail
and wing tips. Price 9/6d. Issued
1967. Deleted 1978. Wing span
150mm. DC/P.

	M/B	M/U	G/C
White, yellow and black	£45	£25	£10
Dark orange and yellow	£35	£15	£5

No. 716. Westland Sikorsky Helicopter   £45   £25   £10

Red body with silver cockpit, red
rotors and cream letters and silver
wheels. With registration G-ATWX.
Price 2/5d. Issued 1957. Deleted
1963. Wing span 89mm.

No. 717. Boeing 737 Plane   £35   £15   £5

Fawn with silver tips on nose and
wings. Dark blue line along centre jets
and tail fins. With black wheels.
'Lufthansa' decals in light blue. Price
8/11d. Issued 1970. Deleted 1976.
Wing span 152mm.

No. 718. Hawker 'Hurricane' Fighter   £45   £25   £10

Green and grey camouflage. Price
55p. Issued 1973. Deleted 1976. Wing
span 188mm.

No. 719. Spitfire Mark II

Green, brown and grey with R.A.F.
decals. With motor driven propeller.
Replaced in 1977 by 741 with same
casting but no motor. Price 17/11d.
Issued 1970. Deleted 1980. Wing span
173mm.

	M/B	M/U	G/C
No. 719	£45	£25	£10
No. 741	£30	£15	£5

No. 721. Junkers Ju 87B Stuka Fighter

£30   £10   £5

Camouflage green and sky-blue and German decals etc. With cap-firing bomb. Price 15/11d. Issued 1970. Deleted 1980. Wing span 191mm.

No. 722. Hawker Harrier Jump Jet

£45   £20   £10

Camouflage green and grey. With all folding wheels. Price 17/11d. Issued 1971. Deleted 1980. Wing span 125mm.

No. 723. Hawker Siddeley HS125 Executive Jet

£45   £20   £10

Red, white and blue livery. With opening door. Price 17/11d. Issued 1975. Deleted 1975. Wing span 132mm.

No. 724. Sea-King Helicopter

£45   £20   £10

Silver and medium blue with U.S.A. stars and stripes. With motor driven rotor blade. Price 21/-. Issued 1972. Deleted 1980. Wing span 179mm.

No. 725. F.4K Phantom II

£45   £20   £10

Dark blue. Royal Navy livery signs etc. With stand-off firing missiles. Price £1.65p. Issued 1972. Deleted 1978. Wing span 132mm.

No. 726. Messerschmitt B.F. 109E

£50   £30   £15

Olive green, with mustard tips and engine cover. Black letters, German cross and swastika. Motor driven propeller. Price 89½p. Issued 1972. Deleted 1976. Wing span 165mm.

No. 728. R.A.F. 'Dominie'

£35   £15   £5

Dark green, medium blue and grey battle colours and R.A.F. decals. The same basic casting as 723. Price 89p. Issued 1972. Deleted 1975. Wing span 132mm.

MODEL	M/B	M/U	G/C

No. 729. 'M.R.C.A.' Swing Wing Fighter

£35 £15 £7

This is a multi role combat aircraft. Grey, green, dark blue and dark yellow battle colours with red and blue circle decals. Black nose tip. Price 89p. Issued 1973. Deleted 1976. Wing span 164mm.

No. 730. Tempest Fighter

– £35 £15

R.A.F. battle livery. Also in silver with red, white and blue roundels. Price 9d. Issued as 701 from 1946 to 1948, and 1952 to 1954, when it was renumbered to 730. Deleted 1957. Never boxed. 51mm. A good investment.

No. 730. U.S. Navy Phantom Fighter

£35 £15 £7

Silver, black and blue with U.S. decals and stars etc. Price 75p. Issued 1972. Deleted 1976. Wing span 132mm.

No. 731. Twin Engined Fighter

– £35 £15

Silver with no markings. A model of a Messerschmitt 110, the model having being planned in 1940, but never released. Then released as a twin-engined fighter as No. 70D, from 1946 to 1948 and from 1950 to 1954. Then renumbered 731. Price 8d. Deleted 1956. 51mm. Never boxed.

No. 731/A. S.E.P.E.C.A.T. Jaguar

£35 £15 £7

Jaguar fighter in green, grey, blue and dark blue battle colours and R.A.F. decals. With opening cockpit and pilot ejector sear. Price 65p. Issued 1973. Deleted 1976. Wing span 106mm.

No. 732. 'Meteor' Twin Jet Fighter

– £25 £10

Price 1/-. Originally issued as 70E from 1946 to 1948. Reissued between 1952 and 1954 as 732. Deleted in 1963. Wing span 66mm. Never boxed.

MODEL	M/B	M/U	G/C

No. 732/A. 'Bell' Helicopter   £35   £15   £7

White, red and dark blue with black
props. With red skis and blue cap
interior with pilot. Police decals in
black. Price £1.75p. Issued 1973.
Deleted 1980. Length 211mm.

No. 733. 'Shooting Star' Jet Fighter   –   £35   £15

Silver body, white stars and blue
circles. Price 1/-. Issued as 70F from
1947 to 1949. Then on sale from 1952
to 1954. Renumbered 733 in 1954.
Deleted 1963. Wing span 60mm.
Never boxed.

No. 734. Supermarine 'Swift' Fighter   £35   £15   £7

Authentic Royal Air Force battle
colours and decals, also metal wheels.
Price 1/9d. Issued 1955. Deleted
1963. Wing span 51mm.

No. 734/A. 'P47 Thunderbolt'   £35   £15   £10

Silver blue metallic with mustard tail,
black and orange nose and prop
design. Red bombs under wings with
Stars and Stripes decals. Black letters
and numbers. Price £1.25p. Issued
1975. Deleted 1978. Wing span
190mm.

No. 735. Gloster 'Javelin' Delta Wing Fighter   £45   £25   £10

Blue, green and grey battle colours
and R.A.F. decals, metal wheels,
silver cockpit. Metal wheels from
1956. Plastic wheels from 1963. Price
2/5d. Issued 1956. Deleted 1965.
Wing span 82mm.

No. 736. Hawker 'Hunter' Fighter   £55   £25   £10

Green, grey and dark blue battle
livery with R.A.F. decals. Metal
wheels. Price 1/9d. Issued 1955.
Deleted 1964. Wing span 54mm.

MODEL	M/B	M/U	G/C

No. 736/A. Bundesmarine Helicopter

	M/B	M/U	G/C
	£35	£15	£7

Silver, red and gold with black wheels and props with motor driven main rotor blades and finger operated winch. Price £2.25p. Issued 1973. Deleted 1978. 179mm.

No. 737. Lightning P.1B Fighter

Silver with R.A.F. roundels, black plastic radar cone and probe fitted to the nose. Metal wheels from 1963. Later the model had paint finish changed to metallic silver grey and from 1965 the model had plastic wheels. Price 2/-. Issued 1959. Deleted 1976. Wing span 64mm.

	M/B	M/U	G/C
Silver metal wheels	£45	£25	£10
Silver grey metal wheels	£35	£15	£7
Plastic wheels	£25	£10	£5

No. 738. D.H. 110 Sea Vixen

	M/B	M/U	G/C
	£45	£15	£7

Silver grey. Price 7/11d. Issued 1956. Deleted 1965. Wing span 184mm.

No. 739. A6M5 Zero-Sen-Fighter Plane

	M/B	M/U	G/C
	£25	£10	£5

Dark green with wide black nose band and wheels. Red Japanese decals and nose point and motor driven props. Price 89p. Issued 1975. Deleted 1978. Wing span 184mm.

No. 997. Sind Caravelle Plane

	M/B	M/U	G/C
	£35	£15	£7

Colours vary. With authentic Caravelle markings and numbers. Price 7/6d. Issued October 1956. Deleted 1965. Wing span 126mm. This is a very good investment.

No. 998. Bristol 'Britannia'

Silver with white upper fuselage and rudder. Canadian Pacific livery, blue letters and CF-CZA registration. Later the paint was changed to metallic silver grey. Metal wheels. Price 9/3d. Issued 1959. Deleted 1975. Wing span 225mm.

	M/B	M/U	G/C
First colour	£55	£35	£15
Metallic colour	£35	£15	£10

No. 999. D.H. 'Comet' Airliner

First colours were blue line trim and silver with wide strip design, black numbers and letters. Then in 1963, metallic silver-grey finish. Originally issued as No. 702 De Havilland Comet introduced in 1954 with the registration G-ALYV. Renumbered 999 in 1955 with G-ALYX. Deleted in 1965. Price 6/4d. Wing span 184mm.

	M/B	M/U	G/C
No. 702	£45	£25	£10
No. 999 Silver	£35	£15	£7
Silver grey	£25	£10	£5

No. 1040. 'Sea King' Helicopter

£35

Diecast metal kit with screws and paint and no glue required. Only mint and boxed price given for these models. Good prices given for finished planes, depending on how good the work is, although collectors like to buy the kits in original condition. Price £1.25p. Issued 1972. Deleted 1977.

No. 1041. Hawker Hurricane Mark II

£45

Diecast metal kit. Price £1.25p. Issued 1973. Deleted 1976.

No. 1042. Spitfire Mark II

£55

Diecast metal kit. Price £1.25p. Issued 1972. Deleted 1977.

No. 1043. S.E.P.E.C.A.T. Jaguar

£35

Diecast metal kit. Price £1.25p. Issued 1974. Deleted 1976.

No. 1044. Messerschmitt BF.109E

£45

Diecast metal kit. Price £1.25p. Issued 1972. Deleted 1975. Kit of model 726.

No. 1. Aero Clockwork Motor   £150

This long running motor was specially
designed to fit into the fuselage of
models made with No. 1, No. 2 or
No. 1 and No. 2 special 'Aero' outfits.
It will rotate at high speed, greatly
adding to the realism of the model or
models which it fits. Price 1/9d.
Issued 1934. Deleted 1940. Mint and
boxed only.

No. 2. Aero Clockwork Motor   £175

A powerful motor and in addition to
rotating the prop, it also drives the
landing wheels of No. 1, No. 2, or
No. 1 or 2 special 'Aero' outfits to
make the machine taxi along the floor
in a very realistic manner. An
adjustable tail-wheel is also supplied
with this motor. Price 3/6d. Issued
1935. Deleted 1940. Mint and boxed
only.

No. 0. Aeroplane Outfit   £250

Outfit was supplied in two different
colour combinations. In red and cream
and in blue and white. One of the
first Dinky outfits produced. In a neat
picturesque box. Designed for
educational purposes and a great
favourite in many schools. One could
make an interesting range of aeroplane
models, including high and low wing
monoplanes, seaplanes and standard
light biplanes. Price 4/6d. Issued
1934. Deleted 1940.

No. 00. Aeroplane Outfit   £275

Red or cream, or blue and white.
Containing a good selection of aero
parts with which delightful models
can be made. Price 3/3d. Issued 1935.
Deleted 1940.

No. 00/a. Aeroplane Outfit   £350

Red and blue, or red and gold, and in
blue and gold. Price 4/6d. Issued
1935. Deleted 1940.

No. 1. Aeroplane Outfit   £350

Red and cream or blue and white.
Parts for making high standard quality
planes etc. Price 7/6d. Issued 1935.
Deleted 1940.

No. 1/a. Aeroplane Constructor Access Outfit

£350

With spare wings, spare wheels etc. Price 6/-. Issued 1936. Deleted 1940.

No. 1/b. Access Outfit No. 2

£250

Spare parts to use with No. 1 Outfit. Price 5/6d. Issued 1936. Deleted 1940.

No. 2. Aeroplane Outfit

£500

Blue and white or red and cream. This kit can make a much wider and larger range of models than No. 1. The parts can make triple-engined monoplanes and biplanes. A racing seaplane of the type which was used in the pre-war Schneider Trophy Contests. A particularly interesting model to be made is that of the Giant Plane Bombing Machine. Also one can build models of amphibians. Price 12/6d. Issued 1936. Deleted 1940.

No. 1. Special Aeroplane Outfit

£750

Red and cream or blue and white. This outfit could build over twenty realistic models of various types of aircraft. The range of special parts included mainplanes, fitted ailerons, tail planes with elevators, movable rudder, radial engine cowling etc. Special manual. Price 12/6d. Issued 1937. Deleted 1940.

No. 1a. Special Aeroplane Accessory Outfit

£350

This outfit will convert a No. 1 Special Aeroplane constructor outfit into a No. 2 Special Outfit. Price 10/-. Issued 1937. Deleted 1940.

No. 2. Special Aeroplane Outfit

£1250

Red and cream or blue and white. Containing a large range of aircraft parts with which practically any type of model aircraft of the pre-war period could be built. Set includes a manual showing forty-four examples of model aircraft with full instructions. Price 21/-. Issued 1937. Deleted 1940. Manual – rare and worth £25.

BOXES AND CATALOGUES

Empty Boxes

We have now come to a period in the world of collecting when not only diecast models are of considerable value, but also the actual empty boxes themselves. It is only common sense to realize that a model has considerably more value when it is in its correct box. For instance, an Esso Tanker valued at £100 without a box, is valued at £175 with a box. A Trojan can can bring £60 unboxed and £175 boxed. Boxes have a psychological effect and it is always easier to sell a model in a box than it is without. At one time the specialist collector, who also paid the highest prices I would not even consider purchasing a model unless it was boxed and in almost perfect condition.

Since the early part of 1978 I began seriously dealing in empty boxes. In both my shops at Leeds and York I had a person who dealt with empty boxes and catalogues alone. It took several months before any of these caught the eye of the serious collector and I had doubts about their value myself until 1979 when suddenly the boxes were all bought up in a matter of days. People began asking about the boxes when they were almost impossible to obtain.

Catalogues

It has always been a well known fact that catalogues dealing with diecast models of all descriptions have been sought after and therefore must hold some considerable value. This is particularly true of French Dinkies. These little booklets not only show pictures and give original prices of the models when first produced, but also give a guide which has in many ways contributed to the publication of my book. Although I have done my best to give a guide to the prices of both boxes and catalogues, I would be very pleased to hear from collectors wherever they may live, should they happen to known of any rare booklets and boxes which I could include in the next edition of this book. Anyone who cares to write care of my editor will receive a reply.

Pre-war boxes

£10–£1000

The boxes which contained models in
half dozens with plain covers are quite
rare.

Pre-war boxes with pictures

£50–£2000

Boxes which contained six or more
models.

Pre-war individual boxes.
Taxis and sports cars

£25–£250

Pre-war individual boxes.
Commercial

£10–£250

Plain.

Pre-war individual boxes.
Commercial

£10–£500

Picturesque.

Pre-war racing cars

£100–£500

Several of these models such as the
Bluebird and Speed of the Wind were
sometimes placed on show at
exhibitions. Great men such as Sir
Malcolm Campbell, and G. E. Eyston
would sign boxes which were specially
made in a limited edition. These are
very rare and very valuable. Some
models such as these even had letters
or certificates in one form or another.

Pre-war exhibition boxes

£25–£2000

Several exhibitions were held where
prominent companies and toy makers
alike would have their goods on
display and any model sold in a box
would bear special dates and details.
There are also rare.

Pre-war gift set boxes

£50–£500

Plain.

Pre-war gift set boxes

£50–£1000

Picturesque.

Pre-war buses and coaches

£10–£1000

Plain.

Pre-war buses and coaches

£25–£1000

Picturesque.

No. 27. Pre-war Tram Car   £25–£1000
Picturesque.

Pre-war ambulances   £10–£250

Pre-war caravans   £25–£250

Pre-war tractors   £25–£250

Pre-war military   £25–£500

Pre-war saloon cars   £25–£500
Plain.

Pre-war saloon cars   £25–£1000
Picturesque.

Pre-war police cars   £25–£500

Pre-war fire engines   £25–£500

Pre-war garages   £25–£500

Pre-war French Dinkies   £25–£500
Plain

Pre-war French Dinkies   £50–£750
Picturesque.

Pre-war trains   £50–£500

Pre-war vans   £30–£300
Plain.

Pre-war vans   £50–£500
Picturesque.

Pre-war ships and boats   £50–£500

Pre-war planes   £30–£300

Post-war models

**Military. Blue and white
  supertoy boxes**   £40–£400

Tractors. Yellow boxes   £20–£200

Tractors. Supertoys   £20–£500

**No. 27N. Field Marshall
  Tractor**   £20–£500

No. 27N. Promotional Tractor	£10
Buses and coaches	£2
No. 283. B.O.A.C. Coach	£5
No. 293/A. Swiss Postal Bus	£5
No. 296. Luxury Coach	£5
No. 949. Wayne School Bus	£25
No. 952. Vega Major Luxury Coach	£10
No. 953. Continental Touring Coach	£4
No. 100. Lady Penelope's Car. Fab 1	£10
No. 106. Thunderbird 2	£10
No. 112. Purdy's TR7	£10
No. 157. Jaguar XK120	£5
No. 354. Pink Panther Car	£10
No. 967. BBC Van	£10
No. 968. BBC Van	£10
No. 969. BBC Van	£10
No. 987. ABC Control Van	£25
No. 988. ABC Transmitter Van	£25
No. 281. Pathé News Car	£25
Dublo Dinky Toys	£25
No. 115. U.B. Taxi	£10
No. 254. Austin Taxi	£5
No. 31B. Dunlop Trojan Van	£25
No. 31C. Chivers Van	£25
No. 31C. Oxo Van	£25

No. 260. Royal Mail Van	£25
No. 261. Telephone Van	£25
No. 262. Swiss Postal Van	£50
Any Ford Transit promotional van	£25
No. 450. Esso Trojan Van	£25
No. 454. Cydrax Trojan Van	£25
No. 455. Brooke Bond Trojan Van	£25
No. 465. Capstan Morris Van	£25
No. 470. Shell Austin Van	£15
No. 471. Nestlés Austin Van	£15
No. 472. Raleigh Austin Van	£15
Nos. 480, 481 and 482. Bedford vans	£10 each
No. 514. Guy Vans. Slumberland, Lyons, or Spratts	£50
No. 514. Guy Weetabix Van	£250
Nos. 918, 919 and 920. Guy vans	£15
No. 923. Heinz Van	£50
No. 60Y. Thompson Aircraft Tender (pre-war)	£10
No. 402. Coca Cola Lorry	£10
Any Bedford box in the 400 Series	£10
No. 428. Large Trailer Box	£5
Any Guy Truck box in the 400 Series	£30
Any Tanker box in the 400 Series	£30
Any Foden Wagon box in the 500 Series	£50

Any Guy box in the 500 Series	£50
No. 582. Pullmore Car Transporter	£25
Any Foden box in the 900 Series	£40
Any Guy box in the 900 Series	£40
Any Leyland Truck box in the 900 Series	£40
No. 950. Transporter Car Set Bob	£25
No. 981. Horse Box	£50
No. 983. Dinky Car Carrier	£25
No. 984. Car Carrier	£25
No. 295. Dinky Trailer	£5
Ships. Any box (large)	£5
Ships. Any box (medium)	£3
Ships. Any box (small)	£2
Planes	£2

Catalogues

Any pre-war Meccano Magazine	£10–£100
Any pre-war Hornby or Dinky Catalogue	£25–£100
Any post-war Dinky Catalogue (first series)	£5–£50
Any post-war Dinky Catalogue (second series)	£3–£30
Any post-war Dinky Catalogue (third series)	50p–£5

Complete Set of Dinky Catalogues

£50–£300

There is a demand for Dinky catalogues in good condition. The numbers in this set range from No. 1 to No. 14. The first of these being printed in 1965 by Lines Brothers. Containing: 1965; 1966; 1967; 1968; 1969; 1970; 1971; 1972; 1973; 1974; 1975; 1976; 1977 and 1978 which was the last catalogue to be published and released. Original prices of catalogues, range from 3d in old coinage to 5p each.

THE MATCHBOX DINKY COLLECTION

I had always hoped that one day someone would revive the greatest name in diecast toys, Dinky. At last it has happened. The firm responsible is Universal Matchbox International Limited to be known as the Matchbox and Dinky Group of Companies.

The first new Dinky model, the 1967 E Type Jaguar, came off the assembly line in November 1988 and was greeted with acclaim by both collectors and casual buyers.

Ten new Dinky models will launch the range and I have given full details below. The superb Stuttgart Bus, due to be released in October 1989, I predict will be an excellent investment.

Dinky was the generic name for model toy cars until 1979 when manufacturing stopped. In their forty six years of business Dinky produced a huge range of different models but the post-war toys were the most successful. Since the late 1970s' collectors and enthusiasts have been asking for models from this era, the nostalgia boom and the lack of supply serving only to increase this demand.

Plans are in hand for developing further models in The Dinky Collection and I wish the project every success.

Please note that the prices given are recommended retail prices and may vary from area to area.

THE NEW DINKY COLLECTION
Dinky is the registered Trade Mark of
the Matchbox Group of Companies.

MODEL
No. DY–1. 1967 'E' Type Jaguar
Introduced in 1961, the series one E
type Jaguar sports car was developed
from the Le Mans winning 'D' type
of 1955–57. The wheelbase is 2.44m.
and the 6 cylinder engine of 4235cc
develops 265b.h.p. giving a top speed
of 145m.p.h. (232KPH) with its
revised headlights and windscreen.
The 1968 car is referred to by
enthusiasts as the 1½ series model in
green livery with silver spoked
wheels, bumpers, windscreen and
trim. Dark green or black hood.
Issued December 1988. 112mm. Price
£4.95p.

No. DY–2. 1957 Chevrolet Bel Air
Pink and cream. Silver trim, wheels,
bumpers, windscreen, lights and
radiator. One of today's true
American Car Classics. The customer
could choose from 5 engines from
140–283hp. It was fitted with the
Turboglide 3 speed automatic gear
box which gave a speed of 77mph
over a quarter mile. This car was very
popular in America in its day and is
the epitome of an American car of the
50s. Price £5.50p. Issued February
1989. Original price £4.95p. 121mm.

No. DY–3. 1965 MGB GT
Dark or mid green. Silver trim,
bumpers, grille, windscreen, hubs.
The MGB was developed from the
1955–62 M.G.A. It was powered by a
4 cylinder O.H.V. engine of 1798cc
with twin carburettors which gave
98bhp at 5400 rpm. In 1965 the G.T.
was introduced which, although
heavier had a higher top speed and
better road holding. It was regarded
as the ideal sports car. Price £4.95p.
Issued January 1989. 52mm.

No. DY–4. 1950 Ford E83 10 cwt.Van (HEINZ 57)

Mustard yellow, with matching wheels. Black tyres, grille, bumpers and roof. The van first appeared in 1938 and used the 1172cc. engine from the 10hp. car. Offsetting the units and placing the driving controls beside the engine gave this van a load length of 2032mm. 3.12cm. capacity on a vehicle with a 2286mm. wheelbase. This vehicle was very popular appearing in many emergency and civilian versions until production stopped in 1957. 90mm. Original price £4.95p. Issued April 1989. 90mm.

No. DY–5–. 1949 Ford V–8 Pilot

Black. Silver grille, bumpers, wheels and headlights. The Ford V8 Pilot was introduced in 1947 to satisfy the great demand for private cars in the late forties and early fifties. 3.6 litre engine produced 83bhp which although being modest, enabled this heavy car (1540kg) to travel at 130kph. Original price £4.95p. Issued May 1989. 101mm.

No. DY–6. 1951 Volkswagen De Luxe Sedan

Blue with matching wheels. Silver trim and bumpers. Grey roof, black tyres. The Volkswagen was designed by Dr. F. Porsche in 1936 to provide transportation for the masses. Production started in 1938 but it was not until 1945 that production started in earnest. This VW was given the nickname 'The Beetle' because of its shape and was in production world wide until the early 80s. The 1951 VW was powered with a 1131cc. rear mounted air cooled engine developing 25bhp. Original price £4.95p. Issued June 1989. 100mm.

No. DY–7. 1959 Cadillac Coupe de Ville

Red and cream with silver trim, grille, bumpers, spoked wheels and lights. The Cadillac's reputation grew to the extent that it became the most prestigious American car available.

The 1959 Coupe de Ville was no exception and continued the reputation with its distinctive styling and extraordinary rear fins. This large car was powered by a 6539cc V8 engine developing 325 gross bhp providing a very smooth ride. This Cadillac is one of the great American car classics. Original price £4.95p. Issued November 1989. 133mm.

No. DY–8. 1948 Commer 8 Cwt. Van

Red with authentic Sharps Toffee motif and adverts. Silver grille bumpers, lights and wheels. The Commer 8cwt. van was produced by the Rootes Motor Company which included such famous Marques as the Humber, Hillman and Sunbeam. The Commer was developed using the same mechanical units as the Hillman Minx. This vehicle featured hydraulic brakes and efficient engines. Price £5.50p. Issued July 1989. 84mm.

No. DY–9. 1949 Land Rover Series 1

Green with yellow cover. Spare wheel on bonnet. Silver trim and bumper. The Rover Company recognised the need for light 4 wheel drive vehicles which were used so effectively during WWII. The Company developed these for farming and in the Colonies where roads were poor. By 1948 the Land Rover was introduced. This robustly built vehicle had a 4 cylinder 1595cc engine with a 4 speed gearbox +2 ratio transfer box to the axles providing the vehicle with 4 wheel drive. £5.50p. Issued September 1989. 90mm.

No. DY–10. Mercedes Benz 03500 Stuttgart Bus

Superb never to be repeated model of an original bus, which was powered by a 4.6 litre 6 cylinder diesel and was capable of 52mph (82kph). Seating for 29, plus fold away seating for extra 7 pasengers when required. Cream with black bonnet, mudguards and tyres. 'Reisebüro Ruoff Stuttgart' wording. Price £15.95p. Issued October 1989. 164mm.

NOTES

NOTES

NOTES

NOTES